Scott Foresman - Addison Wesley

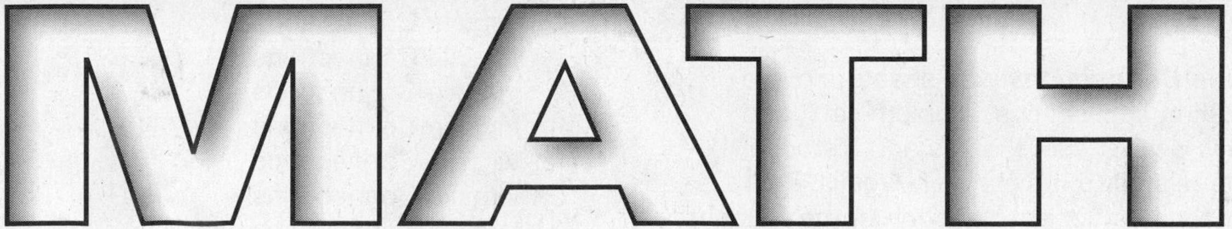

Virginia Math Connections

A Review and Practice Workbook

Project Coordinator
Debbie Owens

Contributing Writers
We wish to thank the following Virginia teachers:
Betsy Barton
Phoebe Clarke
Jill Davis
Sandra Dietz
Penny M. Gilliland
Edward Hockenberry
Kelley J. Miller
J. Diane Stanton
Candace S. Young

Scott Foresman - Addison Wesley

Editorial Offices: Glenview, Illinois • New York, New York
Sales Offices: Reading, Massachusetts • Duluth, Georgia • Glenview, Illinois
Carrollton, Texas • Menlo Park, California

http://www.sf.aw.com

Overview

Virginia Math Connections: A Review and Practice Workbook consists of these four sections of material.

Review worksheets provide practice of key skills and concepts that were covered last year in math class.

Virginia Connections worksheets provide interesting applications, problem sets, and puzzles dealing with themes and historical events related to the state of Virginia. There is one worksheet for each section of the Student Edition. Each worksheet applies and reinforces mathematical content from that section.

Practice worksheets provide additional exercises for students who have not mastered key skills and concepts covered in the Student Edition. A Practice worksheet is provided for each core lesson in the Student Edition. In addition, a Practice worksheet is also provided for each Mixed Practice and Cumulative Review lesson.

Chapter Tests Form A provide practice tests to help students prepare for chapter tests. Feedback from these practice tests can be used by students to assess their knowledge of the material taught in each chapter. Each Form A test covers all of the objectives of the chapter in the Student Edition in a free-response format.

Photo Credits

Photographs in this series courtesy of Virginia Tourism Corp., AP/Wide World Photos, UPI/Corbis-Bettmen, Visuals Unlimited, Library of Congress, International Harvester, The University of Virginia, Richmond Times Dispatch, The Richmond Kickers, Norfolk Zoological Park, Historic Crab Orchard Museum, The Claude Moore Colonial Farm, NASA, The British Museum.

ISBN 0-201-44804-1

Printed in the United States of America

6 7 8 9 10 – PO – 03 02

Contents

Name ______________________________

Tennis Champion From Virginia

Virginia
7B

A tennis player from Richmond, Virginia was ranked as the number-one player in the world in 1975.

To find the name of this famous tennis player, circle the letter that matches the word in each row. Then write the letters in the blanks below.

1. third	C	E	A	G	J	W	Y	O	N	L	X
2. seventh	N	Z	X	V	H	M	R	A	S	D	T
3. ninth	Q	W	E	K	Y	U	A	S	T	H	V
4. sixth	L	K	P	Y	T	H	W	B	M	A	R
5. fourth	X	F	I	U	M	P	E	T	N	Z	C
6. tenth	Q	H	B	P	B	C	J	G	S	R	Y
7. eighth	D	V	Y	O	F	S	W	A	X	E	D
8. second	T	S	L	N	M	G	A	C	M	W	P
9. fifth	F	R	C	B	H	U	N	X	Y	I	K
10. first	E	F	V	P	W	N	L	D	S	C	W

_____ _____ _____ _____ _____ _____   _____ _____ _____ _____

Notes: Make sure that children know that the letter to the farthest left in each row is considered the first letter. Two of the four most important tennis tournaments each year are Wimbledon in England and the U.S. Open. Arthur Ashe was the first African American man to win both of these tournaments. A statue of him stands on Monument Avenue in Richmond.

Extension: Ask children to identify ordinal positions of the letters of the alphabet. For example, the fifth letter is e.

Virginia Mathematics Standards of Learning: (1.5) Identify the ordinal positions first through tenth, using an ordered set of objects.

Name ________________________________

Virginia
8A

You Caught About How Many Fish?

People catch many fish in Virginia's lakes and rivers. Trout and bass are two common types.

Circle groups of 10.
Estimate. Circle about how many.

Count.
Write the number.

1.

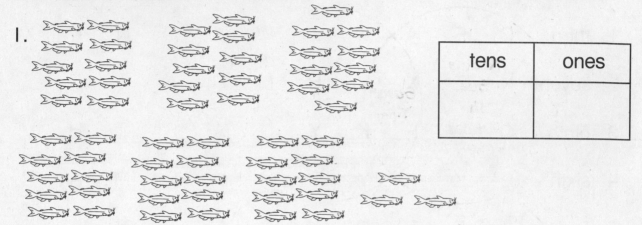

tens	ones

About 50 60 70 ______

2.

tens	ones

About 60 70 80 ______

Notes: Rivers and lakes have freshwater. The Atlantic Ocean and Chesapeake Bay have saltwater. Virginia has both freshwater and saltwater fishing.
Extension: Ask children to estimate classroom quantities such as the number of crayons in a box or the number of cubes in a bucket. Then have children count the objects to find how many.
Virginia Mathematics Standards of Learning: (1.2) Group concrete objects by ones and tens to develop an understanding of place value.

Name ______________________________

Virginia 8B

Going to Lake Anna

Lake Anna State Park is a fun place to visit. People enjoy boating, fishing, swimming, and hiking on one of Virginia's most popular lakes.

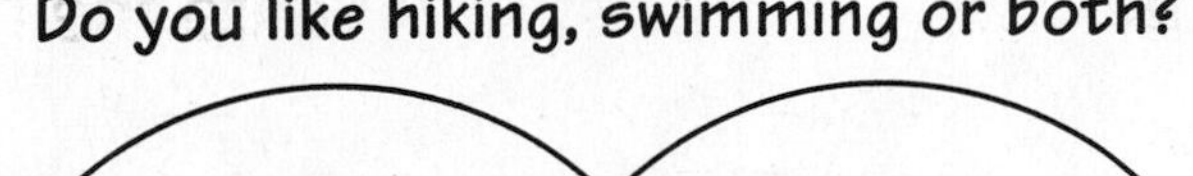

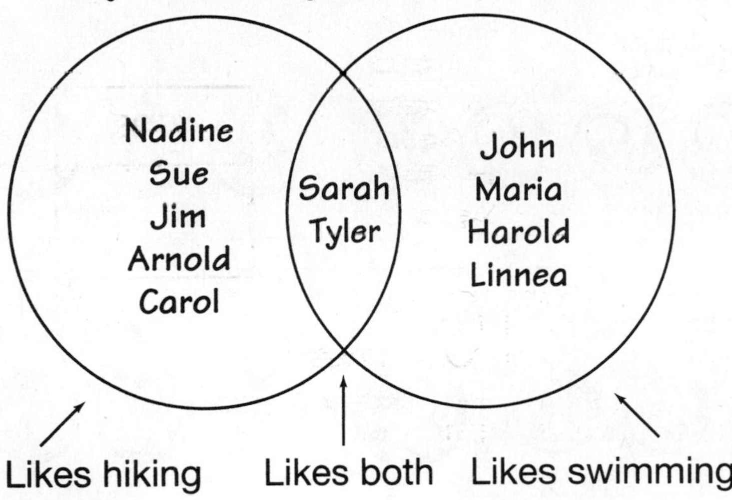

1. How many children like hiking? ________
2. How many children like swimming? ________
3. What does the chart tell you about Sarah? ____________________

   ____
4. Put your own name on the chart. Explain why you wrote your name where you did.

   ____

Notes: Lake Anna is between Fredericksburg and Charlottesville in northern Virginia.
Extension: Gary does not like hiking or swimming. Where could he write his name?
Virginia Mathematics Standards of Learning: (1.18) Investigate, identify, and describe various forms of data collection. (1.20) Sort and classify concrete objects according to one or more attributes.

Name ____

Peanuts and Plenty More

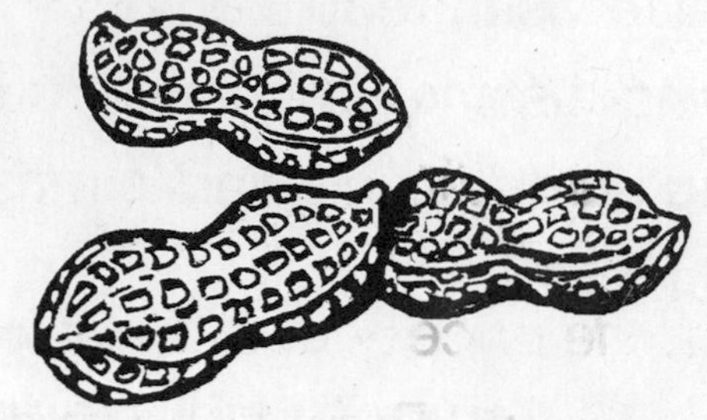

Peanuts are grown in Virginia and are used to make over 300 different items! Some favorites are peanut butter, cookies, and candies.

Circle the coins you need.

1.

2.

3.

4. Draw two different groups of coins you could use to pay for this bag of peanuts.

Notes: The peanut plant is unusual because its pods develop underground. Peanut oil is used as an ingredient in soaps, paint, shoe polish, and ice cream.

Extension: Have children set up a store at school or at home. Children can price items for 50 cents or less and then show coins that would be needed to buy each item.

Virginia Mathematics Standards of Learning: (1.7) Count a collection of pennies, a collection of nickels, and a collection of dimes whose total value is 100 cents or less.

Name ______________________

Virginia 9B

Football Favorites

College football is popular all over our state. Two favorite college teams are from the University of Virginia and Virginia Tech.

Match the price of each item with the group of coins that shows the same amount. Draw a line to match.

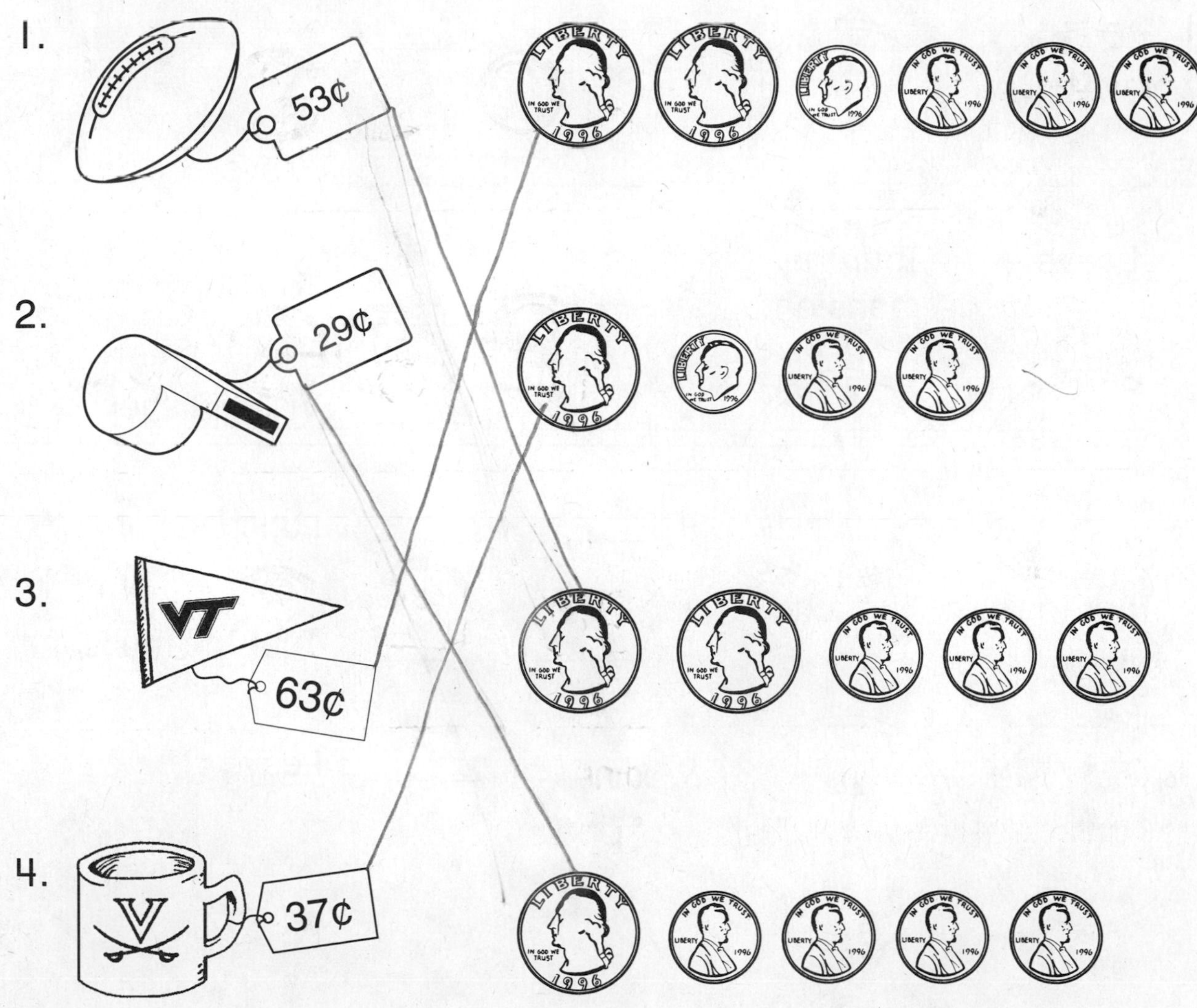

Notes: The University of Virginia is in Charlottesville. Its team is called the Cavaliers. Virginia Tech is in Blacksburg. Its team is called the Hokies.
Extension: Have pairs of children draw pictures of other football items they would like to buy. Have one child give the items prices of 50 cents or less, and have the other child show each amount using coins.
Virginia Mathematics Standards of Learning: (1.7) Count a collection of pennies, a collection of nickels, and a collection of dimes whose total value is 100 cents or less.

Name ______________________________

Virginia
10A

Seeing Mount Vernon

Mount Vernon was the home of George Washington, our country's first president. Many people enjoy visiting Mount Vernon.

Complete the class's schedule for their visit to Mount Vernon.

Leave

Tour the mansion

Tour the museum

Lunch

Arrive

Visit gift shop

1. ____ : ____ Arrive

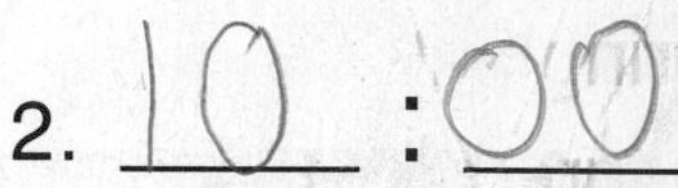

2. ____ : ____ Tour the mansion

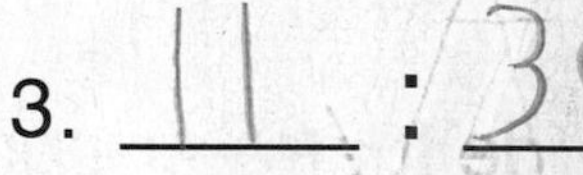
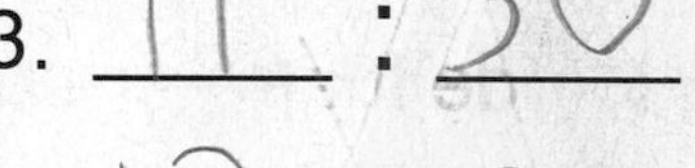

3. ____ : ____ Visit gift shop

4. ____ : ____ Lunch

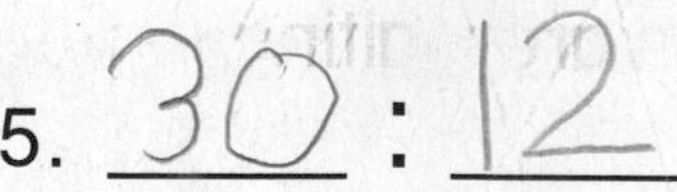
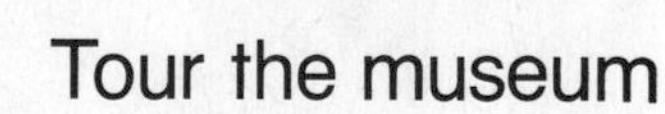

5. ____ : ____ Tour the museum

6. ____ : ____ Leave

Notes: George Washington inherited Mount Vernon from his brother Lawrence. Although he was called away, first to war and later to be president, there was no place George Washington loved more than Mount Vernon. Mount Vernon is located in northern Virginia near Washington, D.C.

Extension: Have the children make a schedule of 5 things that they do on a Saturday.

Virginia Mathematics Standards of Learning: (1.11) Tell time to the half-hour, using an analog or digital clock.

Name ________________________________

Virginia 10B

Magical Busch Gardens

At Busch Gardens in Williamsburg, you can feel like you are in England, Germany, and France without ever leaving Virginia!

Read the stories about Busch Gardens.
Cross out the information that you do not need. Solve.

1. 12 children are on the monorail.
   8 are boys and 4 are girls.
   3 children are wearing hats.
   How many children are not wearing hats? _______ children

---

2. 5 girls are waiting to ride the roller coaster.
   6 boys are waiting to ride the roller coaster.
   The roller coaster ride will last 3 minutes.
   How many children are waiting to ride the roller coaster? _______ children

---

3. Drew saw 8 actors putting on a show.
   He saw 3 birds on a branch.
   He saw 4 actors at a snack bar.
   How many actors did he see? _______ actors

Notes: Busch Gardens in Williamsburg has 9 hamlets modeled after 17th century European villages. The amusement park has over 30 rides, an adventureland, entertainment, food, and shops.
Extension: Ask children to write their own problems that have too much information. Then have each child identify the unnecessary information in another child's problem and solve that problem.
Virginia Mathematics Standards of Learning: (1.9) Solve story and picture problems involving one-step solutions, using basic addition and subtraction facts.

Name ______________________________

Virginia
11A

Colonial Crafts

In Colonial Williamsburg people make candles, shoes, baskets, and other things like they were made long ago.

Estimate how long. Measure with your centimeter or inch ruler.

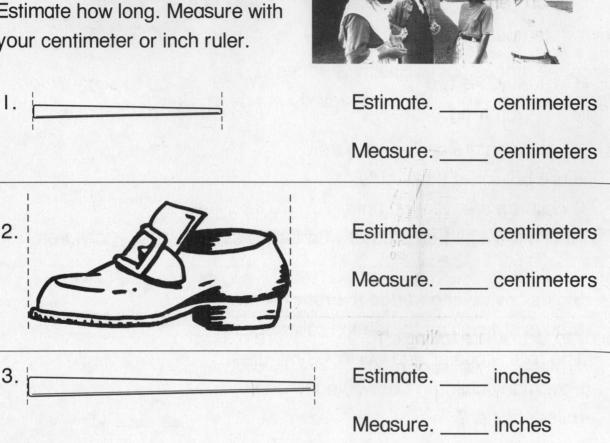

1. Estimate. _____ centimeters

   Measure. _____ centimeters

2. Estimate. _____ centimeters

   Measure. _____ centimeters

3. Estimate. _____ inches

   Measure. _____ inches

4. Explain how you measured the candle in centimeters.

____

____

Notes: Remind children to use the first dashed vertical mark on each object as a place to line up the zero on their rulers and the second dashed vertical mark to read the length of the object from the ruler.
Extension: Ask children to measure the length of a classroom object such as a crayon or pencil in both centimeters and inches. Discuss with children why there are more centimeters than inches in the measurements.
Virginia Mathematics Standards of Learning: (2.12) Estimate and then use a ruler to make linear measurements to the nearest centimeter and inch.

Name ________________________________

Weather or Not!

Virginia
11B

People who live in Virginia enjoy the changes in weather during the four seasons.

Read each sentence. Circle the [thermometer] that shows the correct temperature.

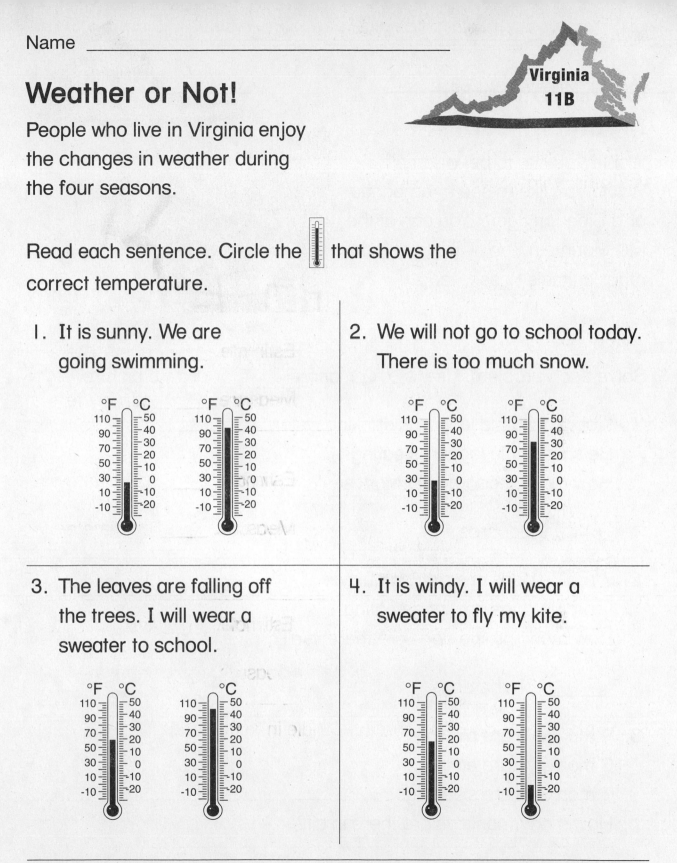

1. It is sunny. We are going swimming.

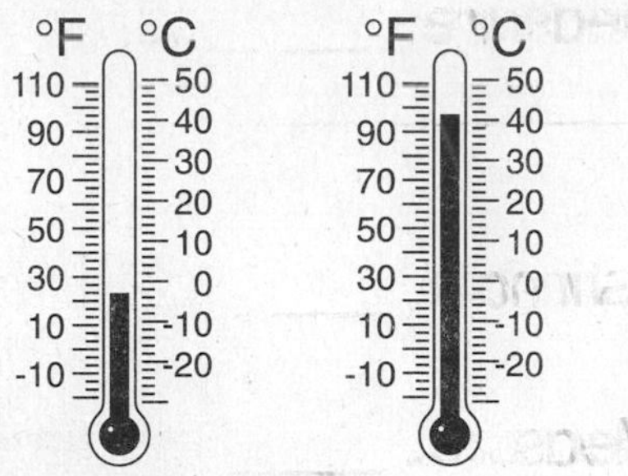

2. We will not go to school today. There is too much snow.

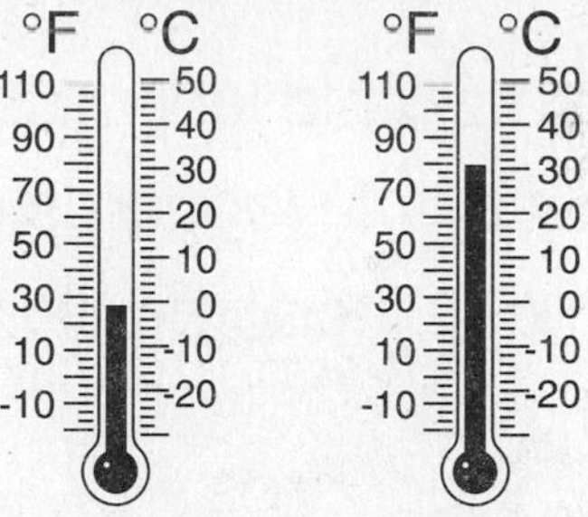

3. The leaves are falling off the trees. I will wear a sweater to school.

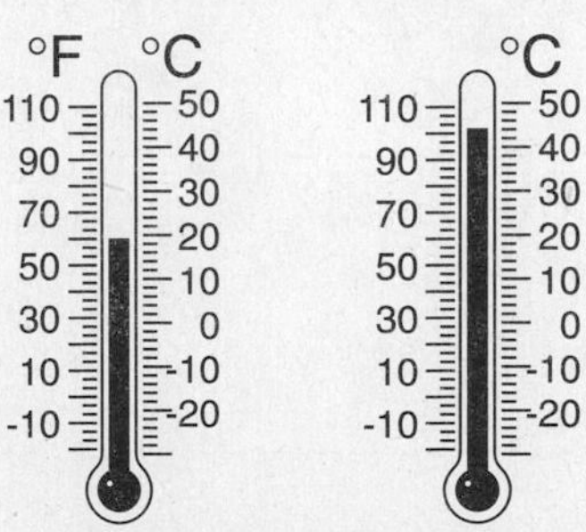

4. It is windy. I will wear a sweater to fly my kite.

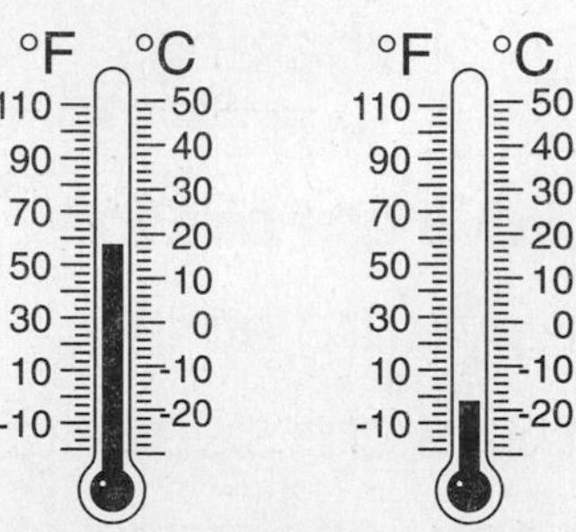

Notes: Temperatures in the eastern part of Virginia are mild because of the ocean. Temperatures vary much more inland, especially in the Appalachian Highlands.
Extension: Use a thermometer in the classroom to record the temperatures at noon for a week. Then have children identify the low and high temperatures for that week. Children can put the temperatures in order from the lowest to the highest temperature or from the highest to the lowest temperature.
Virginia Mathematics Standards of Learning: (1.18) The student will investigate, identify, and describe various forms of data collection in his/her world (e.g., recording daily temperature)

Name ______________________________

Virginia
12A

Come to the Mill Mountain Zoo!

Would you like to pet a llama? Would you like to see a red panda or a Siberian tiger? You can at the Mill Mountain Zoo. There are many other animals to see, too.

Solve each problem. Use ⬭ ⬭ and ▦ ▦ or draw a picture.

1. Mark saw 8 big leopards drinking water.
   He saw 6 little leopards eating.
   How many leopards did Mark see?

   _______ leopards

2. 7 prairie dogs are playing outside.
   9 prairie dogs are inside eating.
   How many prairie dogs are there in all?

   _______ prairie dogs

3. 4 monkeys are playing.
   3 monkeys are eating.
   7 monkeys are sleeping.
   How many monkeys are there in all?

   _______ monkeys

Notes: The Mill Mountain Zoological Park is in Roanoke. You can see 45 different species of animals at the zoo.
Extension: Ask children to explain how they solved each problem.
Virginia Mathematics Standards of Learning: (1.9) Solve story and picture problems involving one-step solutions, using basic addition and subtraction facts.

Name ______________________________

To a Tee

Virginia
12B

Many people in Virginia like to play golf.

Add. Use the addition fact to help you subtract.

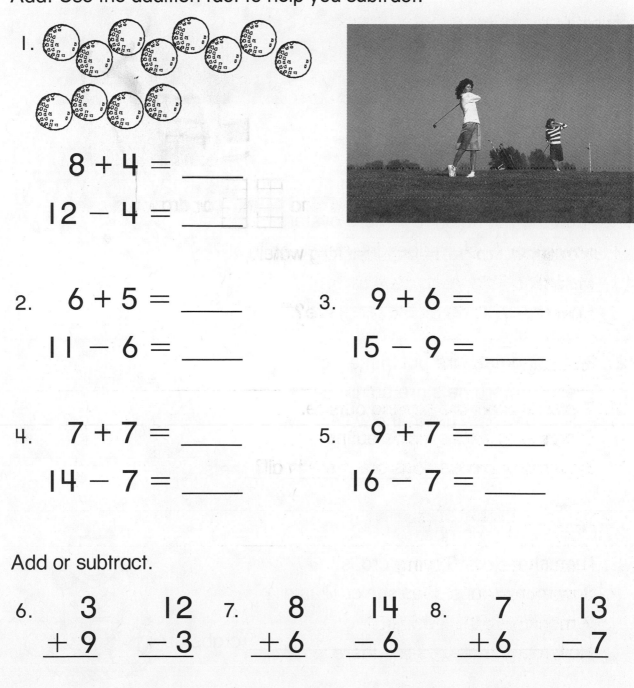

1. 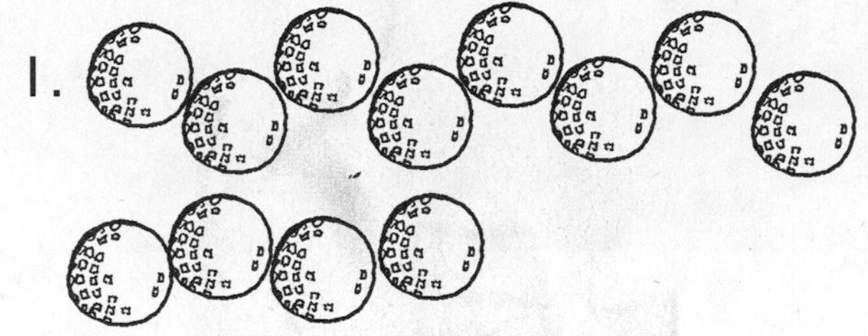

8 + 4 = ____

12 − 4 = ____

2. 6 + 5 = ____

11 − 6 = ____

3. 9 + 6 = ____

15 − 9 = ____

4. 7 + 7 = ____

14 − 7 = ____

5. 9 + 7 = ____

16 − 7 = ____

Add or subtract.

6. $\begin{array}{r} 3 \\ +\ 9 \\ \hline \end{array}$ $\begin{array}{r} 12 \\ -\ 3 \\ \hline \end{array}$

7. $\begin{array}{r} 8 \\ +\ 6 \\ \hline \end{array}$ $\begin{array}{r} 14 \\ -\ 6 \\ \hline \end{array}$

8. $\begin{array}{r} 7 \\ +\ 6 \\ \hline \end{array}$ $\begin{array}{r} 13 \\ -\ 7 \\ \hline \end{array}$

Notes: Virginia has more than 150 public golf courses. Virginia's fine resorts, including The Homestead in Hot Springs, offer golf and other activities for families to enjoy.
Extension: Say an addition fact such as 6 + 4 = 10. Ask children to give a related subtraction fact.
Virginia Mathematics Standards of Learning: (1.8) Recall basic addition facts, sums to 10 or less, and the corresponding subtraction facts.

Name ______________________________

Treasures From the Bay

Virginia is famous for its seafood. Oysters and crabs are favorites.

Use [tens | ones] and [tens rod and ones cubes].

Write the number sentence. Solve.

1. The net catches 31 oysters.
   Then the net catches 9 more oysters.
   How many oysters does the net catch in all?

   ______________________________ oysters

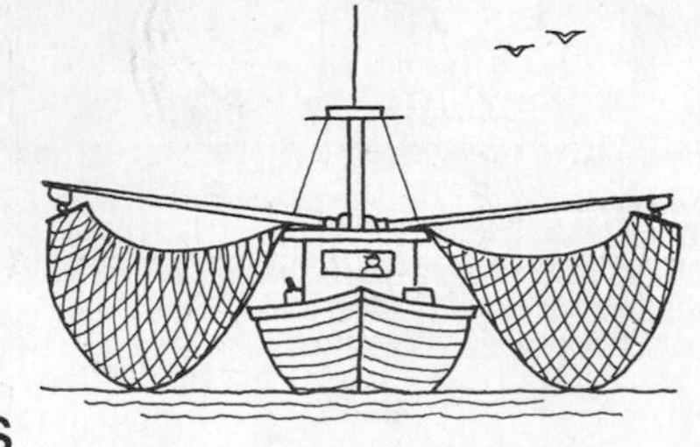

2. 24 fishing nets are put in the water.
   Then 14 more nets are put in the water.
   How many nets are in the water now?

   ______________________________ nets

3. Mary boils 16 crabs.
   Then she fries 10 more crabs.
   How many crabs does she cook in all?

   ______________________________ crabs

Notes: Virginia's yearly fish catch is very valuable. Virginia is a leading state in crab and oyster production. Other important fish catches include striped bass, flounder, menhaden, and bluefish.
Extension: Have children pick two numbers between 10 and 30 and write their own problem about crabs or oysters using these numbers. Children can solve each other's problems.
Virginia Mathematics Standards of Learning: (1.9) Solve story and picture problems involving one-step solutions, using basic addition and subtraction facts. (2.7) Given two whole numbers whose sum is 99 or less, find the sum using various methods of calculation.

Name ______________________

Practice 1-1

Numbers 1, 2, 3

Write 1, 2, and 3.

1. 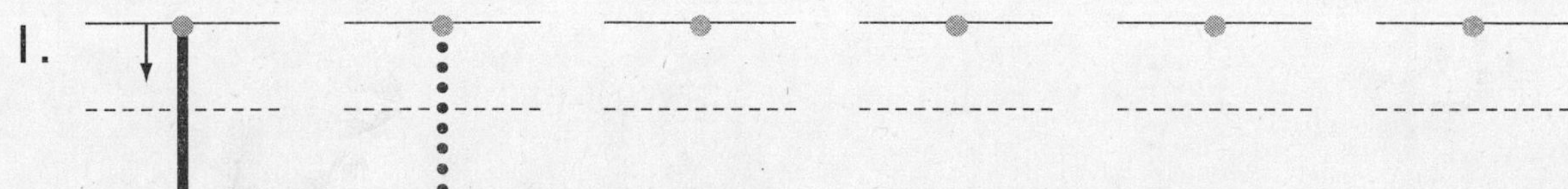

2. 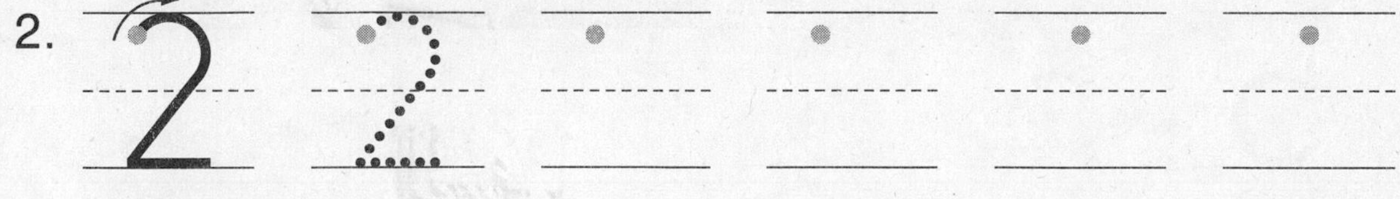

3. 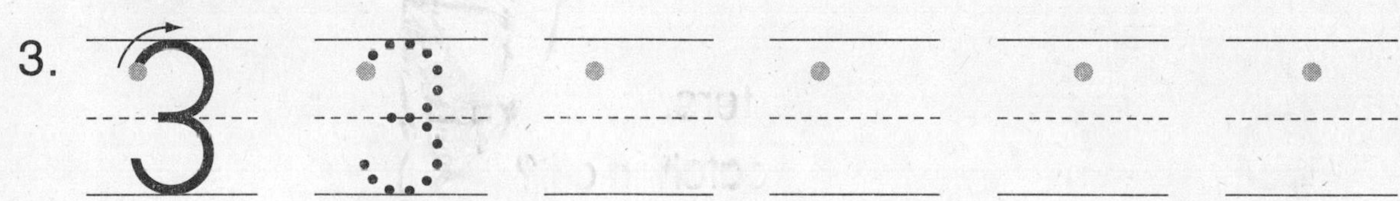

Write how many.

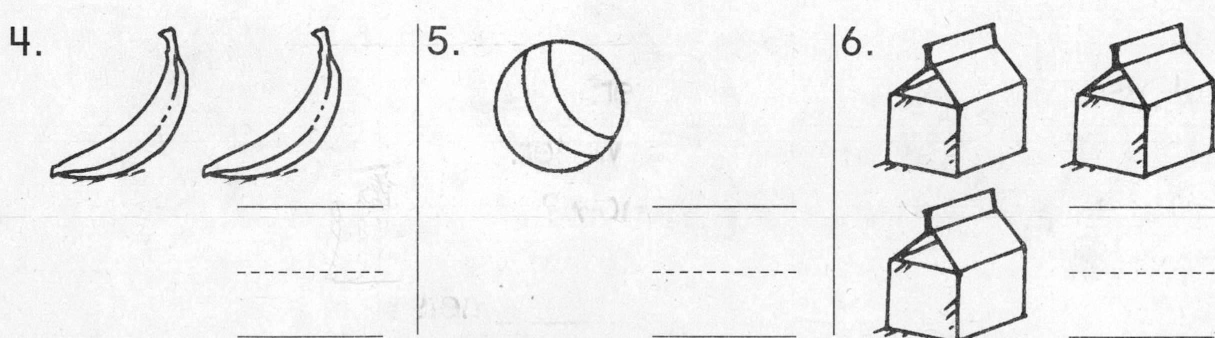

4.

5.

6.

Problem Solving Visual Thinking

Look for a group of 1, 2, or 3 in something you are wearing.

Draw what you see.

Notes for Home Your child wrote the numbers 1, 2, and 3. *Home Activity:* Ask your child to find a group of 1, 2, or 3 objects in the kitchen and write the number for how many.

Name ______________________

Practice 1-2

Numbers 4, 5, 6

Write 4, 5, and 6.

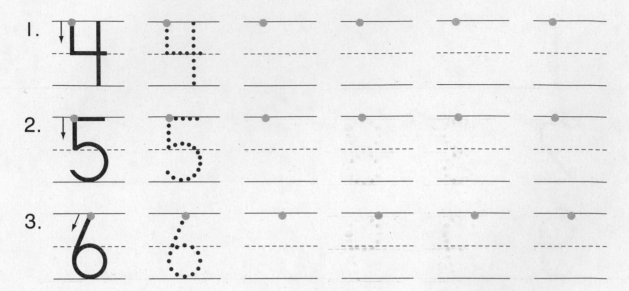

1. 4 4 ___ ___ ___ ___

2. 5 5 ___ ___ ___ ___

3. 6 6 ___ ___ ___ ___

Write how many.

4. ___ 5. ___ 6. ___

Mental Math

Write the next number.

7. 2, 3, 4

8. 4, 5, ___

9. 1, 2, ___

10. 3, 4, ___

Notes for Home Your child wrote the numbers 4, 5, and 6. *Home Activity:* Ask your child to draw groups of 4, 5, and 6 objects on a sheet of paper.

Name ______________________

Practice I-3

Numbers 7, 8, 9

Write 7, 8, and 9.

1.
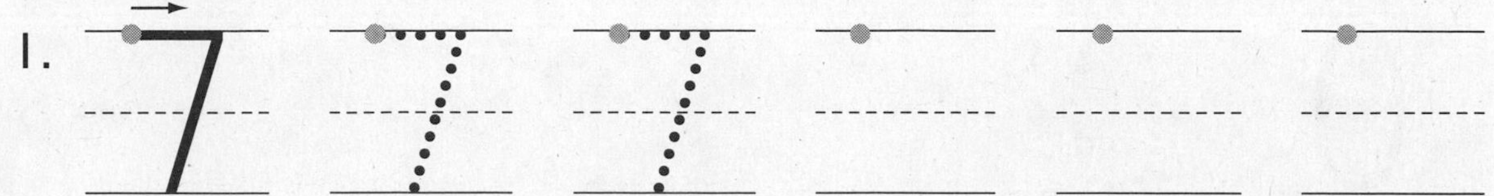

2.
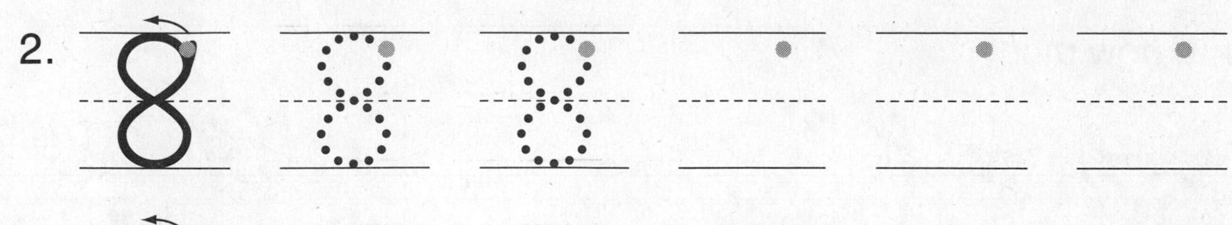

3.
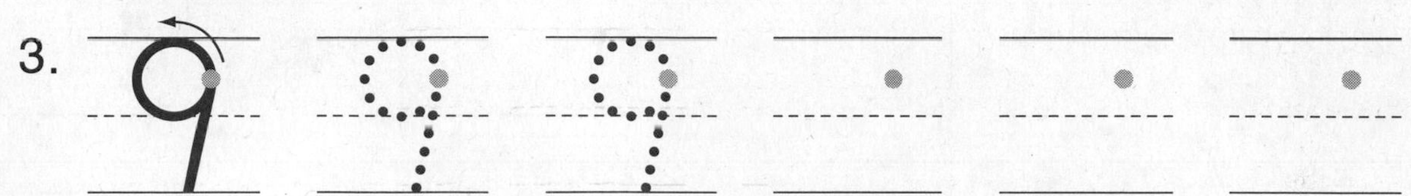

Write how many.

4. 5. 6.

7. 8. 9.
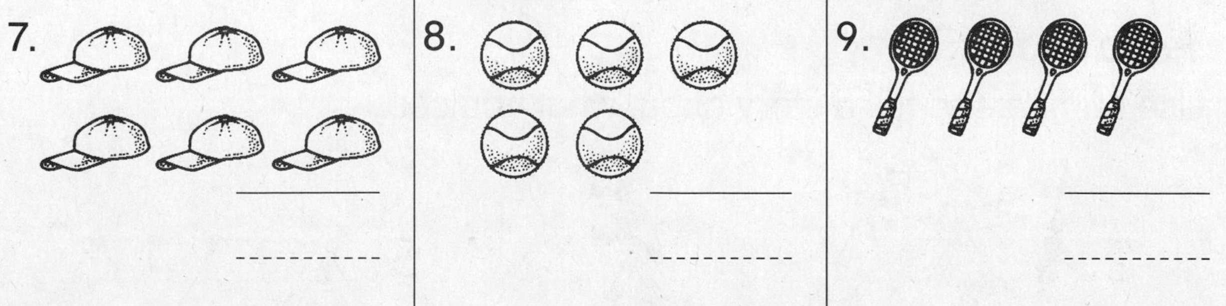

Journal

10. Draw 8 things. 11. Draw 9 things. 12. Draw 7 things.

Notes for Home Your child wrote the numbers 7, 8, and 9. *Home Activity:* Have your child find a group of 7 objects and write the number for how many.

Name ______________________

Practice 1-4

Zero

Write 0.

1. 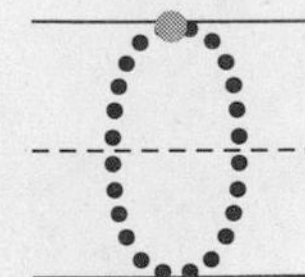  

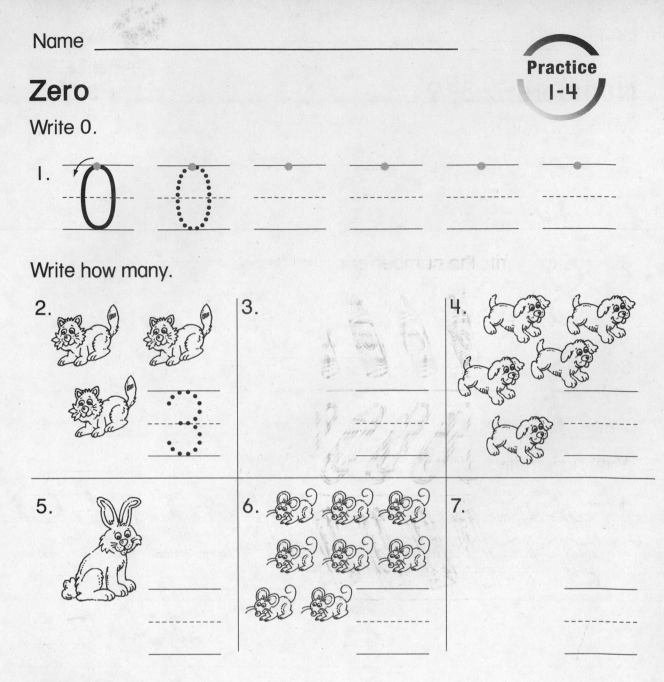

Write how many.

2. 

3. 

4. 

5. 

6. 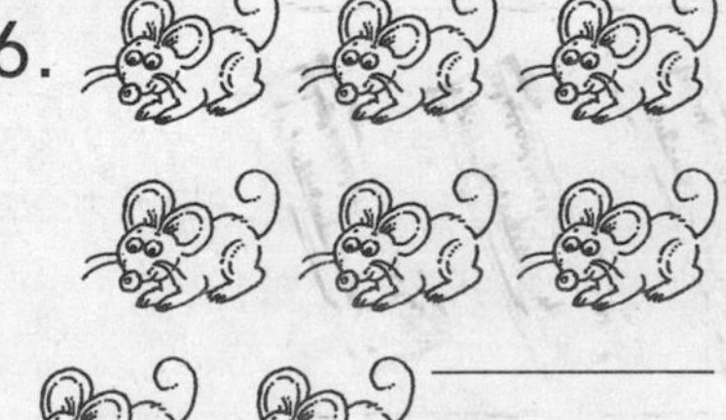

7.

Tell a Math Story

Use numbers to tell a story about what you see.

Notes for Home Your child wrote the number 0. *Home Activity:* Ask your child to make up a math story using any numbers from 0 to 9.

Name ______________________________

Practice 1-5

Numbers to 10

Write 10.

1. 10 10

How many? Write the number or draw the picture.

2. 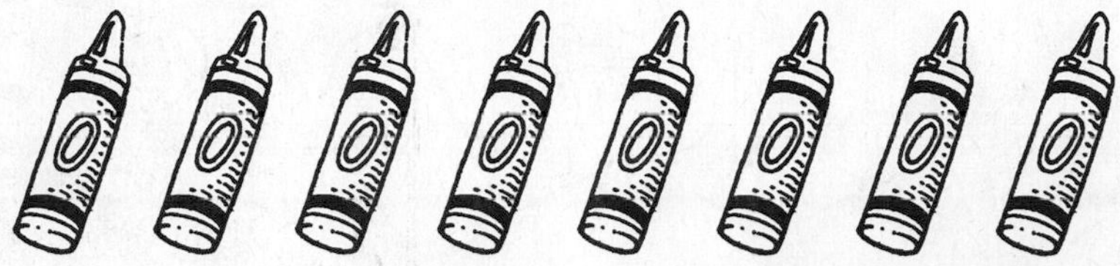 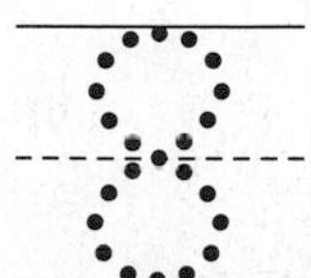

3. 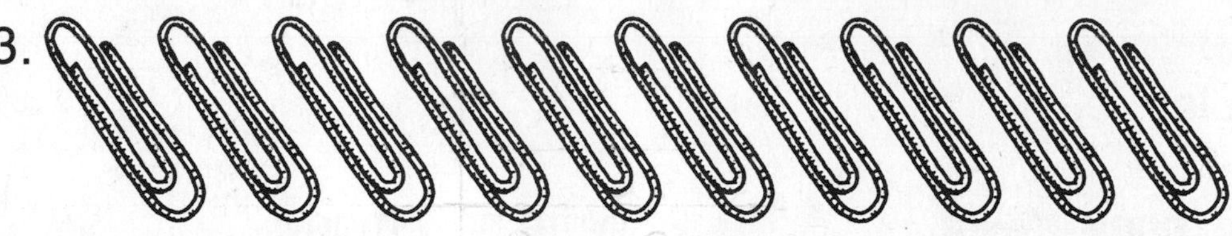

4. 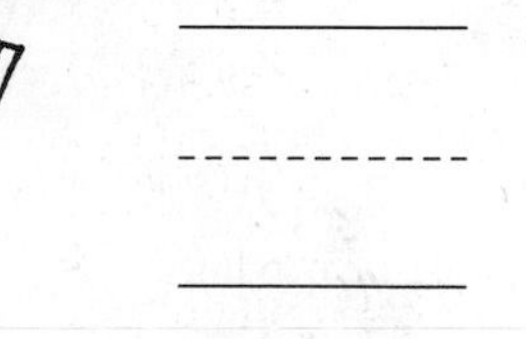

5. 

Problem Solving Visual Thinking

Circle the picture that shows 10.

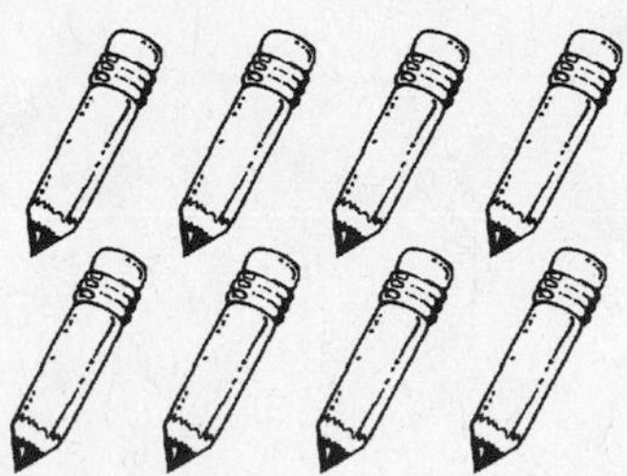 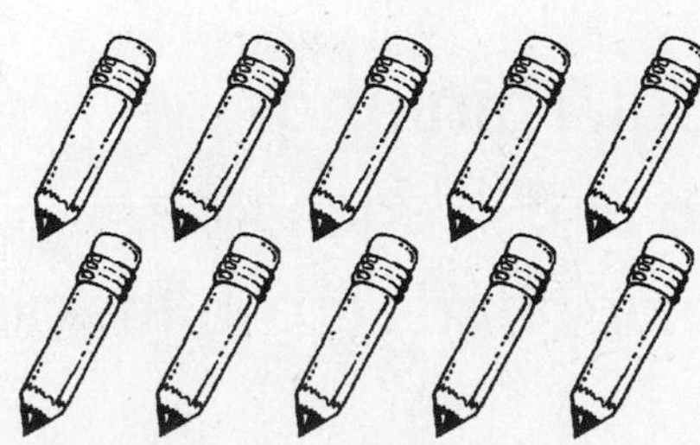

Notes for Home Your child wrote the number 10 and counted and drew up to 10 objects. *Home Activity:* Ask your child to find 10 objects in his or her room and draw a picture of them.

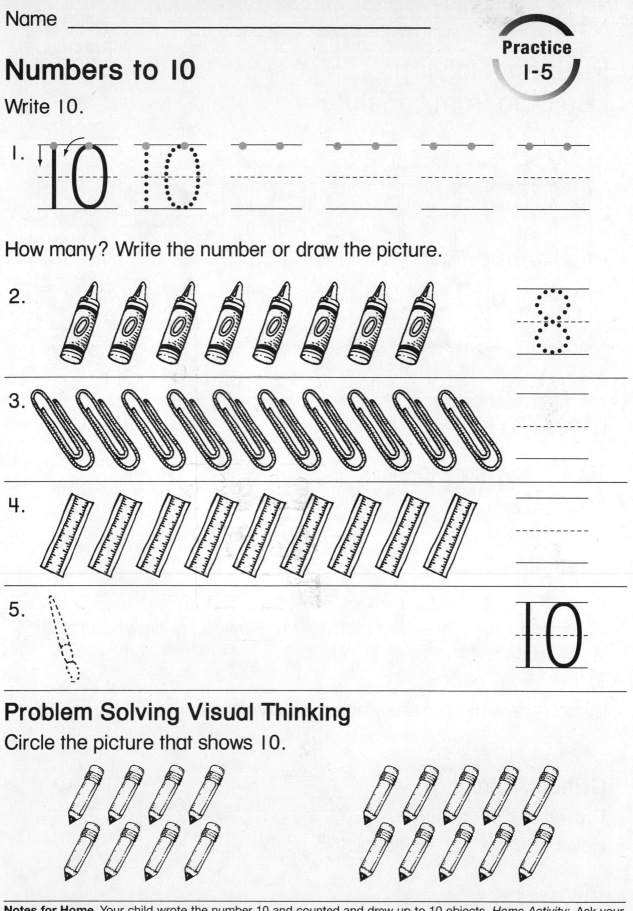

Name ______________________

Practice 1-6

Problem Solving:
Use Data from a Picture

Look at the picture.

1. Write how many .

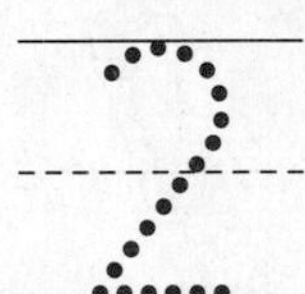

2. Write how many  .

______

3. Draw a for each child.

4. How many did you draw?

______

Critical Thinking

Draw a bird in each tree.

How many birds are in the picture now? ______

Notes for Home Your child solved problems using pictures. *Home Activity:* Ask your child to explain how he or she found the answer for Exercise 3.

Name ______________________

Practice
Chapter 1
A

Mixed Practice: Lessons 1–6

Write how many.

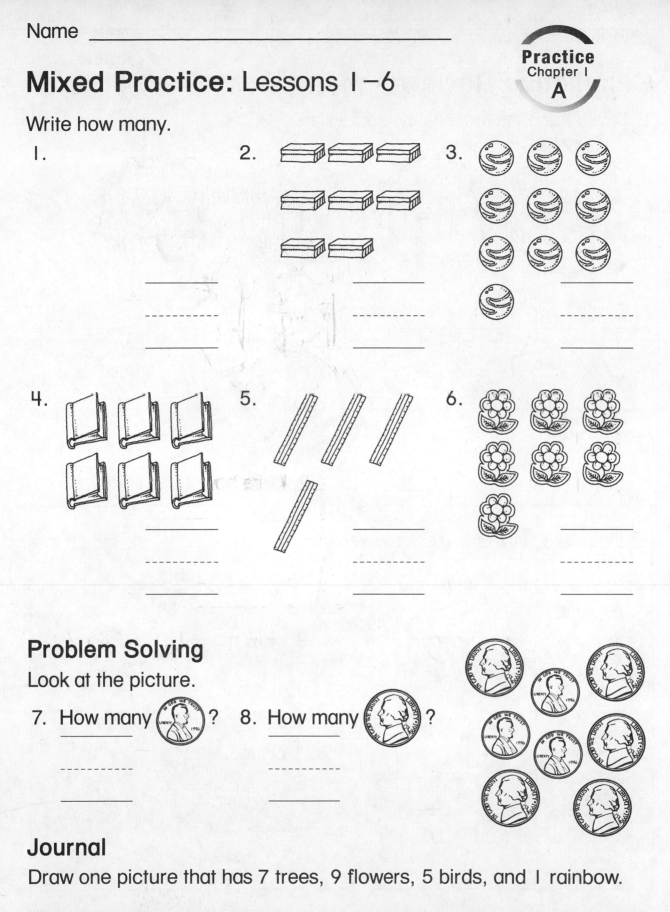

1.

2. 

3.   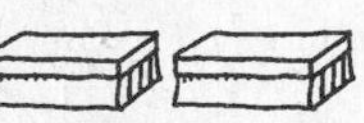   

4. 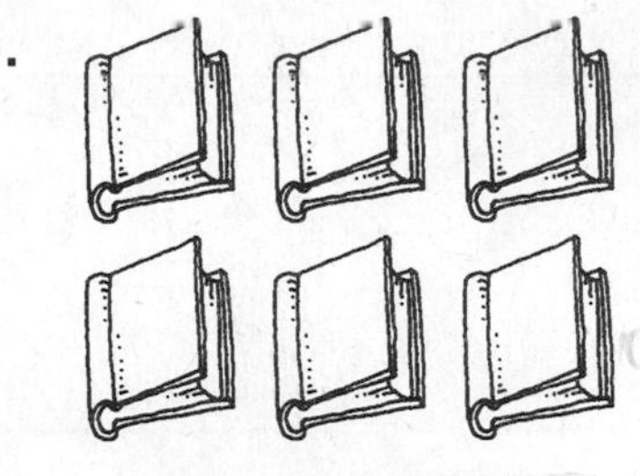

5. 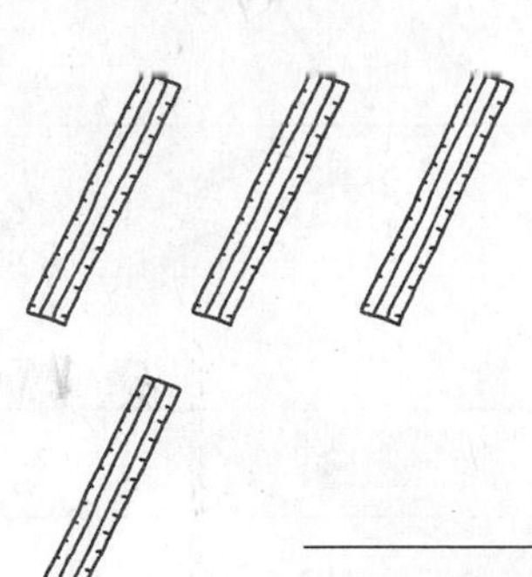

6. 

Problem Solving

Look at the picture.

7. How many  ?

8. How many  ?

Journal

Draw one picture that has 7 trees, 9 flowers, 5 birds, and 1 rainbow.

Notes for Home Your child practiced counting and identifying groups of objects to 10. *Home Activity:* Set out 3 groups of objects containing from 1 to 10 objects each. Ask your child to count the number of objects in each group and to write the numbers.

Use with page 17.

Name ______________________________

Practice
Chapter 1
A

Cumulative Review

1. Circle the ones that are the same size.

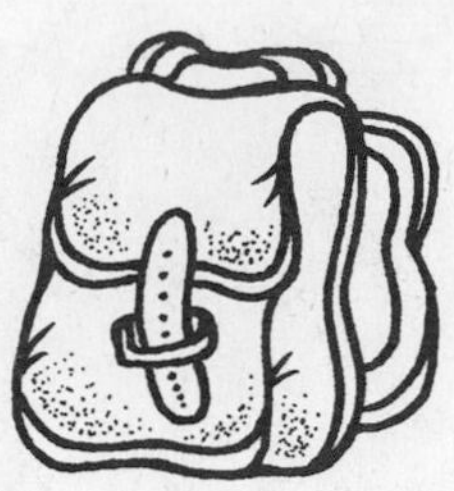
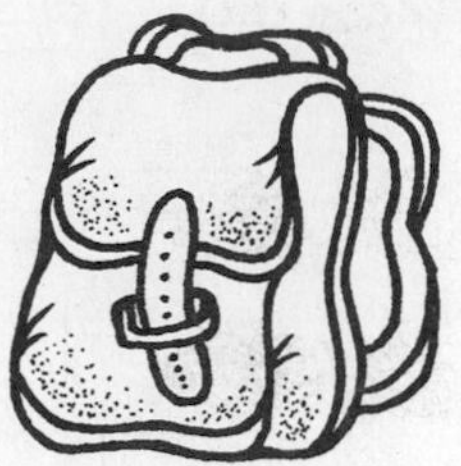
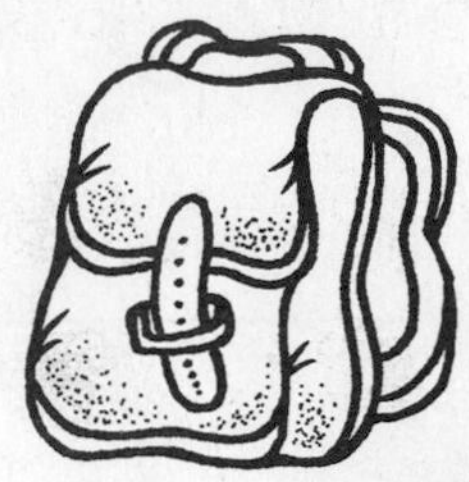

2. Circle the ones that are the same shape.

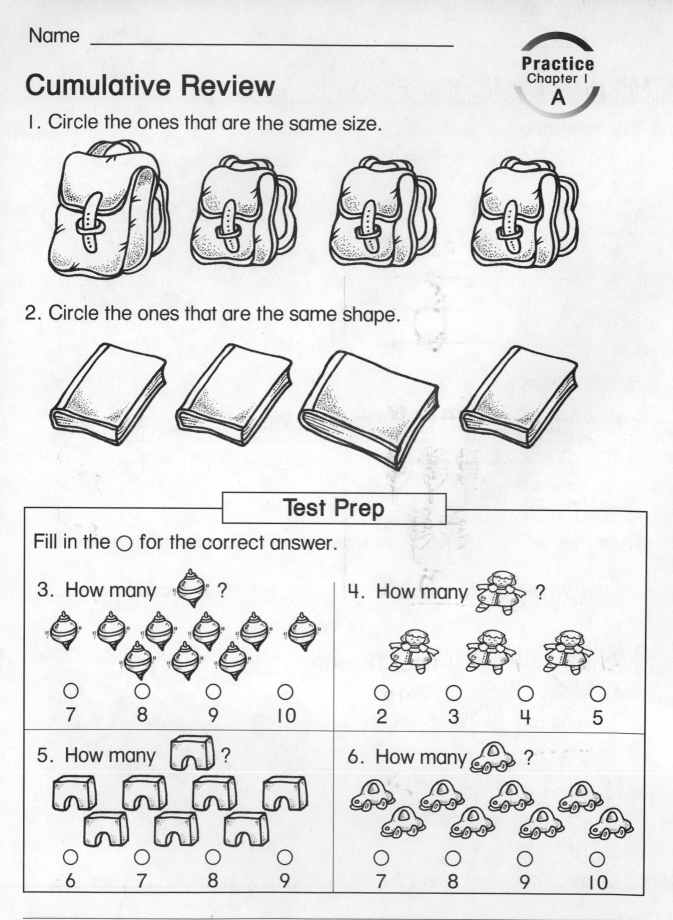

Test Prep

Fill in the ○ for the correct answer.

3. How many ?

○ 7 ○ 8 ○ 9 ○ 10

4. How many ?

○ 2 ○ 3 ○ 4 ○ 5

5. How many ?

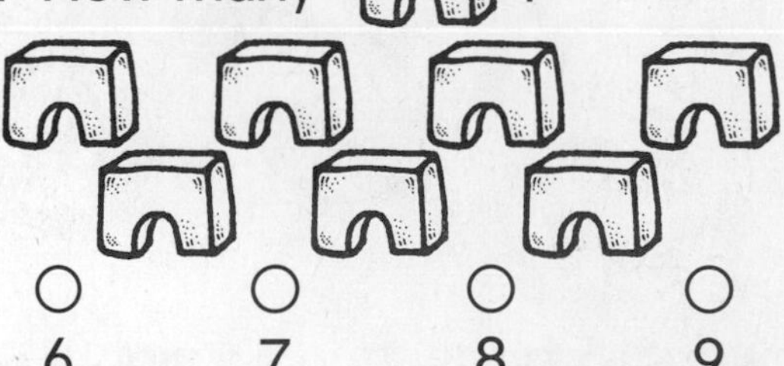

○ 6 ○ 7 ○ 8 ○ 9

6. How many ?

○ 7 ○ 8 ○ 9 ○ 10

Notes for Home Your child reviewed sorting by size and shape, and counting from 1 to 10 objects. *Home Activity:* Ask your child to explain how he or she chose the correct answer in Exercise 6.

Name ___________

Practice I-7

Explore More and Fewer

Write how many.

Circle the group that has more.

1. 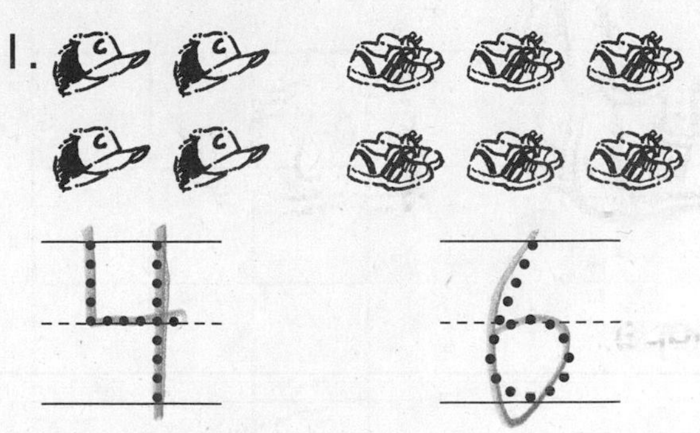

2. 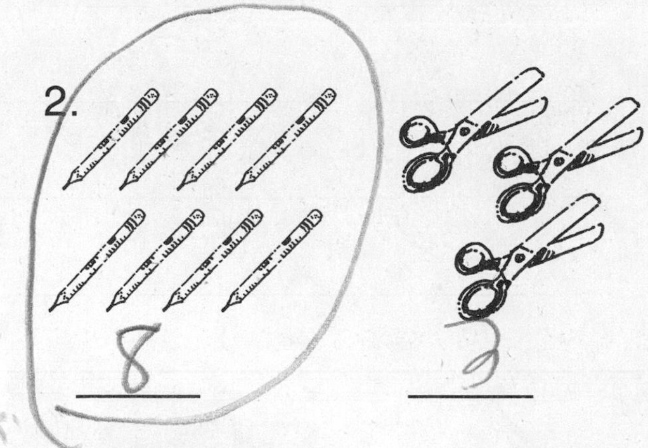

Write how many.

Circle the group that has fewer.

3. 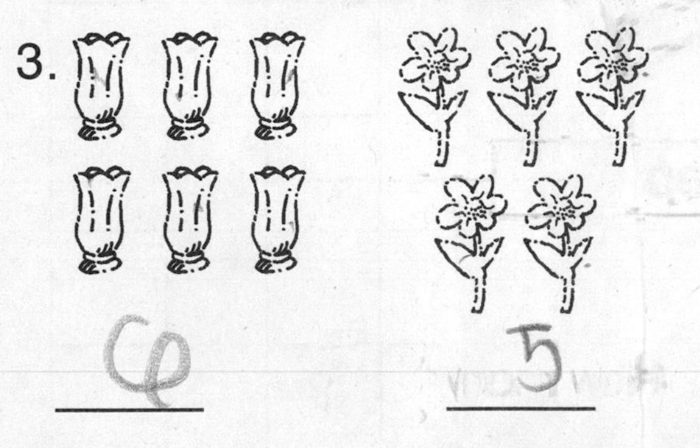

4. 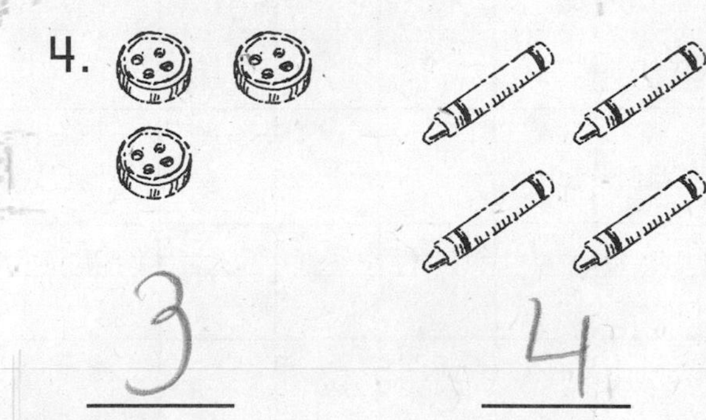

Problem Solving Critical Thinking

Draw a line to give each child a

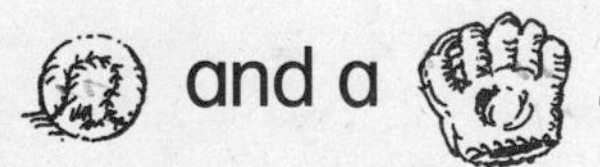 and a .

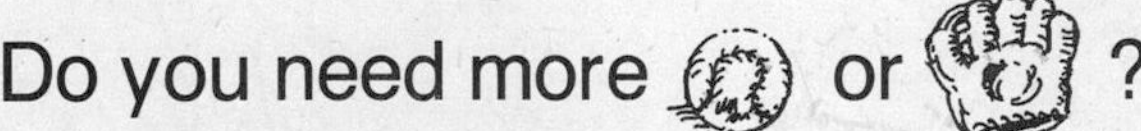

Do you need more or ?

Circle .

Notes for Home Your child practiced telling which group had more and which group had fewer. *Home Activity:* Arrange two unequal groups of objects, each with 10 or fewer. Ask your child to tell which group has fewer.

Name ___________________________

Order Numbers to 10

Draw the missing towers. Write how many.

1.

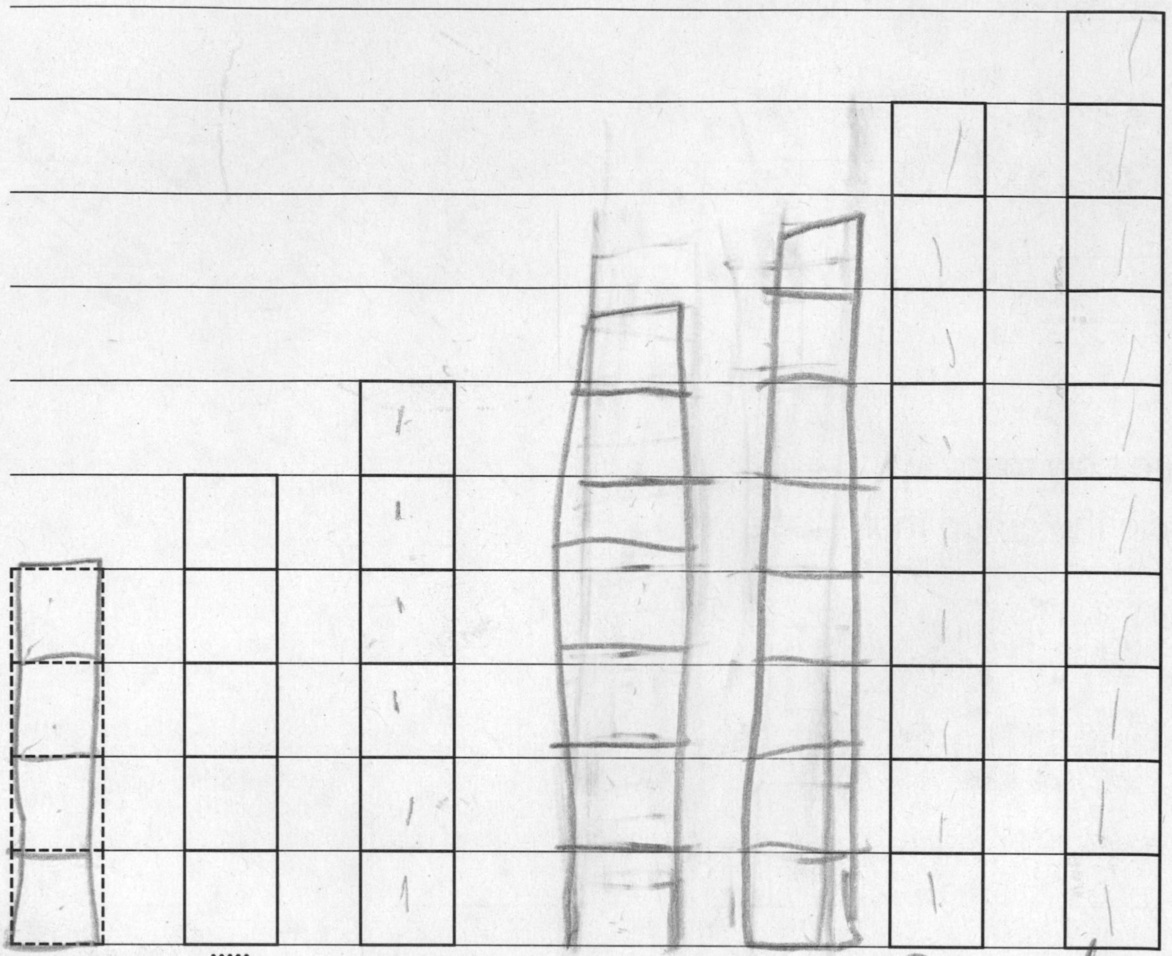

4   5   ___   7   8   ___   ___

Problem Solving Critical Thinking

Connect the dots in order.

What do you see?

____

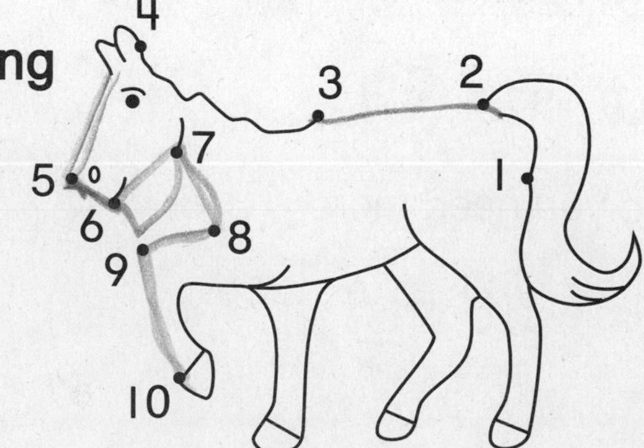

Notes for Home Your child practiced ordering numbers from 1 through 10. *Home Activity:* Say a sequence of two numbers, such as "4, 5," and ask your child to say the number that comes next. (6)

Name ______________________________

Understand 11 and 12

Practice 1-9

Write how many.

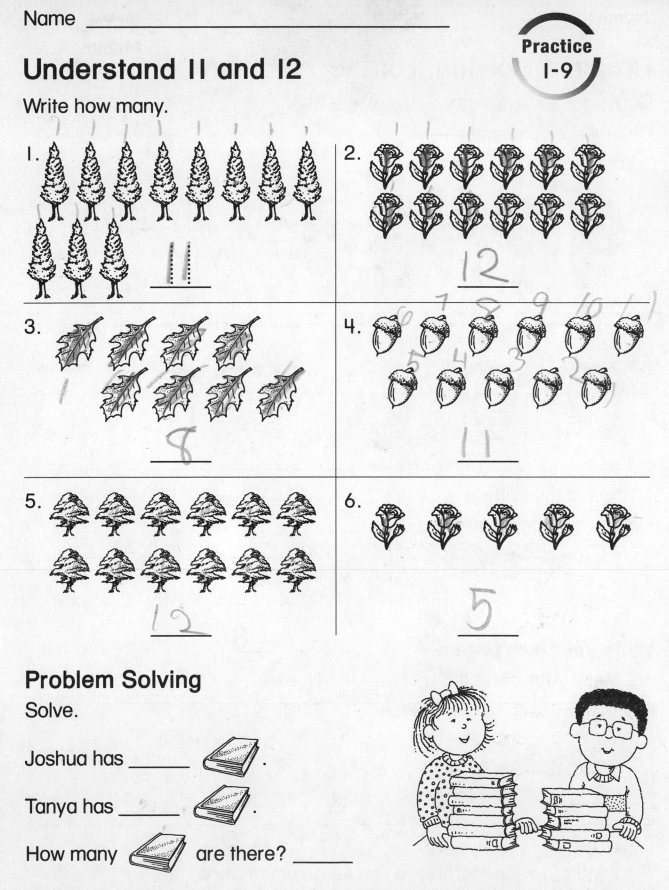

1. 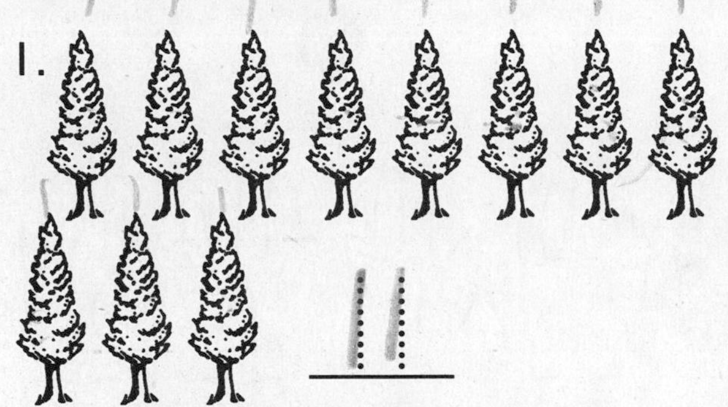 ______

2.  ______

3. 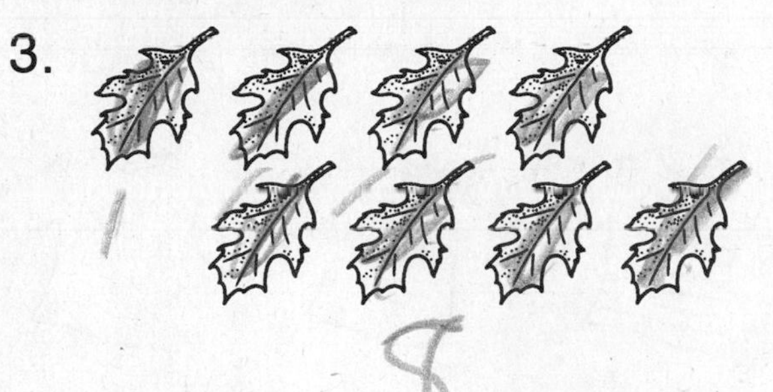 ______

4. 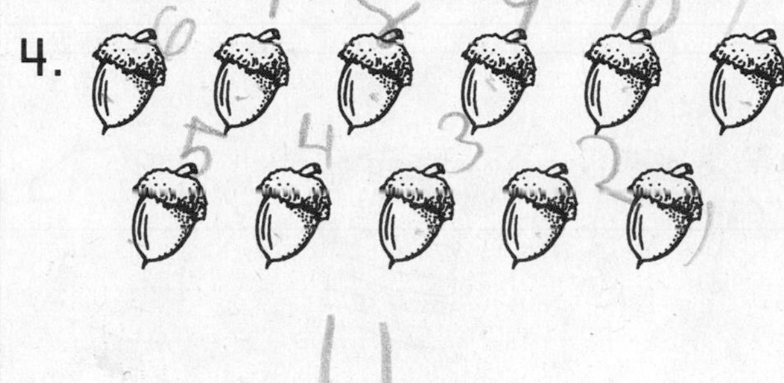 ______

5.  ______

6.  ______

Problem Solving

Solve.

Joshua has ______ .

Tanya has ______ .

How many  are there? ______

Notes for Home Your child counted from 1 to 12 and recognized the symbols for 11 and 12. *Home Activity:* Make groups of 10, 11, and 12 objects, such as paper clips or rubber bands. Then ask your child to count the objects in each group and write the number.

Name ________________________________

Practice
1-10

Problem Solving: Look for a Pattern

Complete each pattern.

Color what comes next.

1. 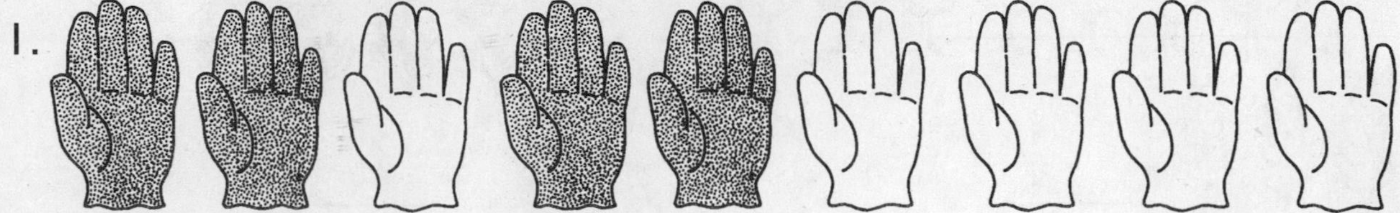

2. 

Complete the pattern.

Draw what comes next.

3.     

Write your own pattern.

4. Make your own pattern. Draw it 3 times.

Journal

Find and draw 3 patterns you can see in your house.

Notes for Home Your child completed a pattern and made his or her own pattern. *Home Activity:* Ask your child to say the pattern in Problem 2 on this page aloud and then make up a new pattern.

 Use with pages 27–28.

Name ______________________

Practice
Chapter 1
B

Mixed Practice: Lessons 7–10

Write how many.
Circle the group that has fewer.

1. ☆☆☆☆ ☆☆☆☆ ☆☆☆   (moons)

____   ____

Write how many.

2.

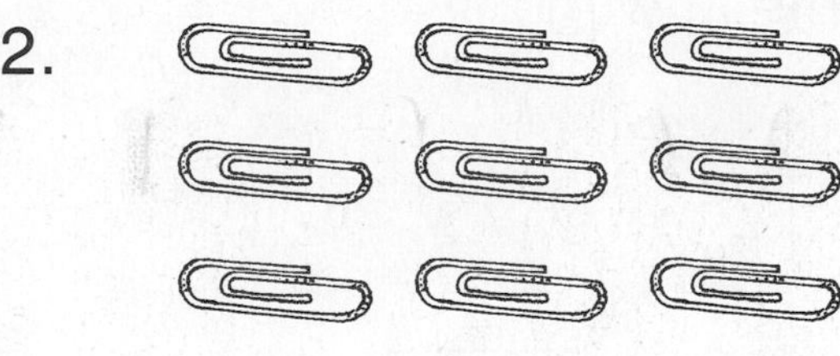

____

Draw the missing towers.
Write how many are in each.

3.

2 ____ 4 ____ 6 ____ 8

Problem Solving

Draw what comes next in the pattern.

Journal

Draw a pattern. Use colors and shapes in your pattern.

Notes for Home Your child reviewed sorting by size and shape, and counting from 1 to 10.
Home Activity: Ask your child to explain how he or she determined what to draw next in the Problem Solving pattern.

Name ______________________________

Cumulative Review

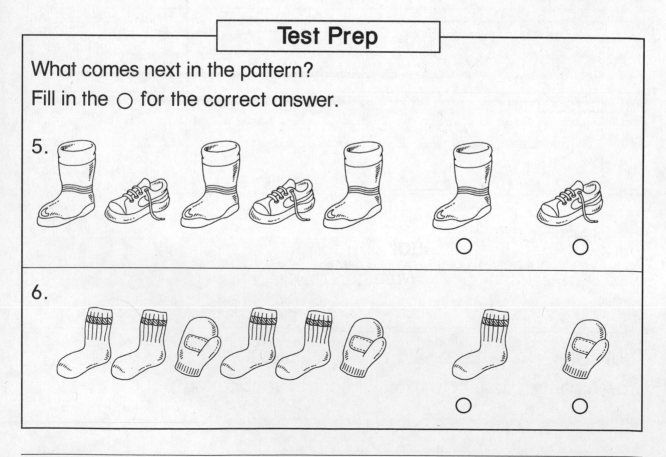

1. Draw 7  .

   Write how many.

   ____

2. Write how many  .

   ____

3. Write the missing numbers.

4. Write the missing numbers.

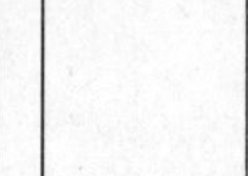

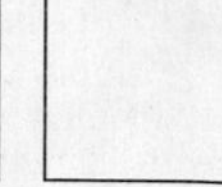

	4		6			9		11	

Test Prep

What comes next in the pattern?

Fill in the ○ for the correct answer.

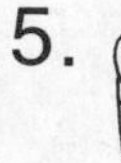

5.

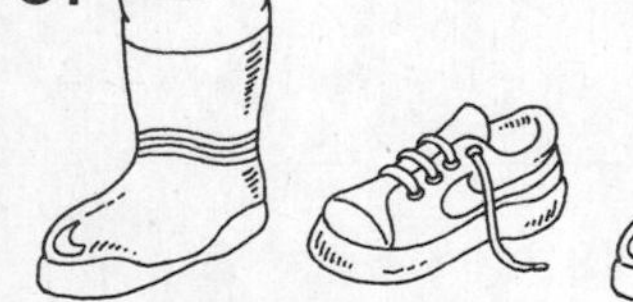

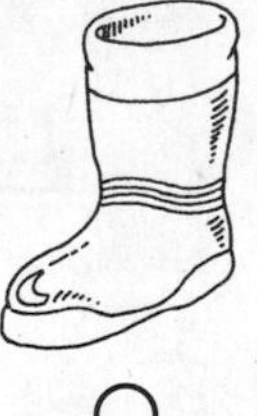

○ ○

6.

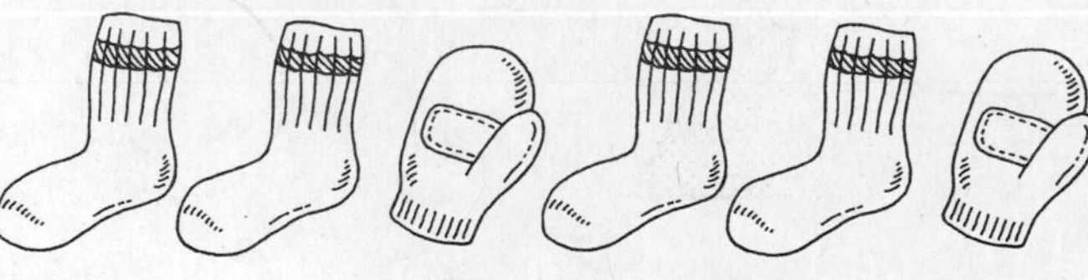
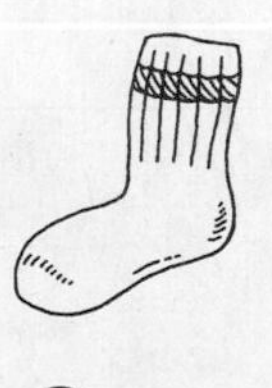

○ ○

Notes for Home Your child reviewed counting and ordering numbers from 1 to 12, and continued a pattern. *Home Activity:* Ask your child to continue the pattern in Exercise 6 by drawing the next three items. (sock, mitten, sock)

Name ___________________________

Explore Sorting and Classifying

Circle the shape that goes with the group.

1.

2.

3.

4.

Problem Solving Visual Thinking

Count the shapes above. Write how many.

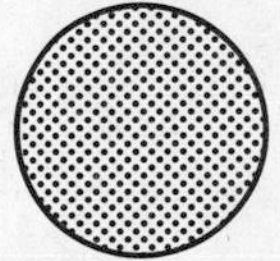
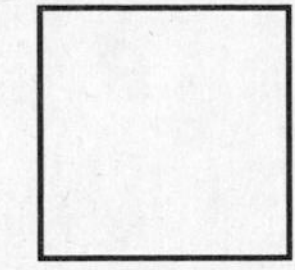

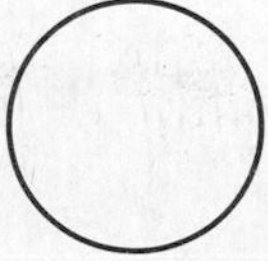

_____ _____ _____ _____

Notes for Home Your child sorted shapes by color and size. *Home Activity:* Ask your child to draw another shape that belongs in each group.

Name ______________________________

Create a Graph

Use the graph.
Which has more?
Circle the answer.

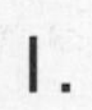
1.  

2.  

3.  

Small Animals We Saw at the Aquarium

Use the graph.
Which has fewer?
Circle the answer.

4.  

5.  

Large Animals We Saw at the Aquarium

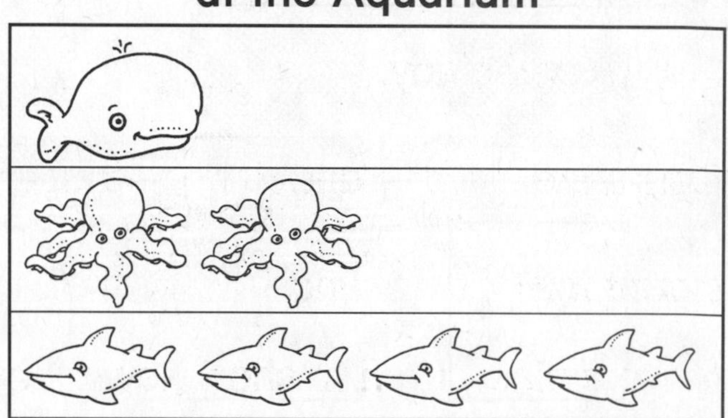

Write About It

Make your own graph.
Draw a picture to complete the sentences.

I have more ________.

I have fewer ________.

My Graph

Notes for Home Your child used a graph to tell if there was more or fewer. *Home Activity:* Ask your child to make a graph of food or snack items at home.

Name ______________________________

Practice 1-13

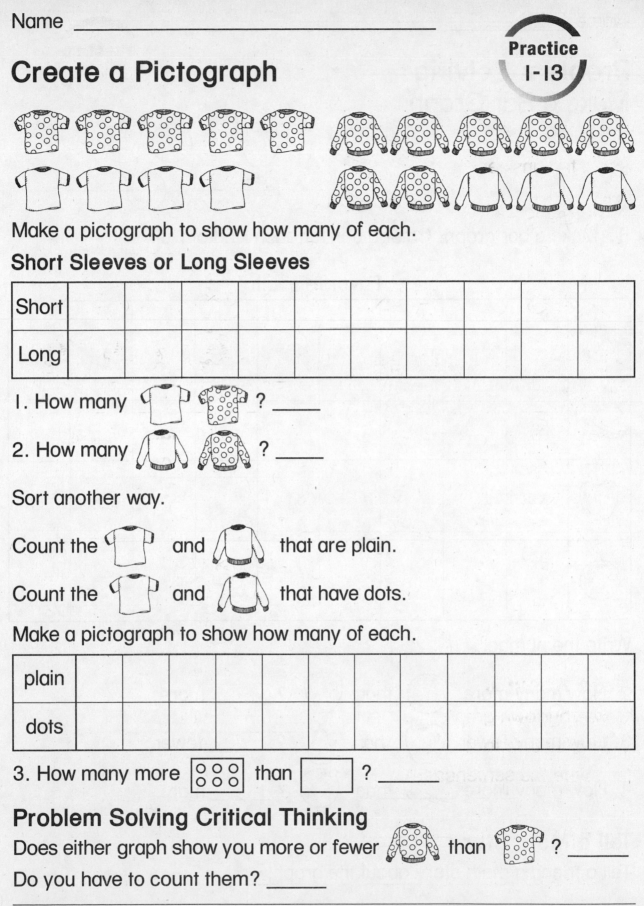

Create a Pictograph

Make a pictograph to show how many of each.

Short Sleeves or Long Sleeves

Short										
Long										

1. How many ? ____

2. How many ? ____

Sort another way.

Count the and that are plain.

Count the and that have dots.

Make a pictograph to show how many of each.

plain											
dots											

3. How many more than ? ____

Problem Solving Critical Thinking

Does either graph show you more or fewer than ? ____

Do you have to count them? ____

Notes for Home Your child created and used a pictograph. *Home Activity:* Ask your child to make a pictograph of two types of objects at home.

Name ______________________________

Practice 1-14

Problem Solving:
Make a Bar Graph

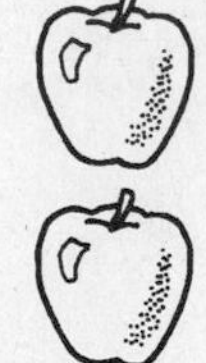
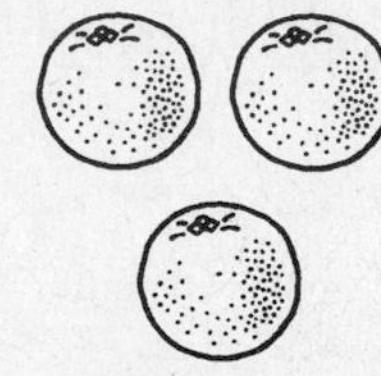

1. Make a bar graph. Color a box for each kind of fruit.

Favorite Fruit

Write the number.

2. How many more  than  ? ______ more

3. How many fewer  than  ? ______ fewer

4. How many more  than  ? ______ more

Tell a Math Story

Tell a friend a math story about the graph.

Notes for Home Your child made a bar graph and told a math story using the information on the graph. *Home Activity:* Ask your child to tell you how many more pears there are than bananas. (2)

Name ______________________________

Practice Chapter 1 C

Mixed Practice: Lessons 11-14

1. Make a pictograph.
   Color a picture for each  and .

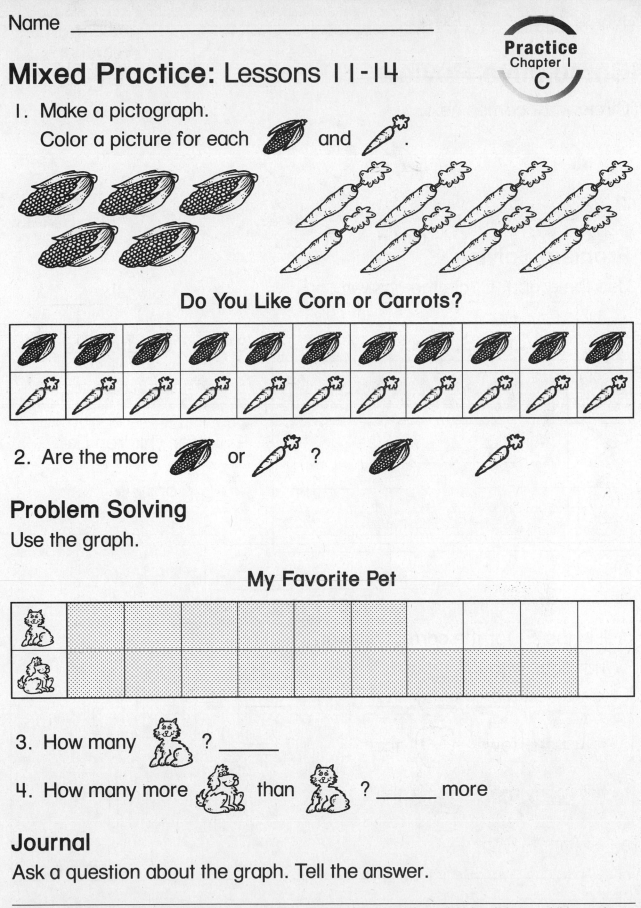

Do You Like Corn or Carrots?

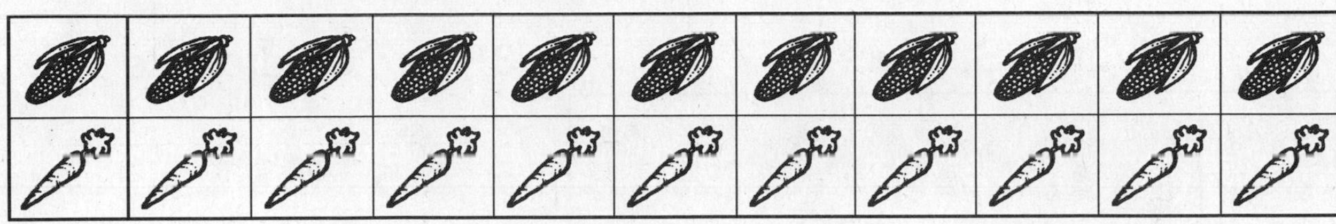

2. Are the more  or ?  

Problem Solving

Use the graph.

My Favorite Pet

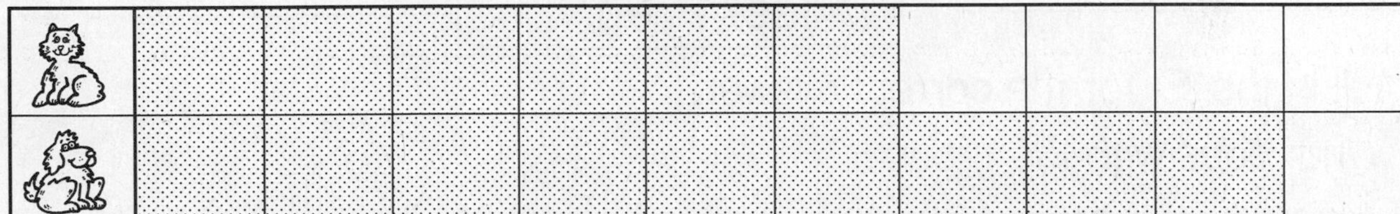

3. How many  ? ______

4. How many more  than  ? ______ more

Journal

Ask a question about the graph. Tell the answer.

Notes for Home Your child practiced using graphs to answer questions. *Home Activity:* Ask your child to make a bar graph of two types of things in his or her room at home.

Name ___________________________________

Cumulative Review

Circle what comes next.

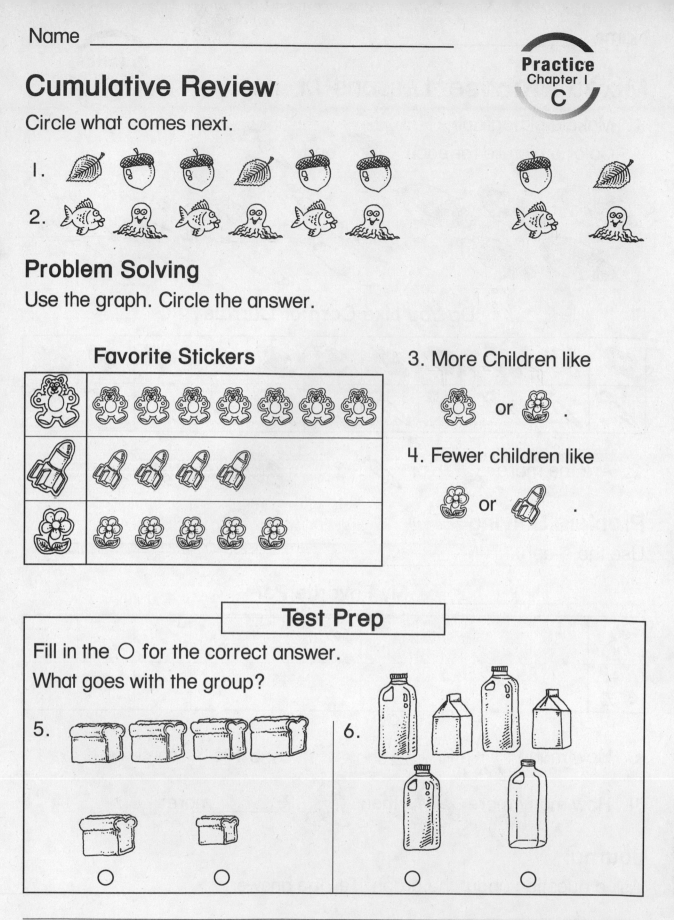

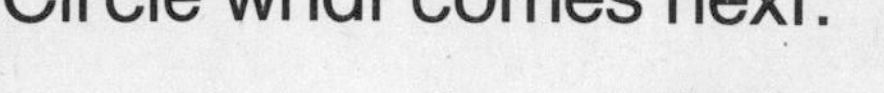

1.  

2.   

Problem Solving

Use the graph. Circle the answer.

Favorite Stickers

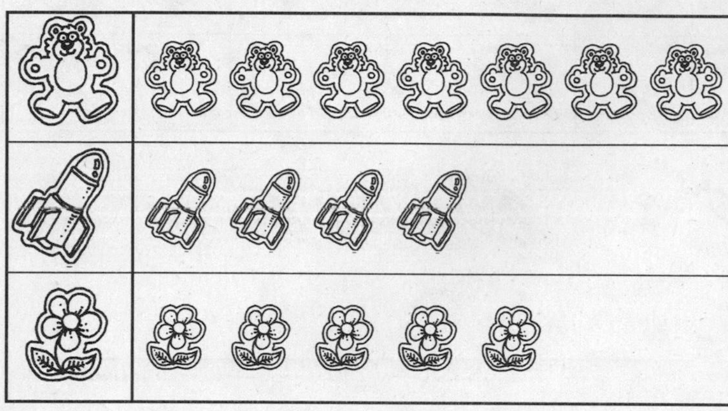

3. More Children like  or .

4. Fewer children like  or  .

Test Prep

Fill in the ○ for the correct answer.

What goes with the group?

5. 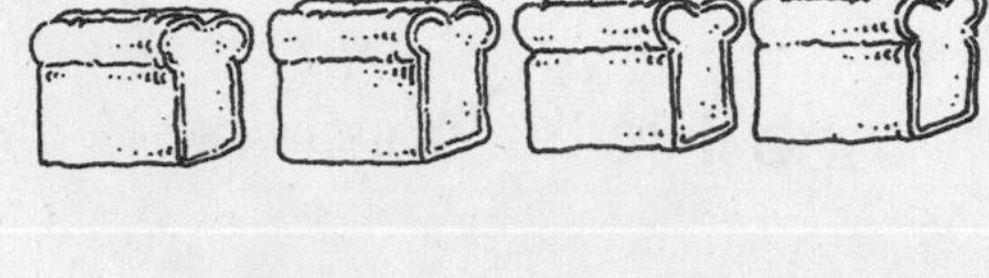

○ ○

6.   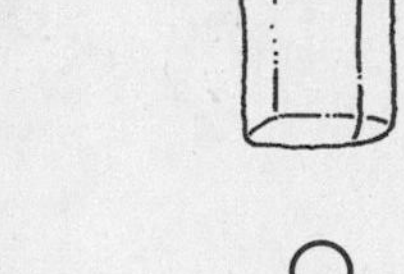

○ ○

Notes for Home Your child reviewed concepts taught in Chapter 1. *Home Activity:* Ask your child to explain how he or she determined what came next in the patterns.

Name ______________________________

Explore Ways to Make 4 and 5

Show ways to make 5. Color the Snap Cubes.
Write the numbers.

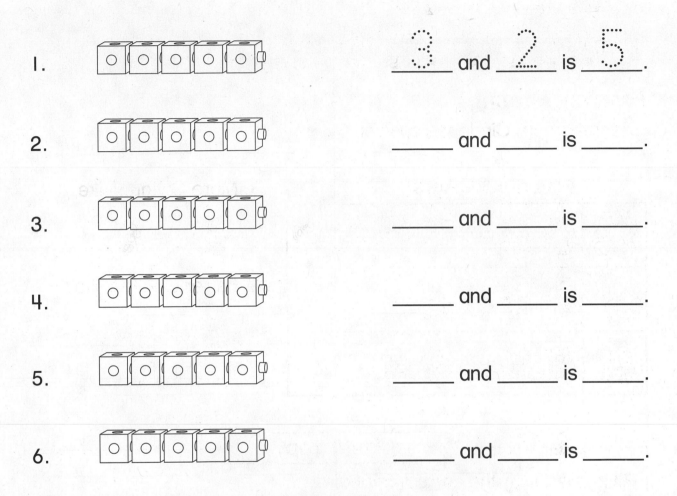

1. 3 and 2 is 5.
2. ______ and ______ is ______.
3. ______ and ______ is ______.
4. ______ and ______ is ______.
5. ______ and ______ is ______.
6. ______ and ______ is ______.

Problem Solving Critical Thinking

7. How can you use a Snap Cube to show that 4 and 1 is the same as 1 and 4?

Notes for Home Your child used Snap Cubes to find ways to make 5. *Home Activity:* Ask your child to find four different ways to make a group of 5 using household objects.

Name ______________________

Ways to Make 6 and 7

Practice 2-2

Show ways to make 6. Color the Snap Cubes.
Write the numbers.

1. 4 and 2 is 6.

2. ______ and ______ is ______.

3. ______ and ______ is ______.

4. ______ and ______ is ______.

5. ______ and ______ is ______.

6. ______ and ______ is ______.

Mental Math

Solve. You have 3.

7. Circle the card you need to make 6.

Notes for Home Your child used Snap Cubes to find different ways to make 6. *Home Activity:* Ask your child to draw groups of 6 and 7 objects.

Name ______________________________

Ways to Make 8 and 9

Practice 2-3

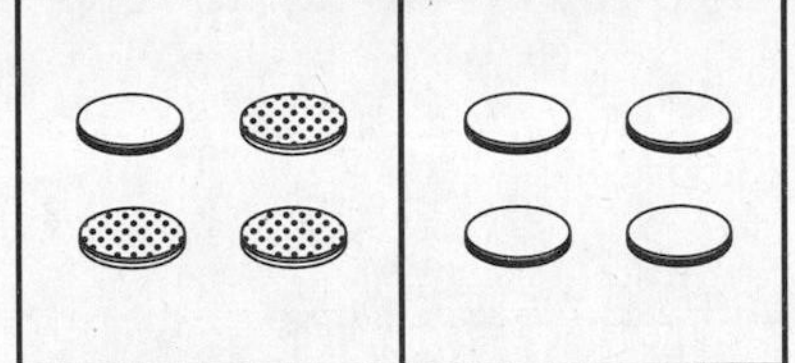

Spill 8 counters.

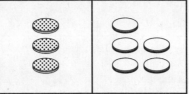

Show gray and white on your mat.

Gray	White	In All
3	5	8

Use the table to record.

Spill counters and show ways to make 8.
Record the ways.

	Gray	White	In All
1.	3	5	8
2.			
3.			
4.			

Problem Solving Visual Thinking

5. Match the groups with the same number.

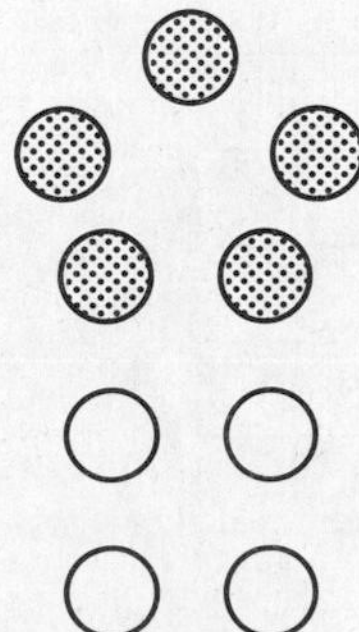

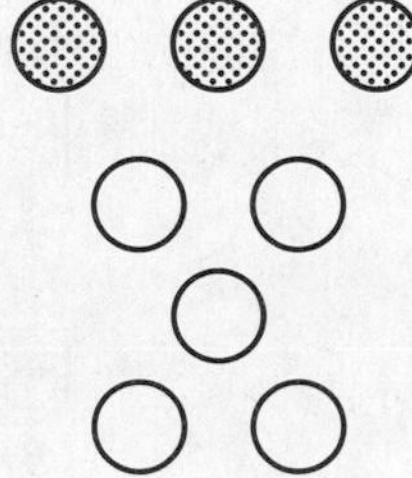

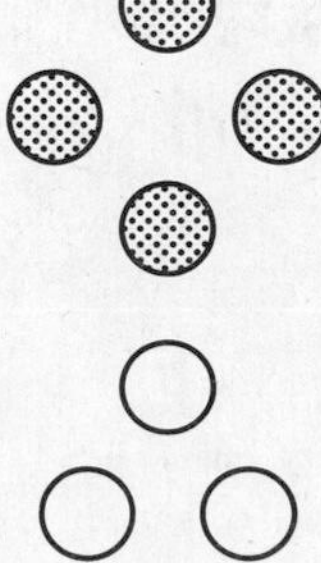

Notes for Home Your child used counters to find different ways to make 8. *Home Activity:* Ask your child to show a way to make 8 using spoons or cups.

Name ______________________

Practice 2-4

Ways to Make 10

Spill 10 ● ○ and show ways to make 10.

Record the ways.

1.

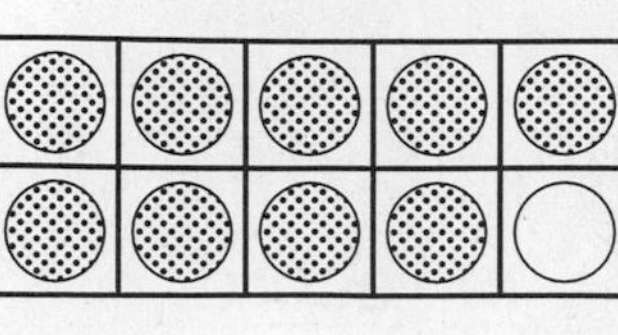

9 and 1 is 10.

2.

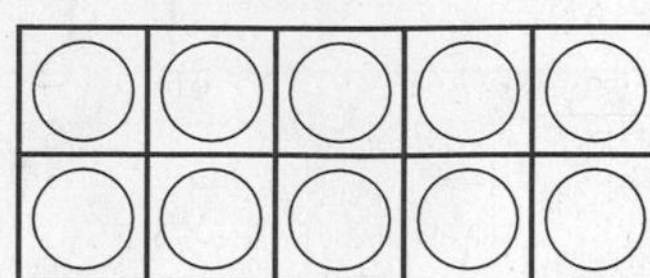

_____ and _____ is _____.

3.

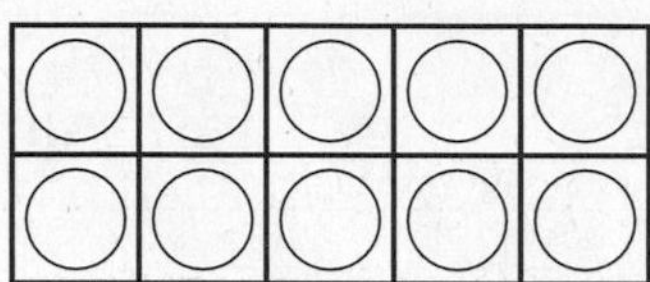

_____ and _____ is _____.

4.

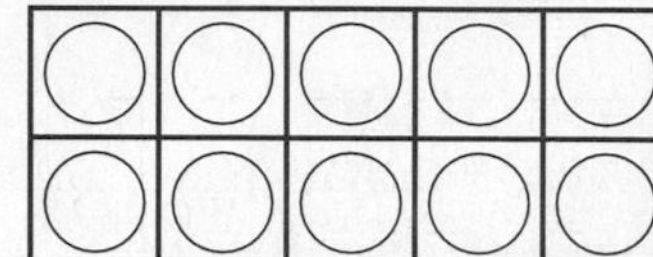

_____ and _____ is _____.

5.

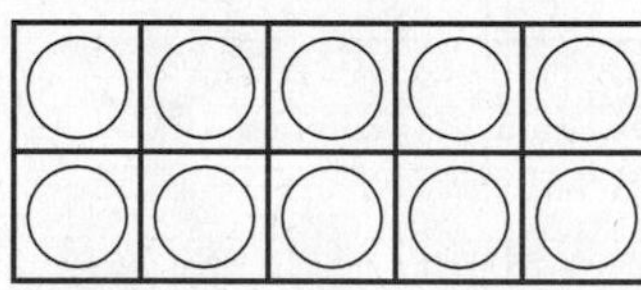

_____ and _____ is _____.

6.

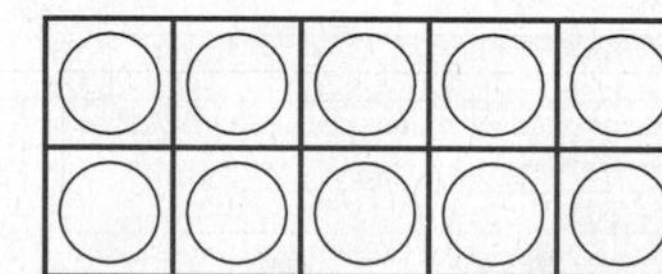

_____ and _____ is _____.

Journal

How are these the same?

How are they different?

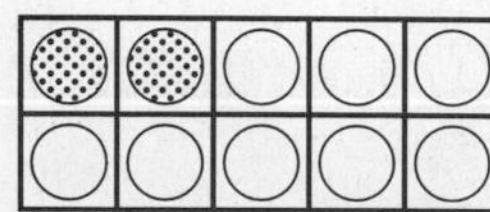

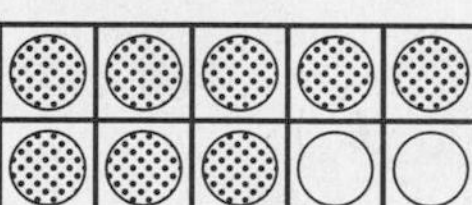

Notes for Home Your child looked for ways to make 10. *Home Activity:* Ask your child to use small objects, such as pennies or buttons, to make groups of ten.

Name ______________________________

Problem Solving: Make a Table

Practice 2-5

1. How many ways can you put

8 in 2  ?

		In All
0	8	8
1	7	8

2. How many ways can you put

10  in 2  ?

		In All
0	10	10

Problem Solving Critical Thinking

3. How many ways are there to make 9? ______________

4. How many ways are there to make 6? ______________

How do you know? ______________________________

Notes for Home Your child made tables to find all the ways to make 8 and 10. *Home Activity:* Ask your child how many ways 9 pencils or pens can be placed in 2 glasses. (10 ways)

Name ______________________________

Mixed Practice: Lessons 1–5

Use 1 or 2 colors to make 7 and 8.
Color. Write the numbers.

1. 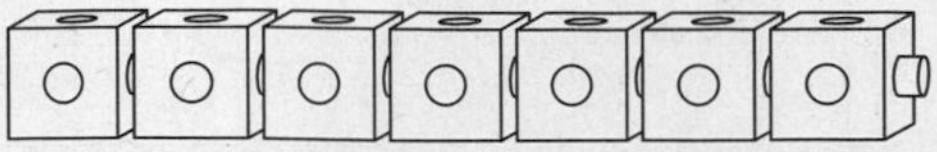

______ and ______ is ______.

2. 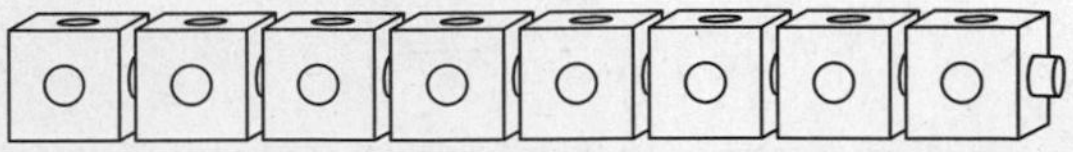

______ and ______ is ______.

Write the number sentence.

3. 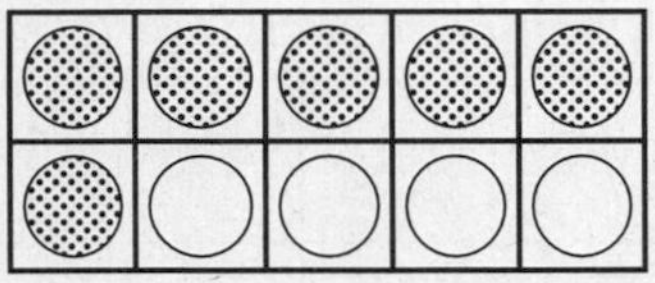

______ and ______ is ______.

Problem Solving

4. How many ways can you put

4  in 2  ?

		In All

Journal

Write a math story about **6 and 4 is 10.**

Notes for Home Your child practiced finding ways to make numbers through 10. *Home Activity:* Ask your child to tell a story about 2 groups of 3 animals.

Name ___________________________

Cumulative Review

Write how many.

1. 

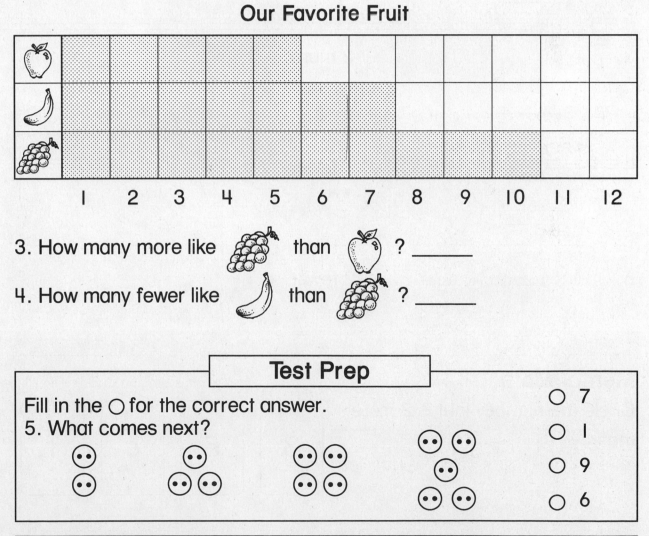

______

2. 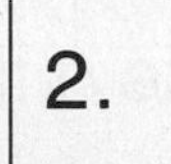   

______

Use the graph. Write the number.

Our Favorite Fruit

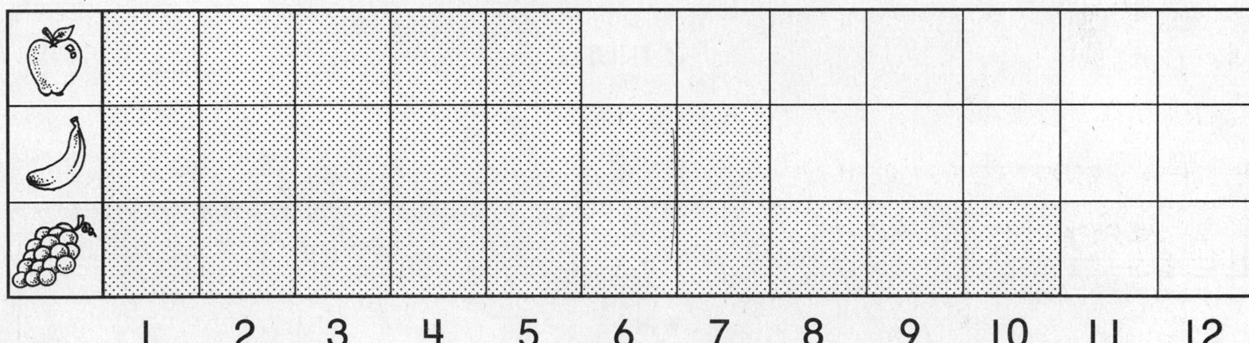

3. How many more like  than  ? ______

4. How many fewer like  than  ? ______

Test Prep

Fill in the ○ for the correct answer.

5. What comes next?

○ 7
○ 1
○ 9
○ 6

Notes for Home Your child reviewed counting to 12 and reading a graph. *Home Activity:* Ask your child to make a graph of your family's favorite animals.

Name ______________________

Practice 2-6

More and Fewer

Use .

Write how many.	Make a train with:	Write how many now.
1. 3	1 more	
2. 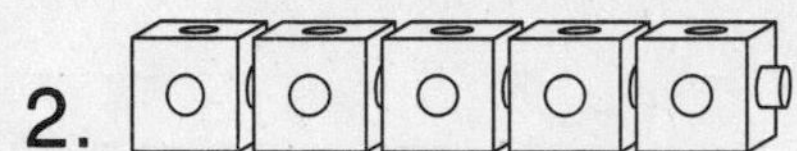 ____	2 fewer	
3. 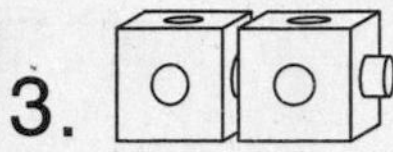 ____	2 more	
4. 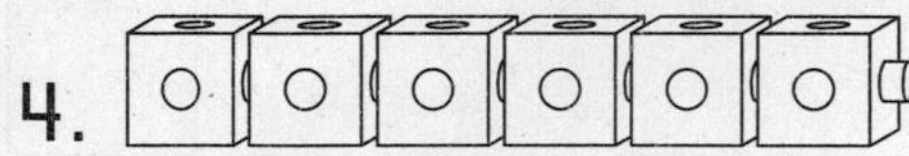 ____	1 fewer	
5. 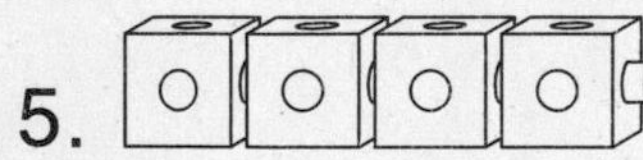 ____	2 fewer	____

Mental Math

Circle the number that is 2 more than 3.

3 5 6 1

Notes for Home Your child showed more or fewer objects than a given amount. *Home Activity:* Ask your child to tell you the number that is 2 less than his or her age and the number that is 2 more than his or her age.

Name ___________________________

Practice 2-7

Odd and Even Numbers

Make pairs. Draw what you make.

Circle odd or even.

1. Use 5 ○.

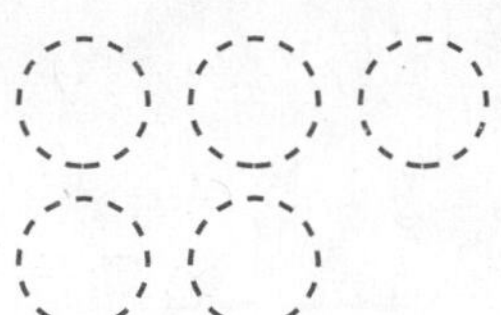

odd

even

2. Use 10 ○.

odd

even

3. Use ○. How many did you use?

odd

even

Problem Solving Patterns

Color even numbers 

. Color odd numbers 

.

1	2	3	4	5	6	7	8	9	10

What color did you color the number 7? ___________________

What pattern do you see? ___________________

Notes for Home Your child used objects to decide whether a number is odd or even. *Home Activity:* Ask your child to draw groups of 3, 4, 5, and 6, and tell whether each group is odd (3, 5) or even (4, 6).

Name ______________________

Practice 2-8

Ways to Make 11 and 12

Use  and 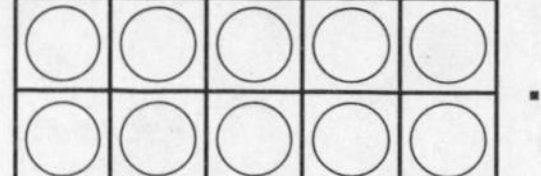.

Spill and show ways to make 11.
Record the ways.

1. 7 and 4 is 11.	2. ______ and ______ is ______.
3. ______ and ______ is ______.	4. ______ and ______ is ______.
5. ______ and ______ is ______.	6. ______ and ______ is ______.
7. ______ and ______ is ______.	8. ______ and ______ is ______.
9. ______ and ______ is ______.	10. ______ and ______ is ______.

Problem Solving Critical Thinking

Use 

, 

, 

to show 11.

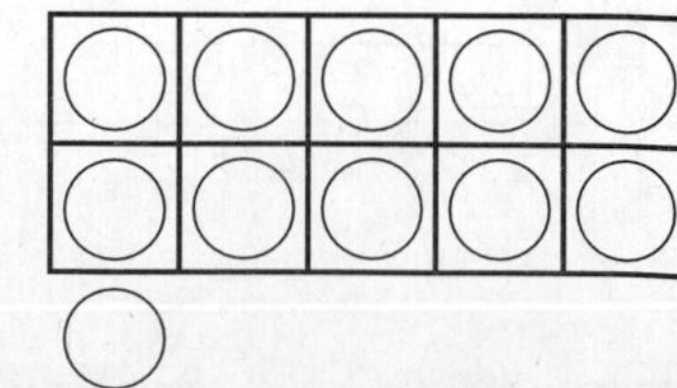

Write the numbers.

______ and ______ and ______ is ______.

Notes for Home Your child used two-colored counters and a ten-frame to find ways to make 11.
Home Activity: Ask your child to use small objects, such as buttons or pennies, to make a group of 11 and a group of 12.

Name ______________________

Practice 2-9

Find Missing Parts Through 7

How many  are under the  ?

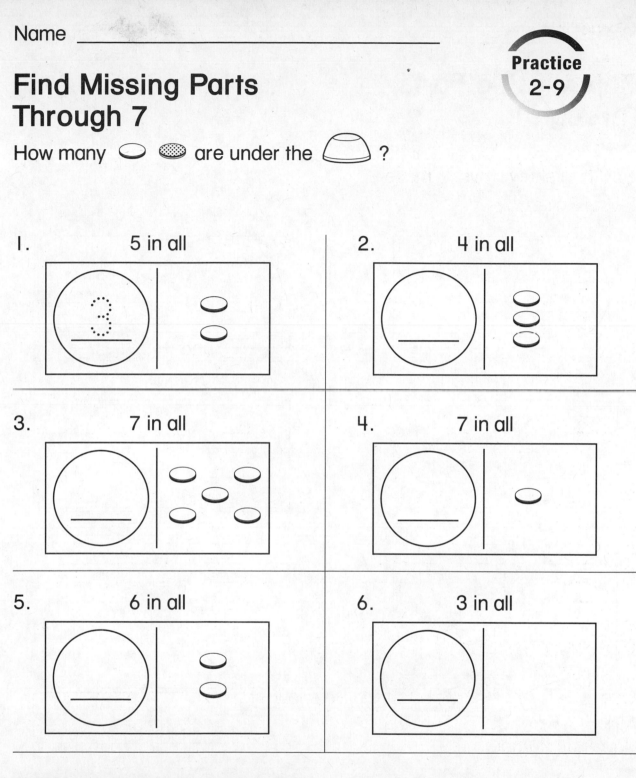

1. 5 in all

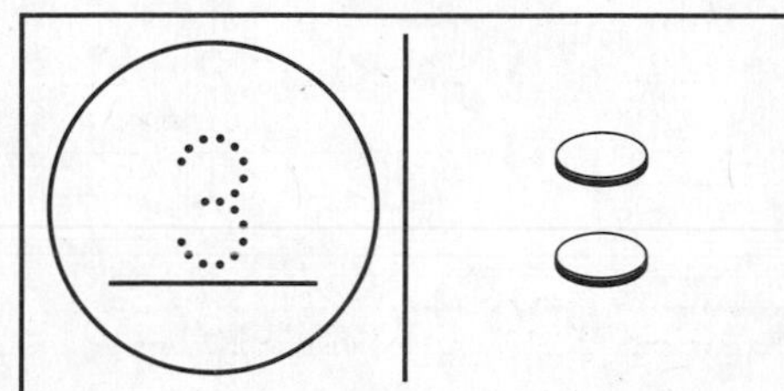

2. 4 in all

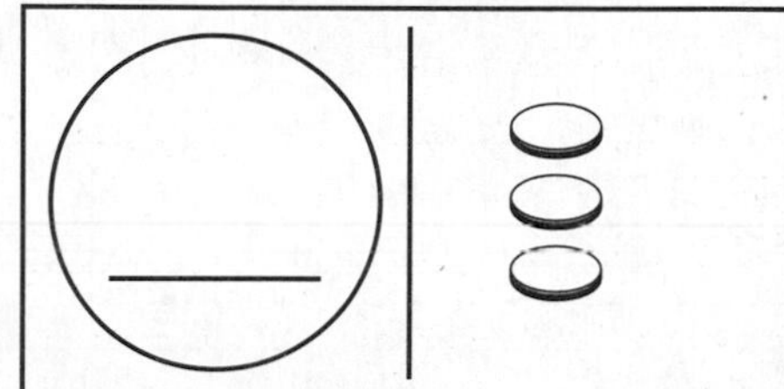

3. 7 in all

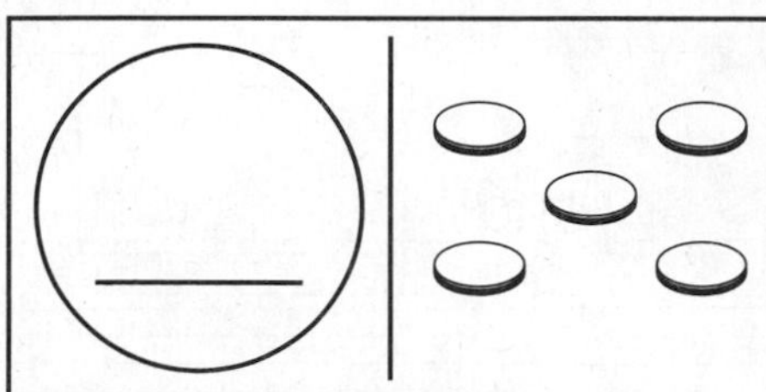

4. 7 in all

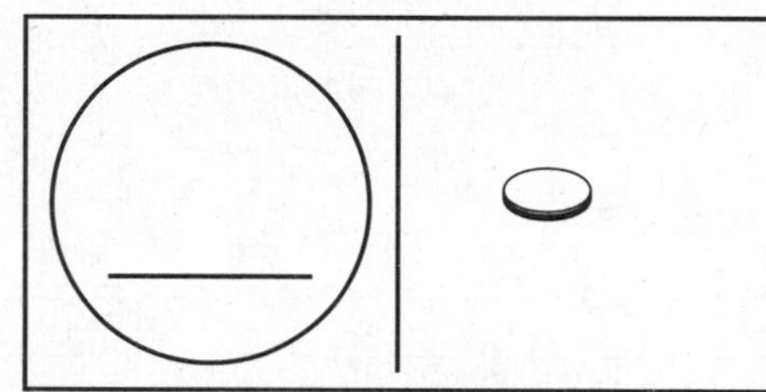

5. 6 in all

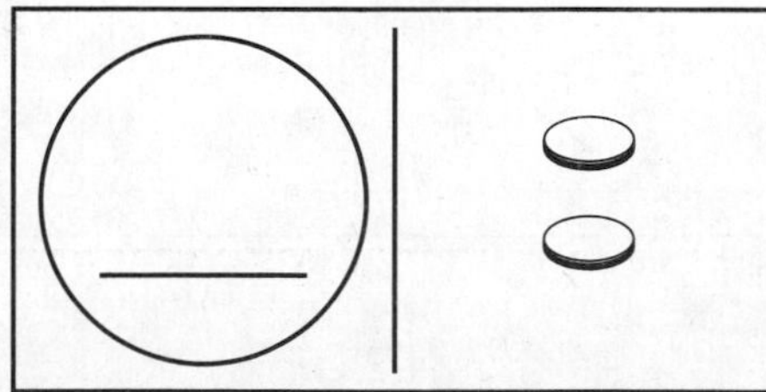

6. 3 in all

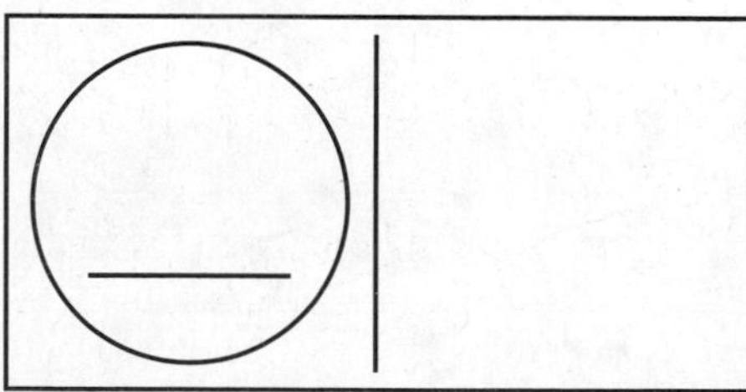

Problem Solving Estimation

7. Work with a friend. Hold some things in a box.
Have your friend estimate how many.
Count them. Take turns.

Notes for Home Your child found how many counters are missing. *Home Activity:* Following the examples on this sheet, take turns finding how many objects are hidden from a group of 6 things.

Name ______________________

Practice 2-10

Find Missing Parts Through 10

How many  are under the ?

1. 8 in all

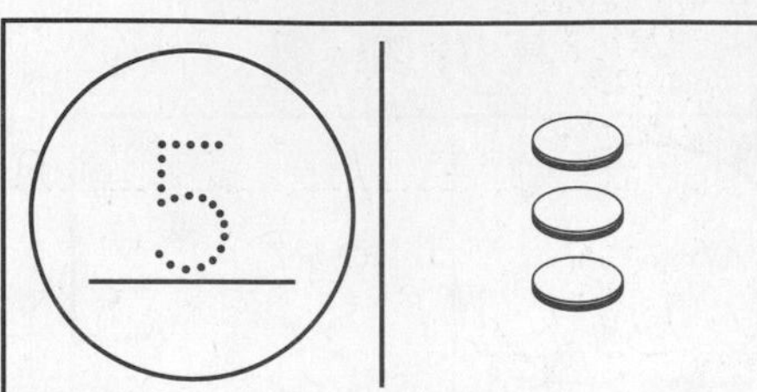

2. 5 in all

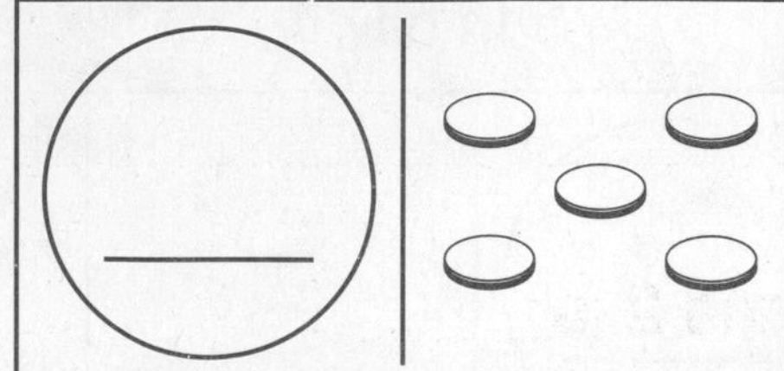

3. 10 in all

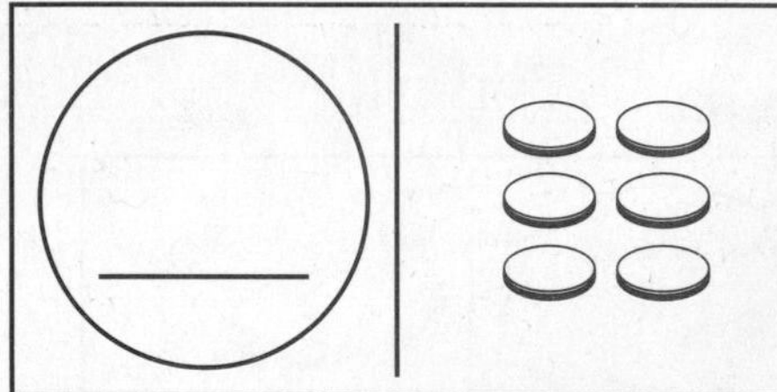

4. 6 in all

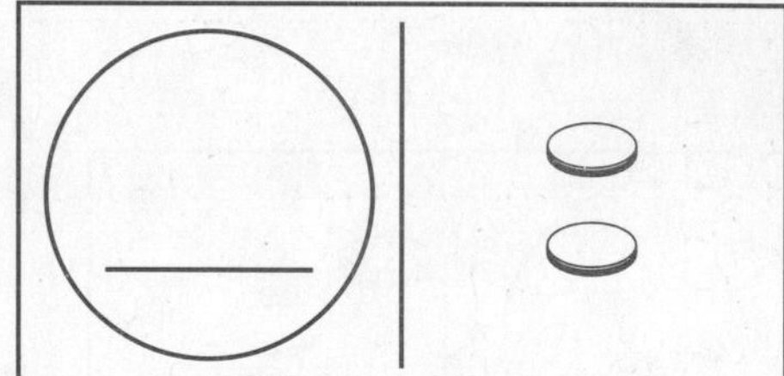

5. 9 in all

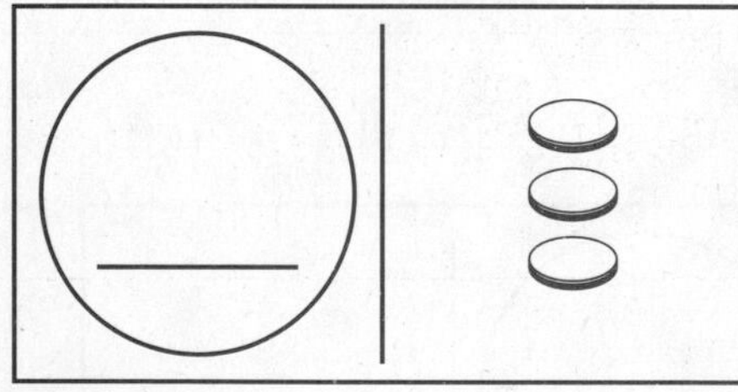

6. 10 in all

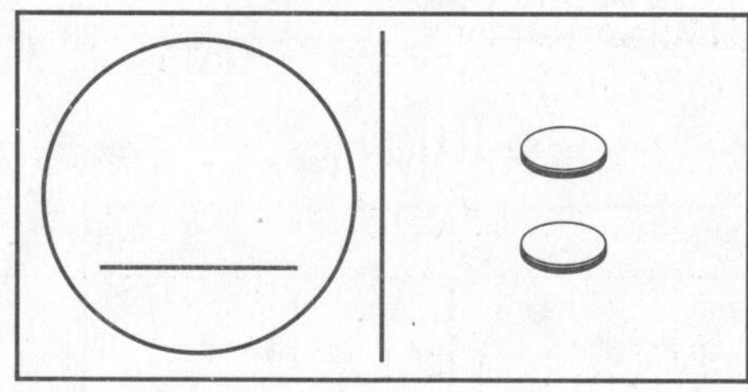

Write About It

Make up your own.

Have a friend solve it.

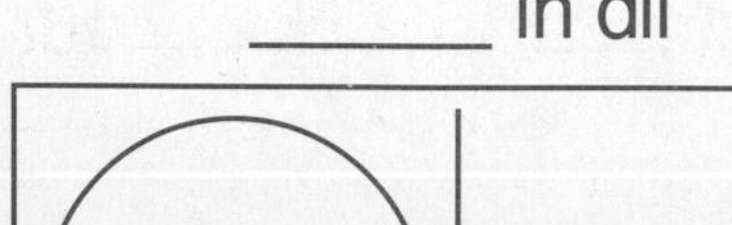

_____ in all

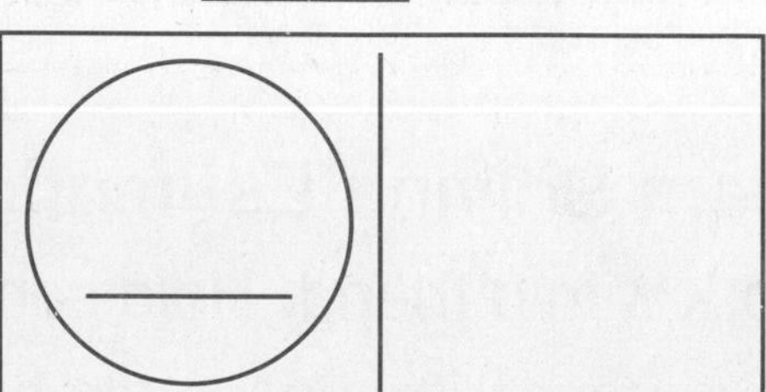

Notes for Home Your child found the missing counters through 10. *Home Activity:* Ask your child to assemble a group of 10 objects, such as paper clips. Put different number of paper clips in your hand and ask your child to tell how many are missing.

Name ________________________

Practice 2-11

Problem Solving: Draw a Picture

Draw a picture to show the problem.
Write how many in all.

1. 2 and 3 is 5.

2. 1 and 2 is ____.

3. 4 and 3 is ____.

4. 3 and 3 is ____.

Tell a Math Story

5. Draw a picture of 3 ducks and 1 cow.
Tell a math story about your picture.

Notes for Home Your child used the strategy Draw a Picture to solve problems. *Home Activity:* Ask your child to draw a picture of children playing and to tell a number story about the picture.

Name ______________________

Mixed Practice: Lessons 6–11

Practice
Chapter 2
B

1. Use [cube]. Write how many. | Make a train with: | Write how many.

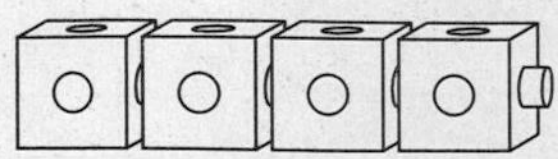

3 more

_____

_____

2. Write the numbers

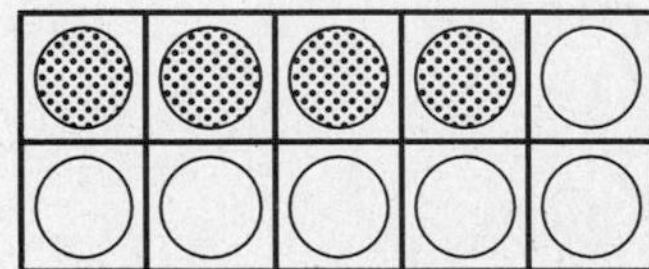

_____ and _____ is _____.

3. How many are under the ?

8 in all

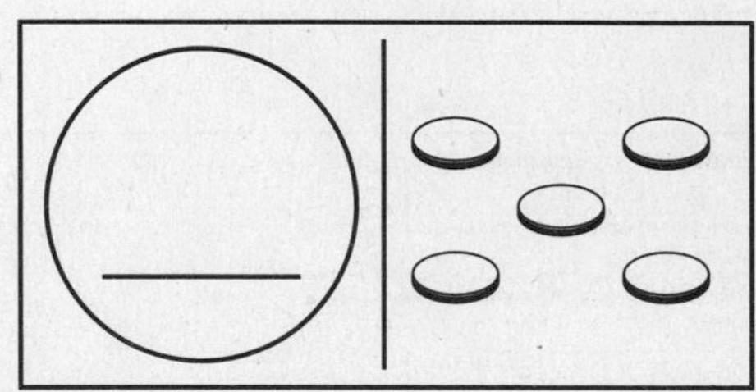

Problem Solving

4. Draw a picture to show the problem.

3 birds flying.
2 more came.

Write how many birds in all.

3 and 2 is _____.

Notes for Home Your child practiced writing number sentences, finding missing numbers, and drawing pictures to solve problems. *Home Activity:* Ask your child to draw a picture to show 3 different ways to make 5.

Name ______________________________

Cumulative Review

Circle the one that belongs.

1. 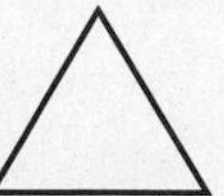  

2. Draw the missing tower. Write how many in each tower.

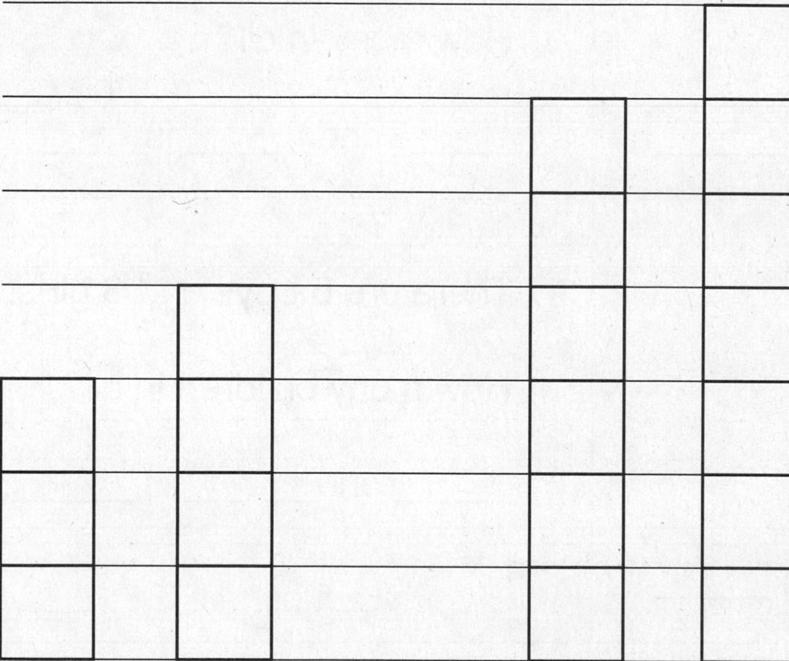

_____ _____ _____ _____ _____

Test Prep

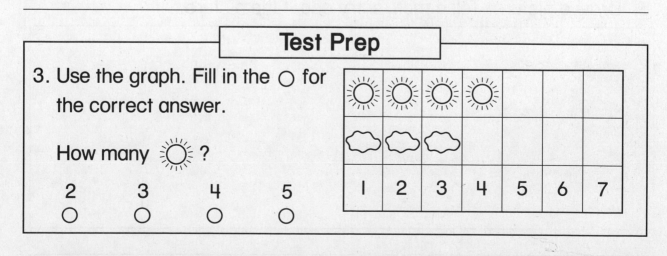

3. Use the graph. Fill in the ○ for the correct answer.

How many ☼?

2 ○ 3 ○ 4 ○ 5 ○

☼	☼	☼	☼			
☁	☁	☁				
1	2	3	4	5	6	7

Notes for Home Your child reviewed counting to 12 and reading a graph. *Home Activity:* Ask your child to make a graph of what he or she had to drink at lunch each day for one week.

Name ________________________________

Practice 3-1

Explore Addition

Solve each problem.

You can use ⬭.

1. There are 3 .

2 more  come.

How many in all?

3 and 2 is 5.

2. There are 6 .

2 more  come.

How many in all?

______ and ______ is ______.

3. There are 5 .

4 more  come.

How many in all?

______ and ______ is ______.

4. There are 5 boys and 3 girls.

How many children in all?

______ and ______ is ______.

Problem Solving Visual Thinking

5. Draw a picture. Tell a math story about the picture.

Notes for Home Your child solved addition problems. *Home Activity:* Ask your child to tell you a math story about Exercise 1.

Name ______________________________

Practice 3-2

Show Addition

You can use ⬭ and ▭▭.
Show the parts.
Write the number sentence.

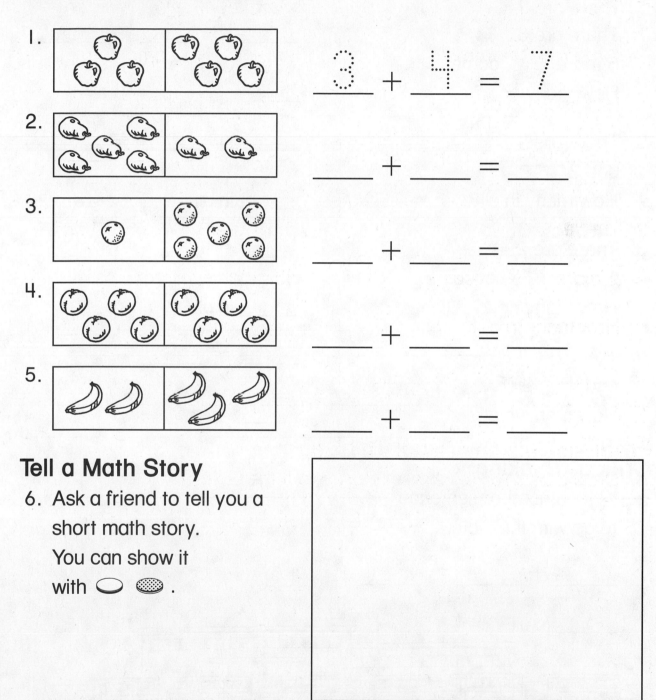

1. 

3 + 4 = 7

2. 

____ + ____ = ____

3. 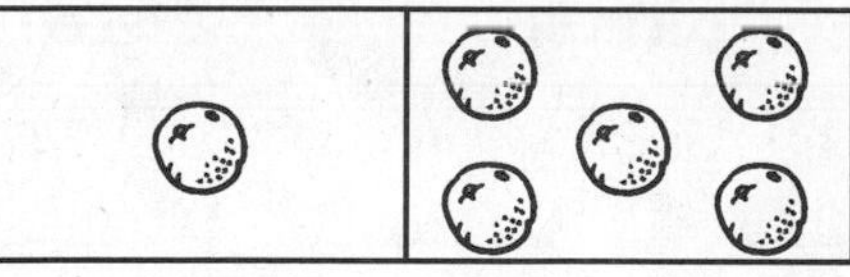

____ + ____ = ____

4. 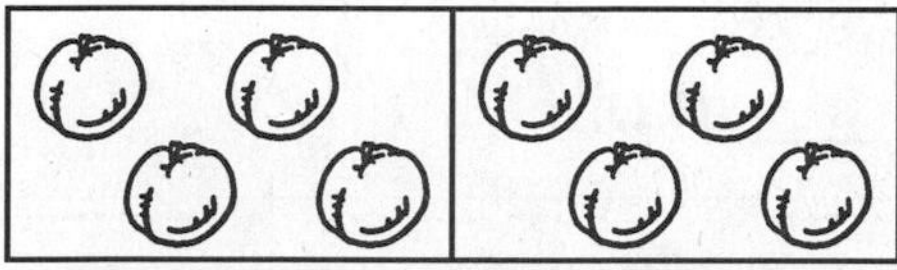

____ + ____ = ____

5. 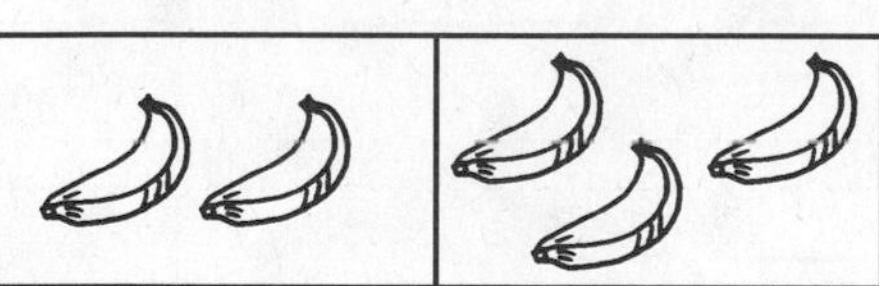

____ + ____ = ____

Tell a Math Story

6. Ask a friend to tell you a short math story. You can show it with ⬭ ⬭.

Notes for Home Your child used counters and wrote number sentences to show addition. *Home Activity:* Ask your child to show 5 + 4 using common objects, such as buttons or pennies.

Name ______________________________

Practice 3-3

Problem Solving: Use Addition

Use ⬭ to show the story.
Write a number sentence.
Write how many in all.

1. There are 3 🚲. 5 more 🚲 come. How many now?

   3 + 5 = 8

   8 🚲

2. There are 4 🚚 and 2 🛻. How many in all?

   ____ + ____ = ____

   ____ in all

3. There are 2 🚌. 3 more 🚌 come. How many now?

   ____ + ____ = ____

   ____ in all

4. There are 4 ✈ and 4 ✈. How many in all?

   ____ + ____ = ____

   ____ ✈

Critical Thinking

5. Write a number sentence to go with the picture.

   ____ + ____ = ____

   ____ in all

Notes for Home Your child wrote number sentences to solve problems. *Home Activity:* Ask your child to draw a picture of his or her favorite form of transportation to show 7 + 2.

Name ______________________________

Practice 3-4

Addition Sentences to 12

Use ⬭ ⬭ .

Show some ways to make each number.

Write the number sentences.

1. **8**

3 + 5 = 8

___ + ___ = ___

___ + ___ = ___

2. **10**

___ + ___ = ___

___ + ___ = ___

___ + ___ = ___

3. **12**

___ + ___ = ___

___ + ___ = ___

___ + ___ = ___

4. **6**

___ + ___ = ___

___ + ___ = ___

___ + ___ = ___

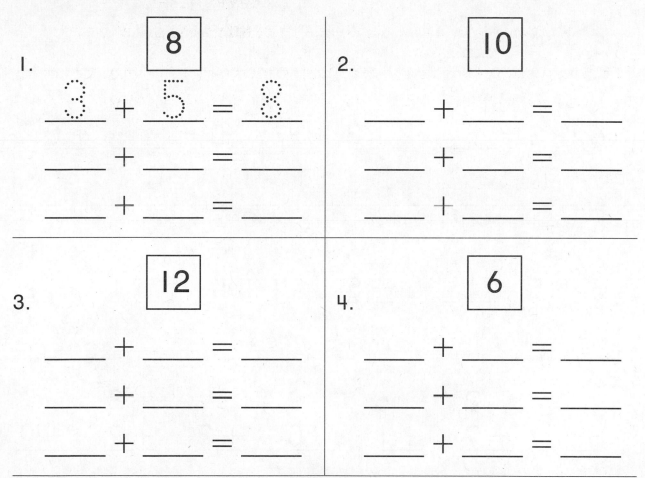

Problem Solving Visual Thinking

5. Draw balls to make 5. Complete the number sentences.

1 + ___ = 5

3 + ___ = 5

4 + ___ = 5

Notes for Home Your child used counters to write addition sentences. *Home Activity:* Ask your child to tell you a math story using 3 different ways to make 12.

Name ______________________________

Practice 3-5

Add in Vertical Form

Write the sums. You can use 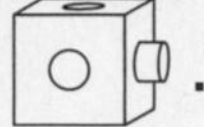.

1.

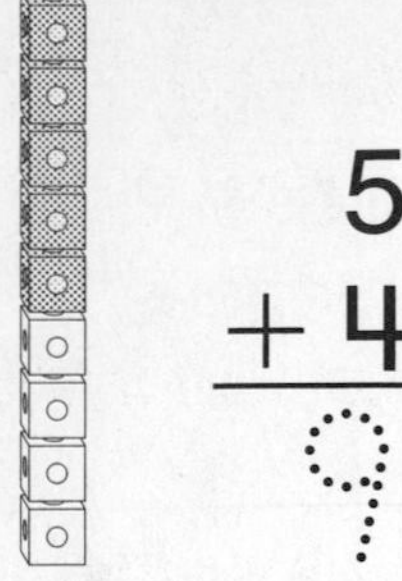

$5 + 4 = $ 9

$$\begin{array}{r} 5 \\ +\ 4 \\ \hline 9 \end{array}$$

2. $6 + 3 = $ ____

$$\begin{array}{r} 6 \\ +\ 3 \\ \hline \end{array}$$

3. $7 + 0 = $ ____

$$\begin{array}{r} 7 \\ +\ 0 \\ \hline \end{array}$$

4. $6 + 5 = $ ____

$$\begin{array}{r} 6 \\ +\ 5 \\ \hline \end{array}$$

5. $4 + 4 = $ ____

$$\begin{array}{r} 4 \\ +\ 4 \\ \hline \end{array}$$

6.

$$\begin{array}{r} 6 \\ +\ 4 \\ \hline \end{array} \quad \begin{array}{r} 2 \\ +\ 9 \\ \hline \end{array} \quad \begin{array}{r} 6 \\ +\ 1 \\ \hline \end{array} \quad \begin{array}{r} 9 \\ +\ 0 \\ \hline \end{array} \quad \begin{array}{r} 4 \\ +\ 3 \\ \hline \end{array} \quad \begin{array}{r} 8 \\ +\ 2 \\ \hline \end{array} \quad \begin{array}{r} 7 \\ +\ 4 \\ \hline \end{array}$$

Problem Solving

Solve each problem.

7. There are 3 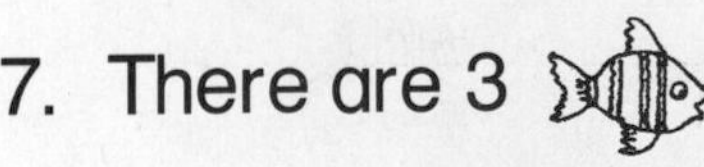  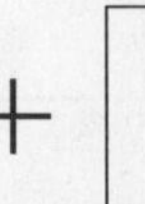 +

and 7 .

How many in all? 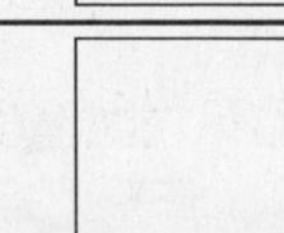

8. There are 8  . +

4 more  come. 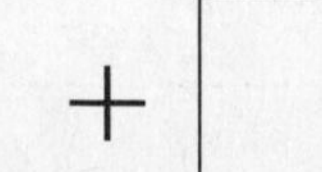

How many now?

Notes for Home Your child solved addition problems that were shown both horizontally and vertically.
Home Activity: Write 3 addition sentences horizontally. Ask your child to write them vertically and to solve them.

Name ______________________________

Practice 3-6

Problem Solving: Draw a Picture

Draw a picture to show the story.
Write a number sentence.

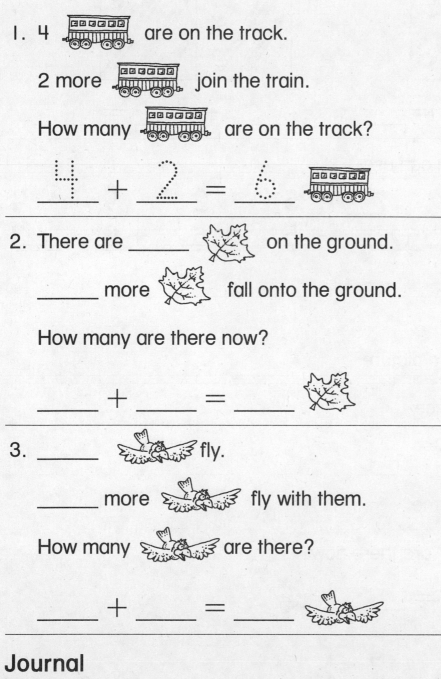

1. 4 are on the track.

   2 more join the train.

   How many are on the track?

   4 + 2 = 6

2. There are ______ on the ground.

   ______ more fall onto the ground.

   How many are there now?

   ______ + ______ = ______

3. ______ fly.

   ______ more fly with them.

   How many are there?

   ______ + ______ = ______

Journal

Write a problem that could be solved by drawing a picture.

Notes for Home Your child solved addition problems by drawing a picture. *Home Activity:* Ask your child to write an addition sentence for a picture in a magazine or book.

Name ______________________________

Practice
Chapter 3
A

Mixed Practice: Lessons 1–6

Write a number sentence.

1. 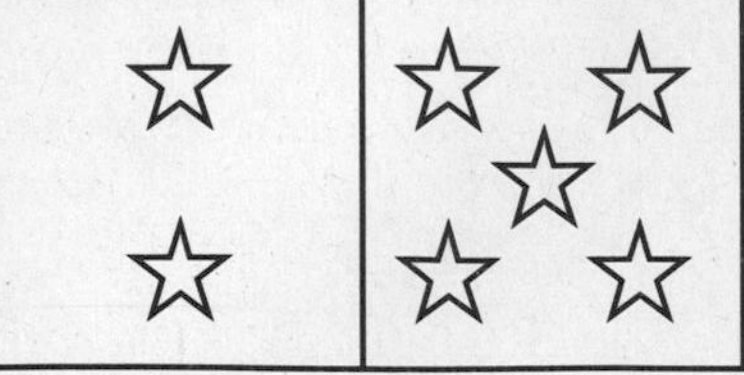

____ + ____ = ____

2. 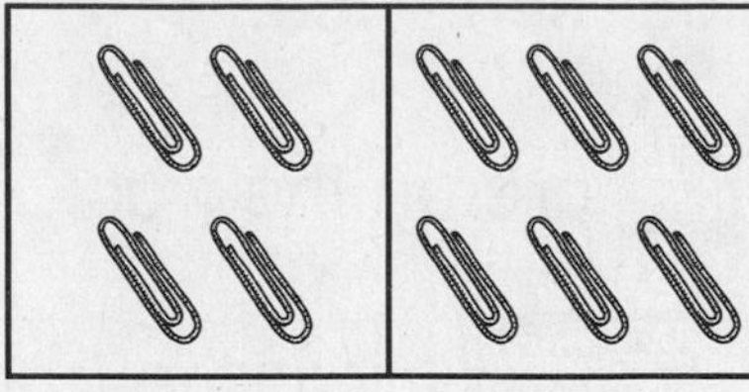

____ + ____ = ____

3. Write the sum. You can use ⬭.

4	5	7	5	2	9	4
+ 0	+ 2	+ 1	+ 5	+ 6	+ 0	+ 3

Problem Solving

Use ⬭ ⬭ or draw a picture.

Write a number sentence.

4. 4  run.

2 more  come.

How many  are there now?

____ + ____ = ____ 

Journal

Draw a picture to show a math story for a problem in exercise 3.
Write the number sentence.

Notes for Home Your child practiced addition for sums through 12. *Home Activity:* Ask your child to chose 3 addition sentences in Exercise 3, and draw a picture for each.

Name ___________________________

Practice
Chapters 1–3
A

Cumulative Review

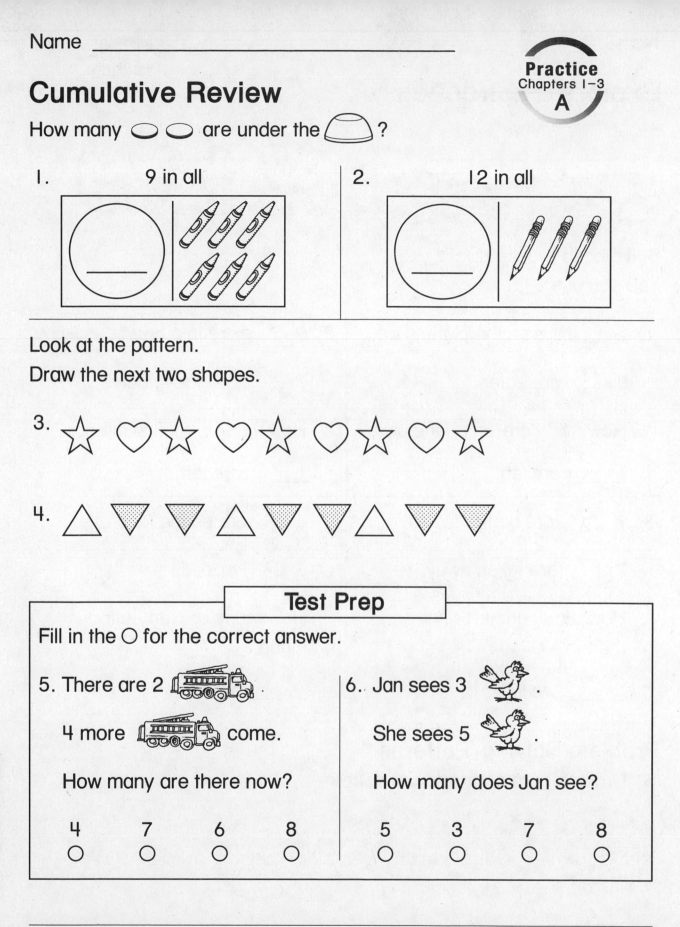

How many ⬭ ⬭ are under the ◠ ?

1. 9 in all

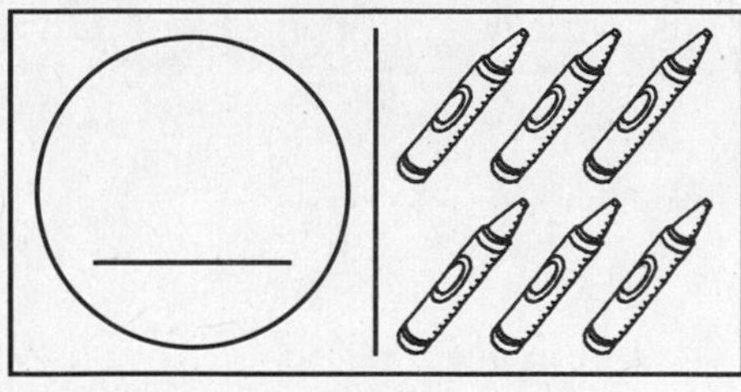

2. 12 in all

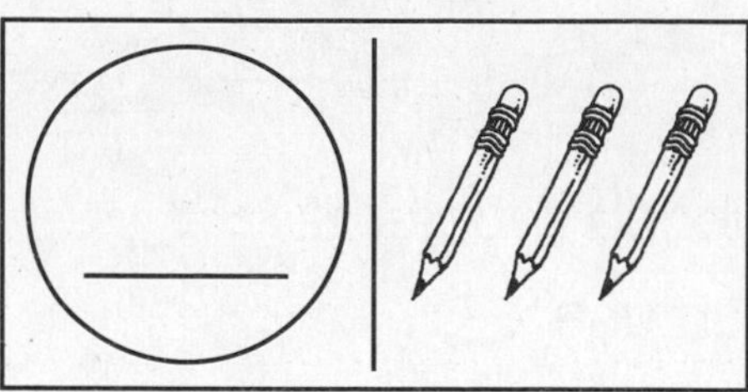

Look at the pattern.

Draw the next two shapes.

3.     

4. 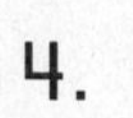        

Test Prep

Fill in the ○ for the correct answer.

5. There are 2  .

4 more  come.

How many are there now?

4	7	6	8
○	○	○	○

6. Jan sees 3  .

She sees 5  .

How many does Jan see?

5	3	7	8
○	○	○	○

Notes for Home Your child reviewed finding missing parts of a number, patterns, and addition. *Home Activity:* Ask your child to draw a pattern using his or her favorite toys.

Name ______________________________

Explore Subtraction

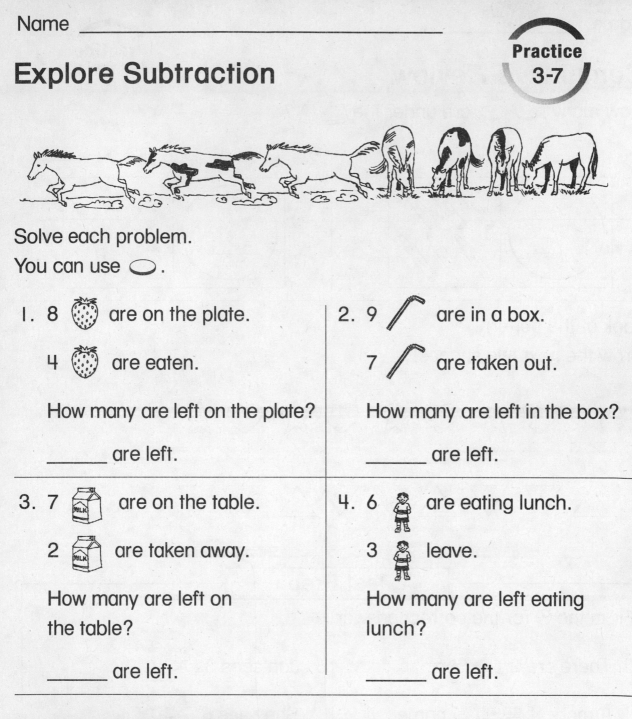

Solve each problem.

You can use ⬭.

1. 8 🍓 are on the plate.

   4 🍓 are eaten.

   How many are left on the plate?

   _____ are left.

2. 9 straws are in a box.

   7 straws are taken out.

   How many are left in the box?

   _____ are left.

3. 7 milk cartons are on the table.

   2 milk cartons are taken away.

   How many are left on the table?

   _____ are left.

4. 6 children are eating lunch.

   3  leave.

   How many are left eating lunch?

   _____ are left.

Problem Solving Patterns

5. Draw pizza slices to complete the pattern.

  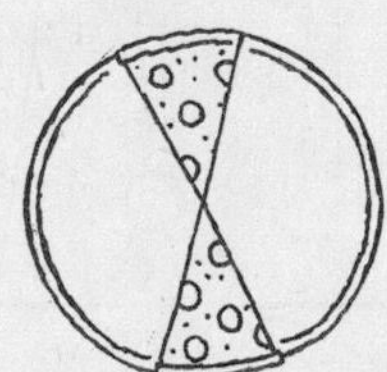 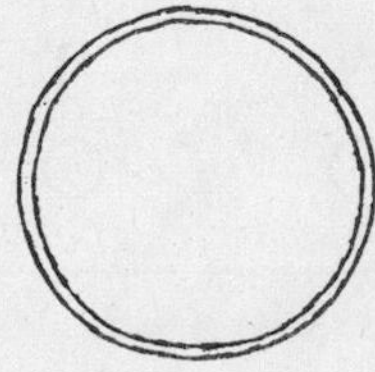

Notes for Home Your child solved subtraction problems. *Home Activity:* Ask your child draw a picture to show 9 – 6 = 3.

Name ______________________________

Subtract in Vertical Form

Practice 3-10

You can use  to subtract.

1. 

$6 - 2 = \underline{4}$

$\begin{array}{r} 6 \\ -\ 2 \\ \hline \end{array}$

2. $11 - 8 =$ ____ $\quad \begin{array}{r} 11 \\ -\ 8 \\ \hline \end{array}$

3. $7 - 7 =$ ____ $\quad \begin{array}{r} 7 \\ -\ 7 \\ \hline \end{array}$

4. $10 - 9 =$ ____ $\quad \begin{array}{r} 10 \\ -\ 9 \\ \hline \end{array}$

5. $12 - 6 =$ ____ $\quad \begin{array}{r} 12 \\ -\ 6 \\ \hline \end{array}$

6. $\begin{array}{r} 5 \\ -\ 1 \\ \hline \end{array} \quad \begin{array}{r} 12 \\ -\ 1 \\ \hline \end{array} \quad \begin{array}{r} 9 \\ -\ 6 \\ \hline \end{array} \quad \begin{array}{r} 8 \\ -\ 8 \\ \hline \end{array} \quad \begin{array}{r} 10 \\ -\ 2 \\ \hline \end{array} \quad \begin{array}{r} 6 \\ -\ 4 \\ \hline \end{array}$

Problem Solving

Solve the problem.

7. There were 12 .
Now there are 7.
How many were eaten?

_____ were eaten.

8. Kara had 8 .
Now she has 3.
How many did she give away?

_____ were given away.

Notes for Home Your child subtracted in horizontal and vertical forms. *Home Activity:* Ask your child to write the Problem Solving problem in horizontal and solve it.

Name ______________________

Relate Addition and Subtraction

You can use  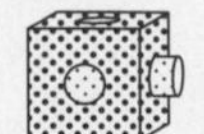.

Complete the number sentences.

1. 5 + 3 = 8
   8 − 3 = 5

2. ____ + ____ = ____
   9 − ____ = ____

3. ____ + ____ = ____
   5 − ____ = ____

4. ____ + ____ = ____
   11 − ____ = ____

Problem Solving Critical Thinking

5. How many ways can you subtract from 2? ____

2 − ____ = ____

2 − ____ = ____

2 − ____ = ____

Notes for Home Your child wrote related addition and subtraction sentences. *Home Activity:* Ask your child write how many ways he or she can subtract from 4. (There are 5 ways: 4 – 0 = 4, 4 – 1 = 3, 4 – 2 = 2, 4 – 3 = 1, 4 – 4 = 0.)

Name ______________________________

Problem Solving:
Choose an Operation

Use  to show the story.

Circle add or subtract. Write the number sentence.

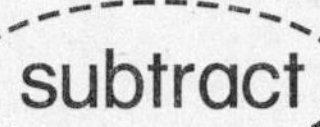

1. There are 12 . add subtract

3 are eaten.

How many are there now? 12  3 = 9

2. There are 2 . add subtract

2 more  are poured.

How many in all? ____ ◯ ____ = ____

3. 4  are on the plate. add subtract

3  are taken away.

How many are on the plate? ____ ◯ ____ = ____

4. 5  on the table. add subtract

Children bring 4 more .

How many are on the table now? ____ ◯ ____ = ____

Journal

Think about 5 things that you have.

Write an addition story.

Write a subtraction story.

Notes for Home Your child read number stories, chose and wrote the addition or subtraction sign, and then solved the problems. *Home Activity:* Ask your child to write an addition and a subtraction story about people who come and go in your family.

Name ______________________

Practice
Chapter 3
B

Mixed Practice: Lessons 7–12

Subtract.

You can use 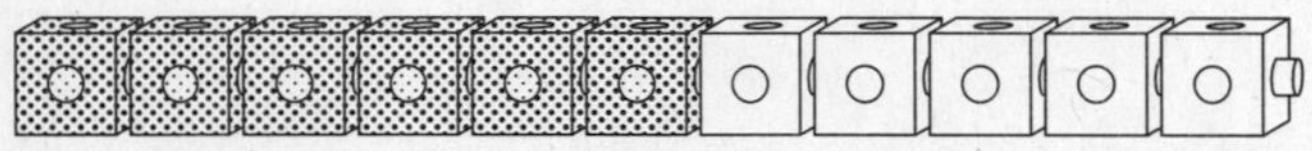.

1. $\begin{array}{r} 7 \\ -5 \\ \hline \end{array}$ $\begin{array}{r} 9 \\ -3 \\ \hline \end{array}$ $\begin{array}{r} 11 \\ -1 \\ \hline \end{array}$ $\begin{array}{r} 4 \\ -4 \\ \hline \end{array}$ $\begin{array}{r} 8 \\ -6 \\ \hline \end{array}$ $\begin{array}{r} 7 \\ -2 \\ \hline \end{array}$ $\begin{array}{r} 10 \\ -5 \\ \hline \end{array}$

2. Write the number sentences.

____ + ____ = ____

11 − ____ = ____

Problem Solving

Write the number sentence.

3. There are 8 .

6 more  come.

How many are there now?

____ ◯ ____ = ____

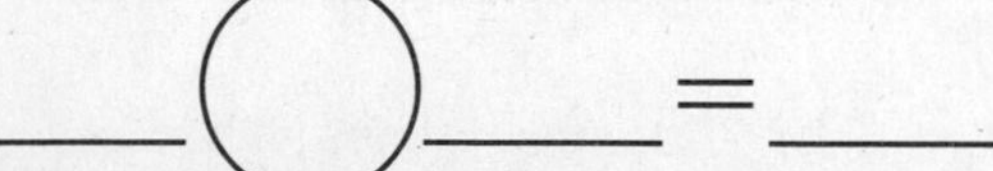

4. There are 6 .

2 fly away.

How many are left?

____ ◯ ____ = ____

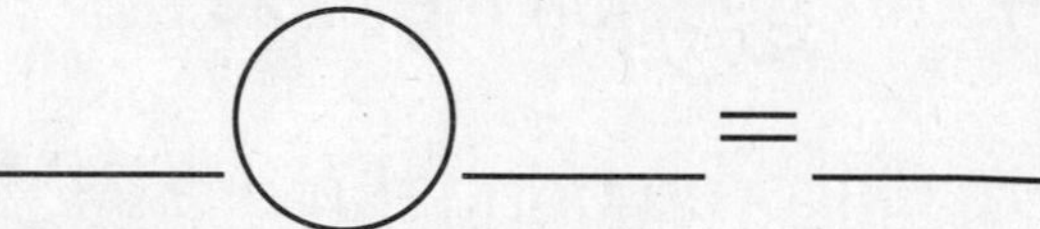

Journal

Write a math story that has the number 5 in it.

Draw a picture.

Write a number sentence for your story.

Notes for Home Your child practiced subtraction concepts, and relating addition and subtraction.
Home Activity: Ask your child to write a math story about a game he or she has played at school.

Name ______________________

Practice
Chapters 1–3
B

Cumulative Review

Use 1 or 2 colors.
Color to show 2 ways to make the number.
Write a number sentence.

1.

_____ and _____ is 6. _____ and _____ is 6.

Draw a picture to match the number sentence.
Write how many in all.

2. 

$3 + 1 =$ _____.

Test Prep

Choose the number sentence.
Fill in the ○ for the correct answer.

3. 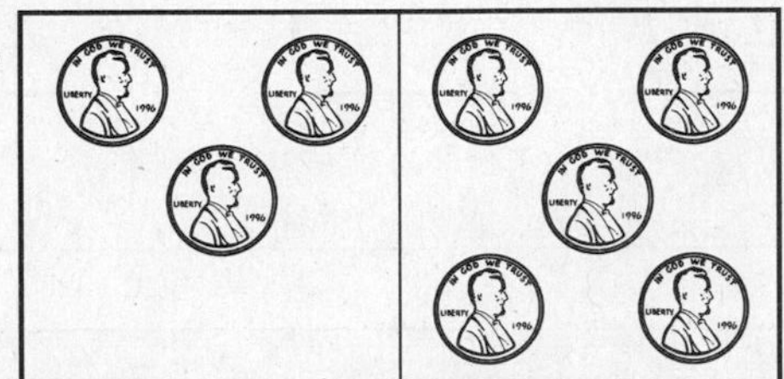

○ $5 - 2 = 3$
○ $3 + 8 = 11$
○ $8 - 3 = 5$
○ $3 + 5 = 8$

4. There are 8  and 2 come.
How many in all?

○ $8 - 2 = 6$
○ $8 + 2 = 10$
○ $10 + 2 = 12$
○ $10 - 2 = 8$

Notes for Home Your child reviewed finding combinations for numbers and drawing a picture to solve a problem. *Home Activity:* Ask your child to draw pictures for Exercise 1.

Name ______________________________

Count On 1 or 2

Count on to add.

1. 

$7 + 1 = 8$

$$\begin{array}{r} 7 \\ +\ 1 \\ \hline 8 \end{array}$$

2. 

$7 + 2 =$ ____

$$\begin{array}{r} 7 \\ +\ 2 \\ \hline \end{array}$$

3. $6 + 2 =$ ____ $3 + 1 =$ ____ $1 + 2 =$ ____

4. $4 + 2 =$ ____ $1 + 1 =$ ____ $4 + 1 =$ ____

5. $\begin{array}{r} 5 \\ +\ 1 \\ \hline \end{array}$ $\begin{array}{r} 5 \\ +\ 2 \\ \hline \end{array}$ $\begin{array}{r} 9 \\ +\ 1 \\ \hline \end{array}$ $\begin{array}{r} 9 \\ +\ 2 \\ \hline \end{array}$ $\begin{array}{r} 3 \\ +\ 1 \\ \hline \end{array}$ $\begin{array}{r} 3 \\ +\ 2 \\ \hline \end{array}$

6. $\begin{array}{r} 2 \\ +\ 2 \\ \hline \end{array}$ $\begin{array}{r} 6 \\ +\ 1 \\ \hline \end{array}$ $\begin{array}{r} 7 \\ +\ 2 \\ \hline \end{array}$ $\begin{array}{r} 8 \\ +\ 2 \\ \hline \end{array}$ $\begin{array}{r} 7 \\ +\ 1 \\ \hline \end{array}$ $\begin{array}{r} 8 \\ +\ 1 \\ \hline \end{array}$

Problem Solving Patterns

Complete the pattern.
What pattern do you see?

Notes for Home Your child added 1 or 2 to a number. *Home Activity:* Ask your child to draw a small object. Then ask him or her to add 1 or 2 of the objects to the picture several times and to find each total.

Name ______________________

Practice 4-2

Explore Turnaround Facts

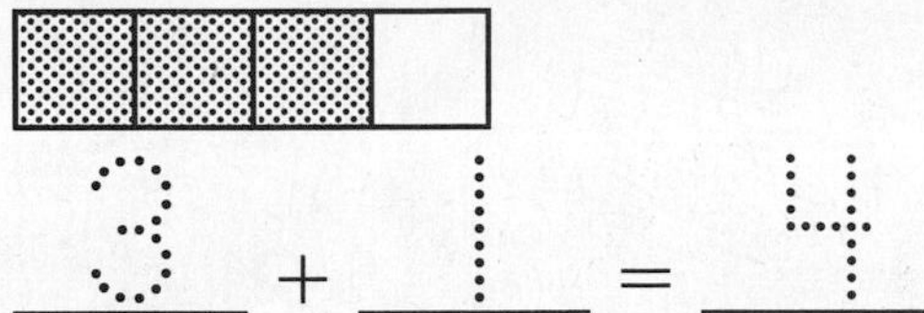

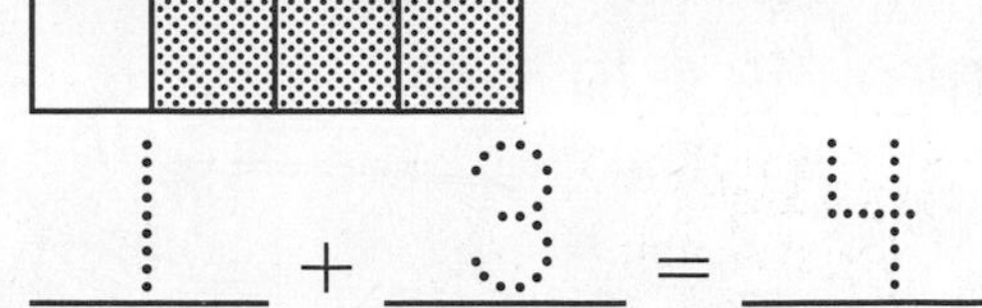

3 + 1 = 4   1 + 3 = 4

1. Make a 6 train. Write 2 turnaround facts.

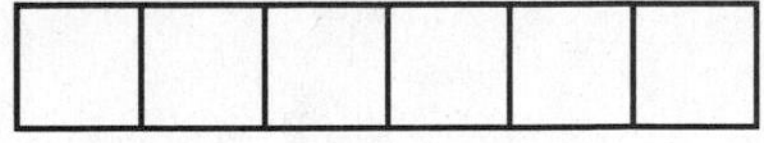

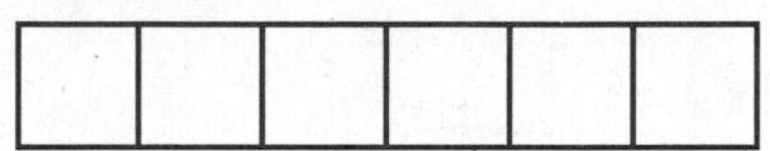

____ + ____ = ____   ____ + ____ = ____

2. Make a 9 train. Write 2 turnaround facts.

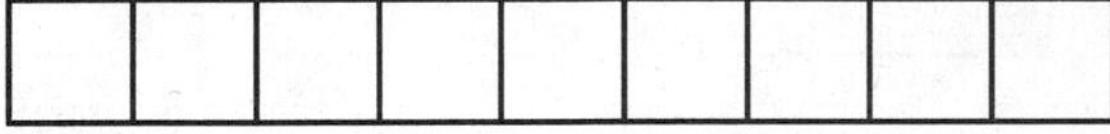

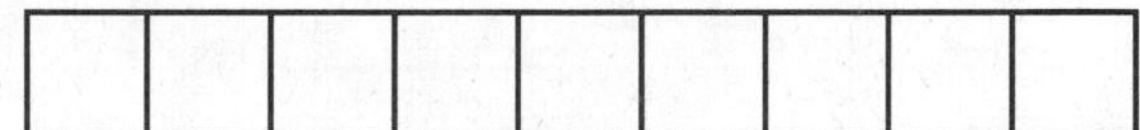

____ + ____ = ____   ____ + ____ = ____

3. Make a 7 train. Write 2 turnaround facts.

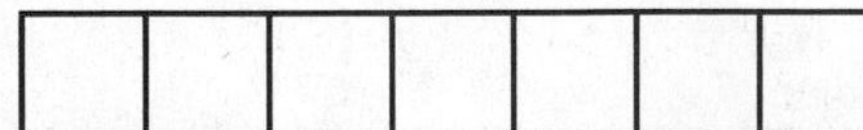

____ + ____ = ____   ____ + ____ = ____

Problem Solving Visual Thinking

4. Tell how the trains are alike and different.

Notes for Home Your child learned that turnaround facts like 1 + 3 and 3 + 1 always have the same sum. *Home Activity:* Ask your child to make an 8 train and show 2 turnaround facts.

Name ______________________

Practice 4-3

Count On from Any Number

Think of the greater number.

Count on to add.

1.

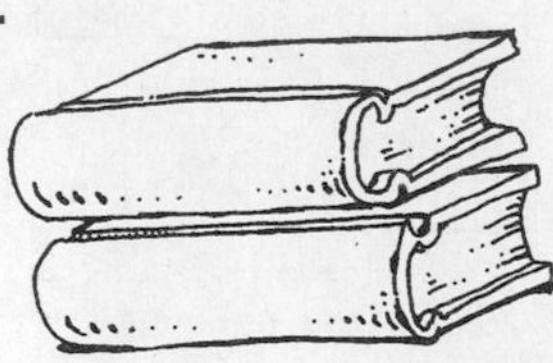

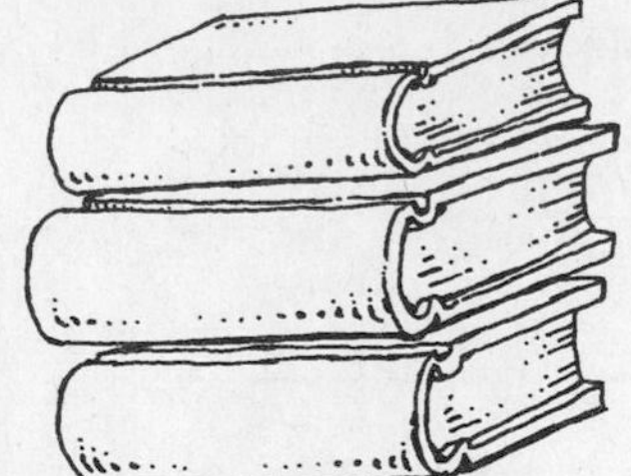

$2 + 3 = \underline{5}$

$$\begin{array}{r} 2 \\ +3 \\ \hline 5 \end{array}$$

2. $4 + 3 =$ ____ | $8 + 1 =$ ____ | $4 + 2 =$ ____

$3 + 4 =$ ____ | $1 + 8 =$ ____ | $2 + 4 =$ ____

3.

$$\begin{array}{r} 4 \\ +1 \\ \hline \end{array} \quad \begin{array}{r} 1 \\ +4 \\ \hline \end{array} \quad \begin{array}{r} 5 \\ +2 \\ \hline \end{array} \quad \begin{array}{r} 2 \\ +5 \\ \hline \end{array} \quad \begin{array}{r} 3 \\ +7 \\ \hline \end{array} \quad \begin{array}{r} 7 \\ +3 \\ \hline \end{array}$$

4.

$$\begin{array}{r} 6 \\ +2 \\ \hline \end{array} \quad \begin{array}{r} 2 \\ +6 \\ \hline \end{array} \quad \begin{array}{r} 1 \\ +9 \\ \hline \end{array} \quad \begin{array}{r} 9 \\ +1 \\ \hline \end{array} \quad \begin{array}{r} 1 \\ +3 \\ \hline \end{array} \quad \begin{array}{r} 3 \\ +1 \\ \hline \end{array}$$

Tell a Math Story

5. Look at the picture.
   Think of a math story.
   Tell it to a friend.

Notes for Home Your child added 1, 2, or 3 to the greater number. *Home Activity:* Ask your child to choose a number sentence in Exercise 5 and to illustrate it.

Name ______________________

Practice 4-4

Use a Number Line to Count On

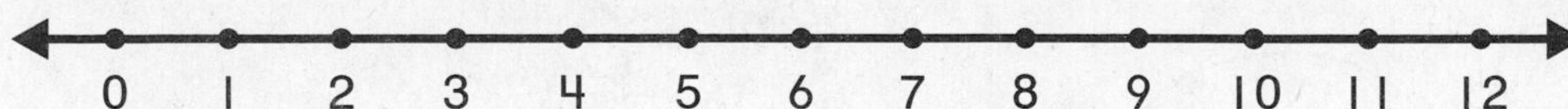

You can use the number line. Write the sum.

1. 5 + 2 = 7   4 + 3 = ____   3 + 1 = ____

2. 6 + 1 = ____   2 + 3 = ____   8 + 1 = ____

3. 4 + 1 = ____   2 + 7 = ____   3 + 5 = ____

4.

8	3	2	5	1	6
+ 3	+ 6	+ 3	+ 1	+ 9	+ 2

5.

2	1	7	3	2	1
+ 4	+ 7	+ 3	+ 3	+ 9	+ 2

Write your own number sentences.

6. ____ + 1 = ____   ____ + 2 = ____

Mental Math

7. What number is 3 more than 6? How can the number line help?

____

____

Notes for Home Your child used a number line to add numbers. *Home Activity:* Write 3 addition facts such as 4 + 5, 2 + 7, and 6 + 3, and ask your child to find the sums using a number line.

Name ________________________________

Practice 4-5

Add Zero

Add.

1. 

$3 + 0 = \underline{3}$

2. 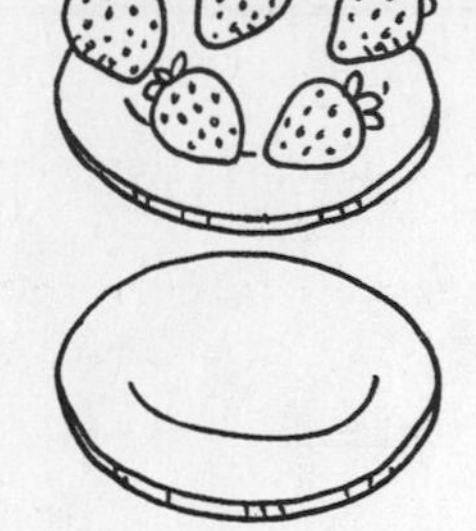

$$\begin{array}{r} 5 \\ +\ 0 \\ \hline \end{array}$$

3. $5 + 2 =$ ____ $3 + 0 =$ ____ $1 + 3 =$ ____

4. $2 + 0 =$ ____ $0 + 0 =$ ____ $0 + 6 =$ ____

5. $\begin{array}{r} 0 \\ +\ 4 \\ \hline \end{array}$ $\begin{array}{r} 1 \\ +\ 0 \\ \hline \end{array}$ $\begin{array}{r} 3 \\ +\ 5 \\ \hline \end{array}$ $\begin{array}{r} 7 \\ +\ 0 \\ \hline \end{array}$ $\begin{array}{r} 2 \\ +\ 2 \\ \hline \end{array}$ $\begin{array}{r} 9 \\ +\ 1 \\ \hline \end{array}$

6. $\begin{array}{r} 8 \\ +\ 0 \\ \hline \end{array}$ $\begin{array}{r} 9 \\ +\ 2 \\ \hline \end{array}$ $\begin{array}{r} 0 \\ +\ 5 \\ \hline \end{array}$ $\begin{array}{r} 2 \\ +\ 1 \\ \hline \end{array}$ $\begin{array}{r} 6 \\ +\ 0 \\ \hline \end{array}$ $\begin{array}{r} 0 \\ +\ 0 \\ \hline \end{array}$

Problem Solving Critical Thinking

Try this super fact.

$800 + 0 =$ ____

Write your own super fact. ____ $+ 0 =$ ____

Notes for Home Your child added zero. *Home Activity:* Ask your child to write and solve 3 addition sentences that include adding zero.

Name ____________________

Add with 5

Add.

1. $7 + 5 = \underline{12}$ $\quad 5 + 5 = \_\_\_\_$ $\quad 1 + 5 = \_\_\_\_$

2.

2	4	3	0	5	5
+ 5	+ 5	+ 5	+ 5	+ 4	+ 6

Mixed Practice

Add.

3.

9	7	8	6	5	2
+ 3	+ 0	+ 1	+ 2	+ 5	+ 3

4.

3	2	4	0	9	1
+ 1	+ 7	+ 1	+ 8	+ 0	+ 5

Problem Solving Critical Thinking

5. Circle what you can buy with  and      .

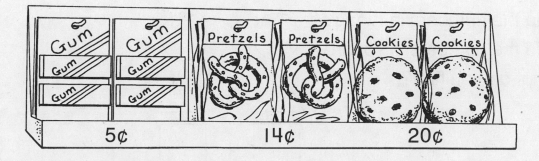

Gum Gum Pretzels Pretzels Cookies Cookies

5¢ 14¢ 20¢

Notes for Home Your child added 5, 0, and 1, 2, or 3. *Home Activity:* Ask your child to draw a picture that shows adding 0.

Name ______________________

Practice 4-7

Problem Solving: Make a List

Choose 2 boxes. Make a list.

1. Your friend wants exactly 12 party favors.

I box of __9__ favors and I box of __3__ favors

I box of _____ favors and I box of _____ favors

I box of _____ favors and I box of _____ favors

2 boxes of _____ favors.

2. You want exactly 9 party favors.

I box of _____ favors and I box of _____ favors

I box of _____ favors and I box of _____ favors

I box of _____ favors and I box of _____ favors

Critical Thinking

3. Add the numbers in circles.
Add the numbers in triangles.
Add the numbers in squares.
What do you find?

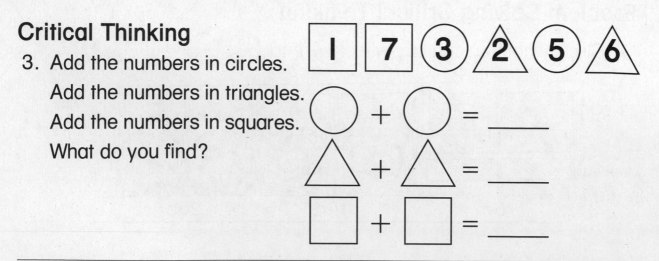

Notes for Home Your child solved problems by choosing numbers to get a given sum. *Home Activity:* Ask your child to list 4 ways to get 10 party favors. (Answers will vary, but may include: 5 + 5, 6 + 4, 8 + 2, 7 + 3.)

Name ______________________________

Mixed Practice: Lessons 1–7

Practice
Chapter 4
A

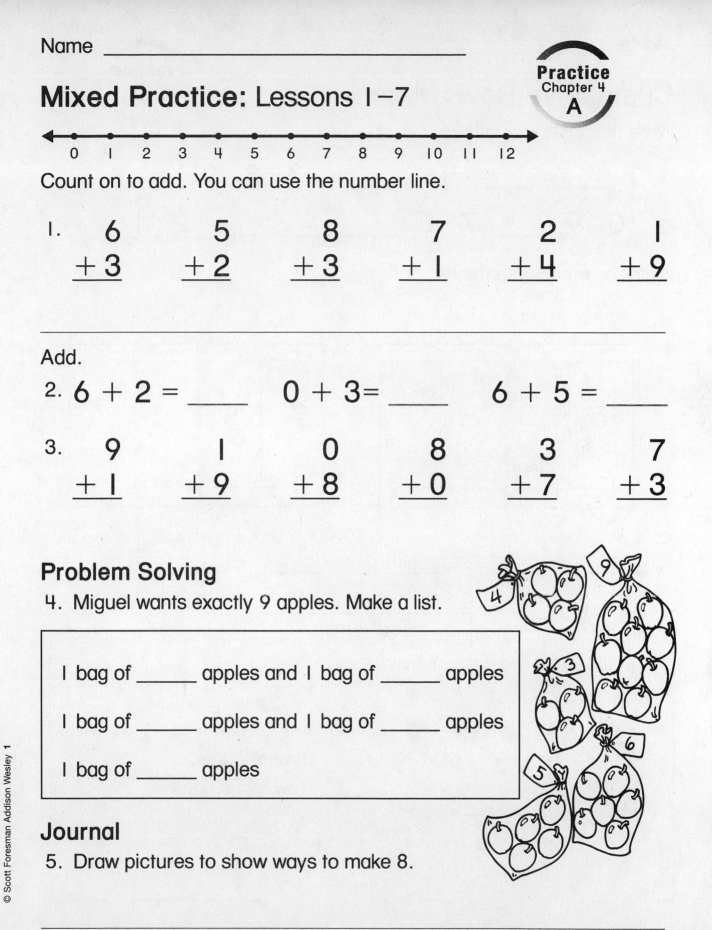

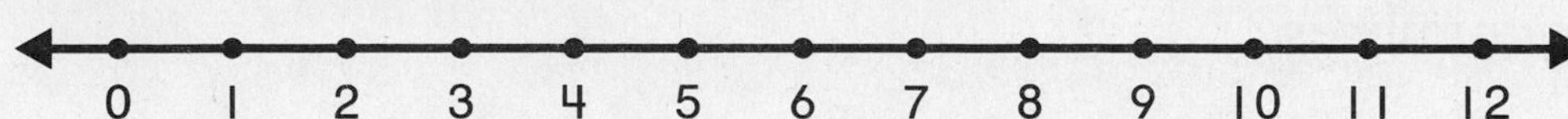

Count on to add. You can use the number line.

1.

6	5	8	7	2	1
+ 3	+ 2	+ 3	+ 1	+ 4	+ 9

Add.

2. 6 + 2 = ____   0 + 3 = ____   6 + 5 = ____

3.

9	1	0	8	3	7
+ 1	+ 9	+ 8	+ 0	+ 7	+ 3

Problem Solving

4. Miguel wants exactly 9 apples. Make a list.

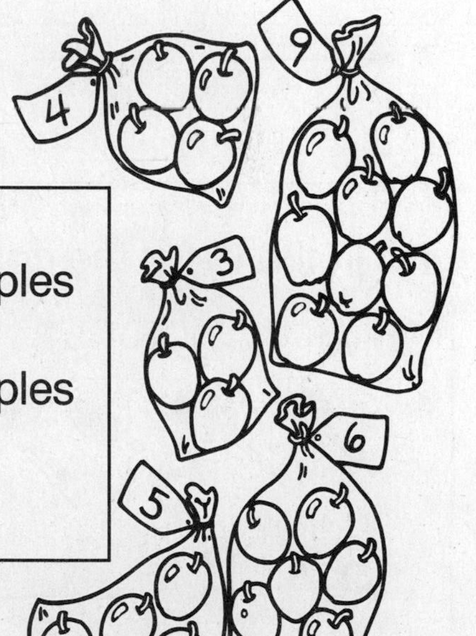

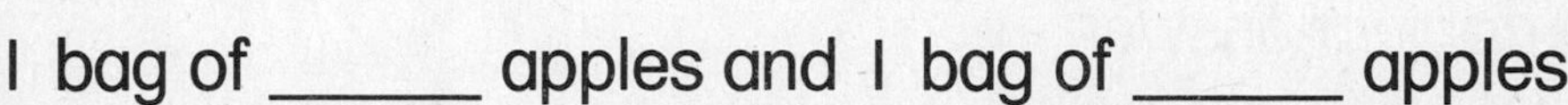

1 bag of _____ apples and 1 bag of _____ apples

1 bag of _____ apples and 1 bag of _____ apples

1 bag of _____ apples

Journal

5. Draw pictures to show ways to make 8.

Notes for Home Your child practiced addition facts to 12. *Home Activity:* Ask your child to list 3 ways to make 2 groups of food items, such as eggs, that make 12. (Answers will vary, but may include: 10 + 2, 6 + 6, 4 + 8.)

Name ______________________________

Practice
Chapters 1–4
A

Cumulative Review

Write the missing numbers.

1. 1 ____ ____ 4 ____ 6 7 8 9 ____

2. 10 9 ____ 7 6 ____ ____ ____ 2 1

Write the number sentence.

3.

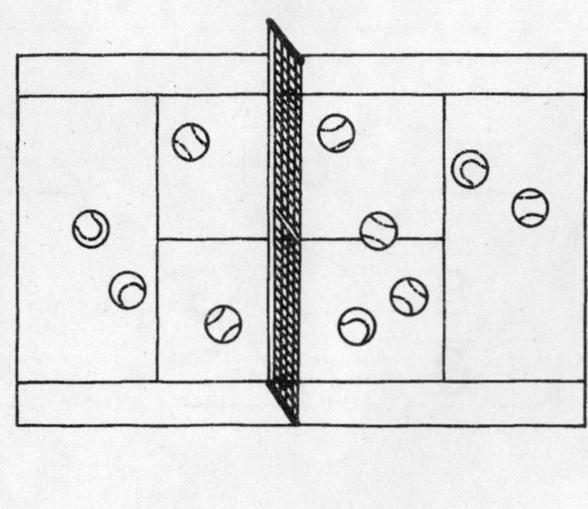

____ + ____ = ____

4.

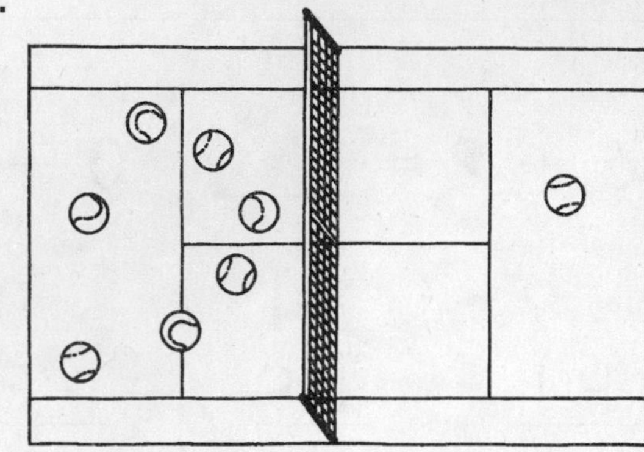

____ + ____ = ____

Test Prep

Fill in the ○ for the correct answer.

Solve.

5.

5 − 2 = ____

1	2	3	4
○	○	○	○

6. 4  play.
3 more come.
How many now?

5	8	7	6
○	○	○	○

Notes for Home Your child reviewed ordering numbers, addition, and subtraction. *Home Activity:* Ask your child to create and solve 4 addition sentences using the fingers of each hand to show the addends.

Name ________________________________

Practice 4-10

Subtract All and Subtract Zero

Solve.

1. There are 5 bananas. All are eaten. How many are left?

$5 - 5 = $ 0

$\begin{array}{r} 5 \\ -\ 5 \\ \hline 0 \end{array}$

2. There are 8 cherries. No one ate any. How many are left?

$8 - 0 = $ ____

$\begin{array}{r} 8 \\ -\ 0 \\ \hline \end{array}$

Subtract.

3. $9 - 0 = $ ____ $9 - 9 = $ ____ $11 - 0 = $ ____

4. $\begin{array}{r} 7 \\ -\ 7 \\ \hline \end{array}$ $\begin{array}{r} 7 \\ -\ 0 \\ \hline \end{array}$ $\begin{array}{r} 5 \\ -\ 5 \\ \hline \end{array}$ $\begin{array}{r} 6 \\ -\ 6 \\ \hline \end{array}$ $\begin{array}{r} 12 \\ -\ 0 \\ \hline \end{array}$ $\begin{array}{r} 12 \\ -\ 12 \\ \hline \end{array}$

Mixed Practice Subtract.

5. $6 - 1 = $ ____ $5 - 2 = $ ____ $2 - 0 = $ ____

6. $\begin{array}{r} 1 \\ -\ 1 \\ \hline \end{array}$ $\begin{array}{r} 9 \\ -\ 2 \\ \hline \end{array}$ $\begin{array}{r} 10 \\ -\ 1 \\ \hline \end{array}$ $\begin{array}{r} 6 \\ -\ 6 \\ \hline \end{array}$ $\begin{array}{r} 8 \\ -\ 2 \\ \hline \end{array}$ $\begin{array}{r} 4 \\ -\ 3 \\ \hline \end{array}$

Problem Solving Critical Thinking

7. Try this super fact. $200 - 0 = $ ____

Write your own super fact. ____ $- 0 = $ ____

Notes for Home Your child subtracted all or 0. *Home Activity:* Have your child use small objects, such as beans, to show show you 8 – 0 and 8 – 8.

Name ______________________

Practice 4-11

Subtract with 5

Subtract.

1. 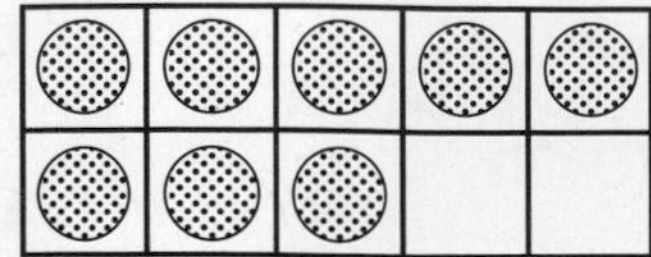

$8 - 5 =$ 3

2. 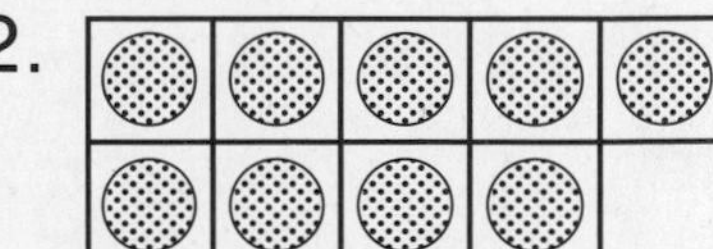

$9 - 5 =$ ____

3. $6 - 5 =$ ____ $10 - 5 =$ ____ $7 - 5 =$ ____

4. $\begin{array}{r} 9 \\ -5 \\ \hline \end{array}$ $\begin{array}{r} 11 \\ -5 \\ \hline \end{array}$ $\begin{array}{r} 12 \\ -5 \\ \hline \end{array}$ $\begin{array}{r} 8 \\ -5 \\ \hline \end{array}$ $\begin{array}{r} 5 \\ -5 \\ \hline \end{array}$ $\begin{array}{r} 10 \\ -5 \\ \hline \end{array}$

Mixed Practice Subtract.

5. $\begin{array}{r} 10 \\ -0 \\ \hline \end{array}$ $\begin{array}{r} 6 \\ -3 \\ \hline \end{array}$ $\begin{array}{r} 12 \\ -5 \\ \hline \end{array}$ $\begin{array}{r} 11 \\ -1 \\ \hline \end{array}$ $\begin{array}{r} 8 \\ -8 \\ \hline \end{array}$ $\begin{array}{r} 9 \\ -2 \\ \hline \end{array}$

6. $\begin{array}{r} 7 \\ -2 \\ \hline \end{array}$ $\begin{array}{r} 11 \\ -2 \\ \hline \end{array}$ $\begin{array}{r} 5 \\ -0 \\ \hline \end{array}$ $\begin{array}{r} 9 \\ -1 \\ \hline \end{array}$ $\begin{array}{r} 10 \\ -10 \\ \hline \end{array}$ $\begin{array}{r} 12 \\ -2 \\ \hline \end{array}$

Problem Solving

7. There are 9 🍎 in all.
How many are in the bag?

____ 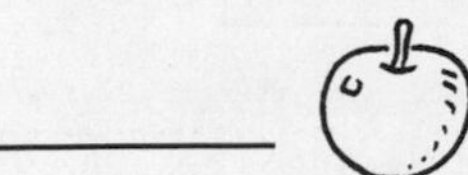

Notes for Home Your child subtracted with 5, counted back 1 or 2, and subtracted 0. *Home Activity:* Write 3 subtraction sentences on a piece of paper. Ask your child to solve each subtraction sentence and to draw pictures representing each sentence.

Name ______________________

Practice Chapters 1–4 B

Cumulative Review

Add.

1.

2	9	4	6	4	1	10
+ 7	+ 2	+ 5	+ 4	+ 4	+ 8	+ 0

Problem Solving

Use the graph. Write the number.

2. How many more  than bird? ______ more

3. How many fewer  than ? ______ fewer

Test Prep

Fill in the ○ for the correct answer.

You can use the number line to count on.

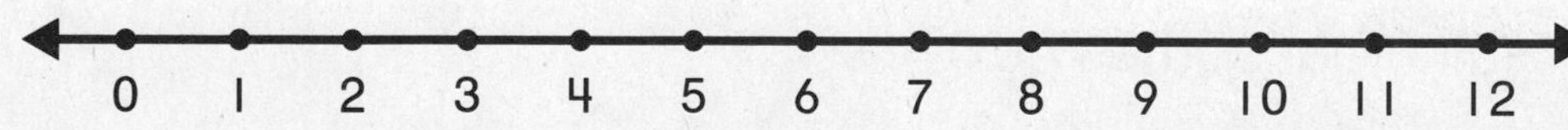

4. $8 + 2 =$ ______

○ 9 ○ 10 ○ 11 ○ 12

5. $6 + 3 =$ ______

○ 8 ○ 9 ○ 10 ○ 11

Notes for Home Your child reviewed using a graph and addition. *Home Activity:* Ask your child to solve the problem 8 + 3. (11)

Name ______________________________

Practice 5-1

Explore Solids

 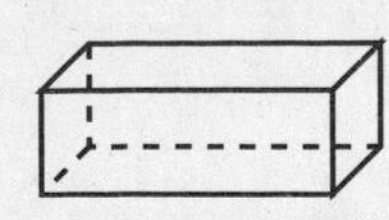 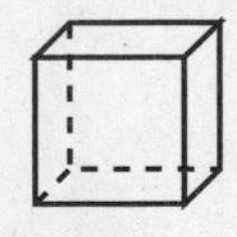

pyramid rectangular prism cube

These can stack and slide.

 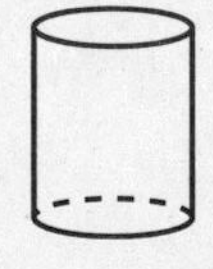 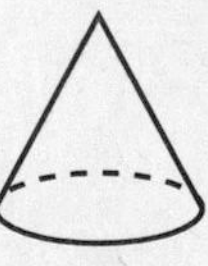

sphere cylinder cone

These are round and curved. They roll.

Draw a solid that belongs.

Draw a solid that does not belong.

	belongs	does not belong
1.		
2.		

Problem Solving Patterns

Circle the solid that comes next.

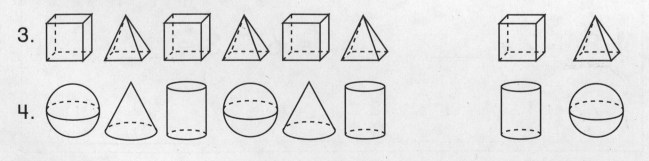

3. 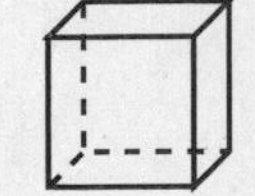  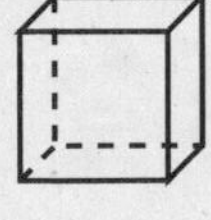  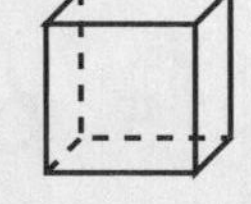  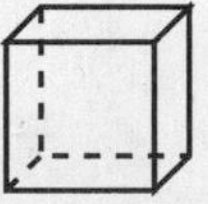 

4. 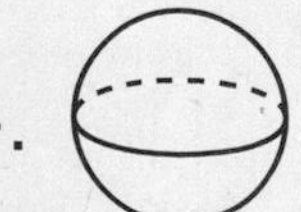   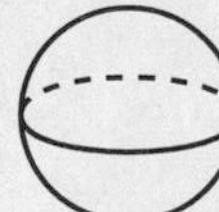 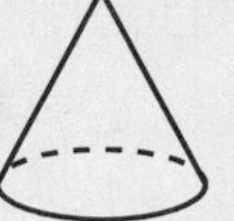 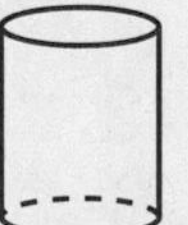 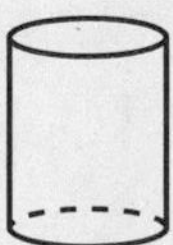 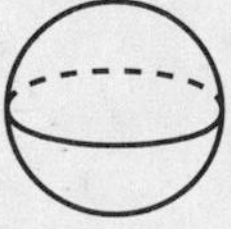

Notes for Home Your child identified and described differences between solid shapes. *Home Activity:* Ask your child to point to kitchen objects that have shapes similar to those in Exercise 1.

Name ________________________________

Faces of Solids

Kim drew around these solids.

Find the shape she made.

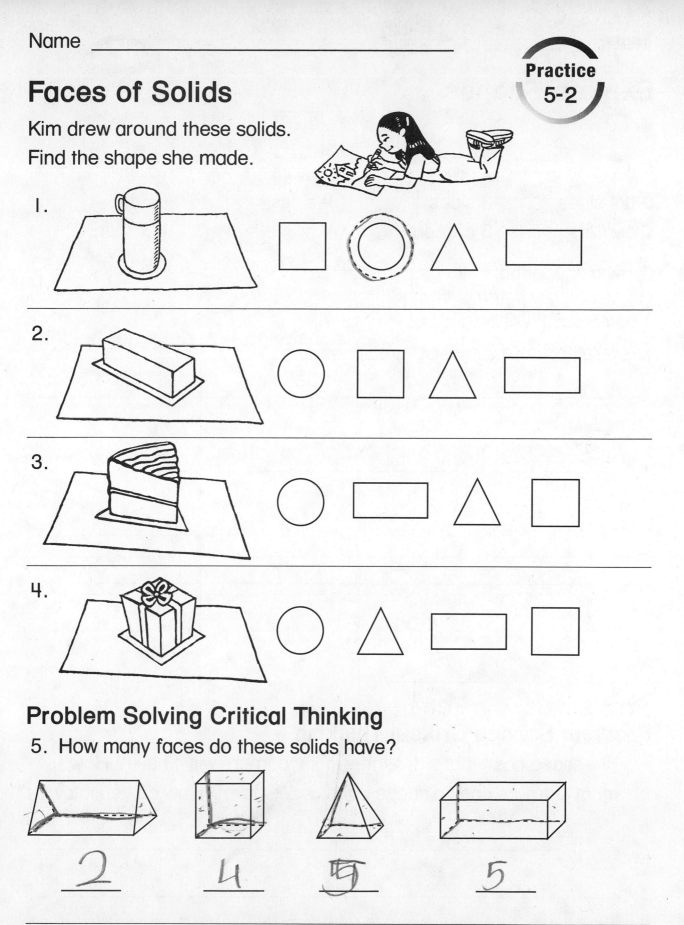

1.

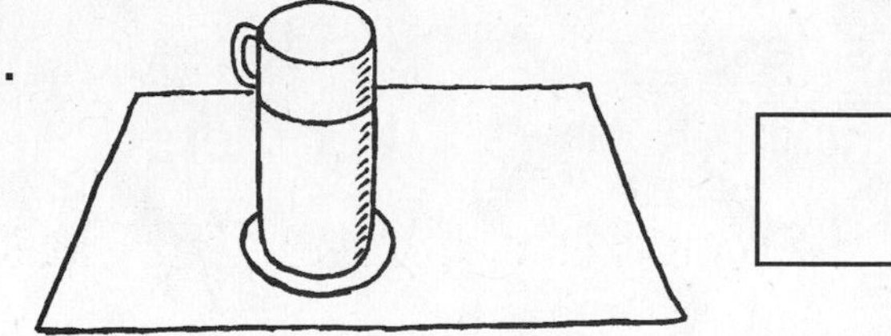
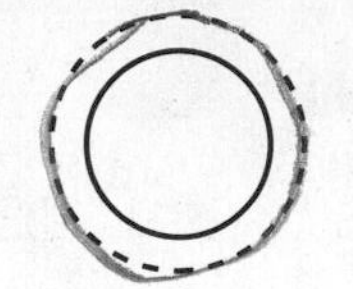
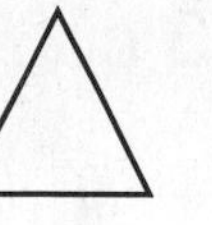
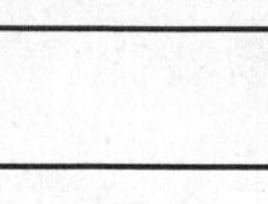

2.

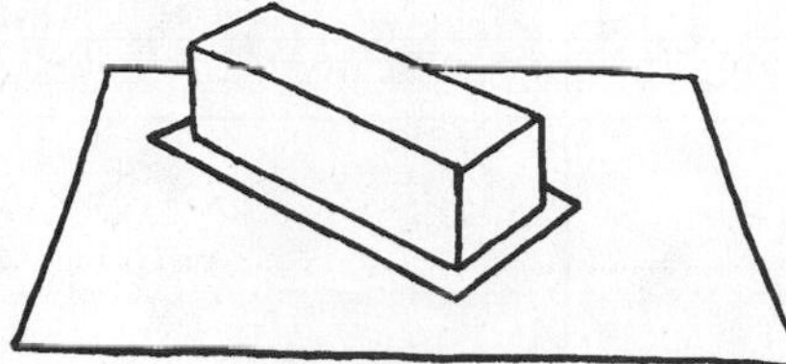
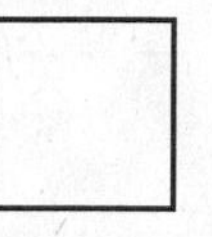

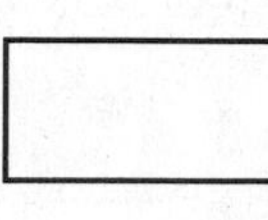

3.

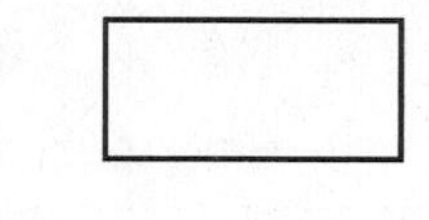
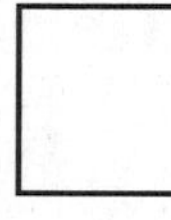

4.

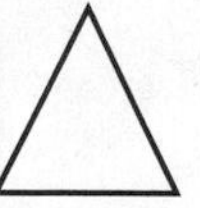
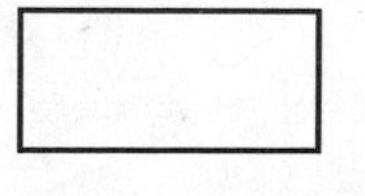

Problem Solving Critical Thinking

5. How many faces do these solids have?

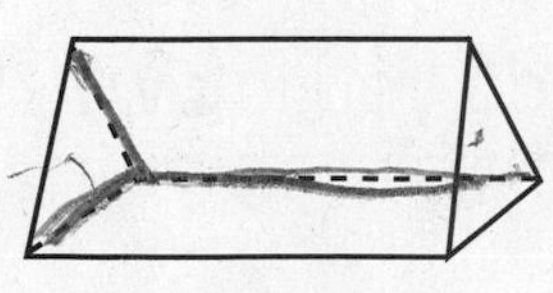
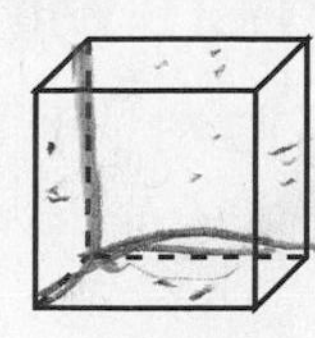

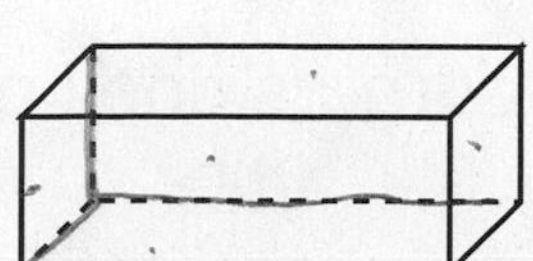

2 ______ 4 ______ 5 ______ 5 ______

Notes for Home Your child predicted the shape that would be made by tracing around each solid. *Home Activity:* Ask your child to point to solids with 6 sides on this worksheet. (Possible answers: rectangular prism; cube)

Name ______________________________

Practice 5-3

Explore Shapes

	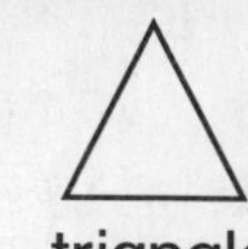		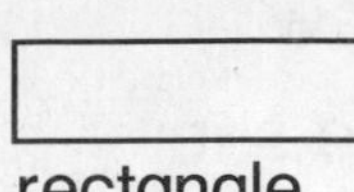
circle	triangle	square	rectangle
0 flat sides	3 sides	4 sides	4 sides
0 corners	3 corners	4 corners	4 corners

Draw a shape that belongs.
Draw a shape that does not belong.

	belongs	does not belong
1.		
2.		
3.		

Problem Solving Critical Thinking

4. If a shape has 0 flat sides, how many corners will it have? How many corners does a shape with 3 sides have? How do you know?

____

____

Notes for Home Your child compared shapes to find similarities and differences. *Home Activity:* Ask your child to point to 5 objects in a room that have a square or rectangular shape.

Name ______________________________

Same Size and Shape

Practice 5-4

Circle the ones that are the same size and shape.

1. 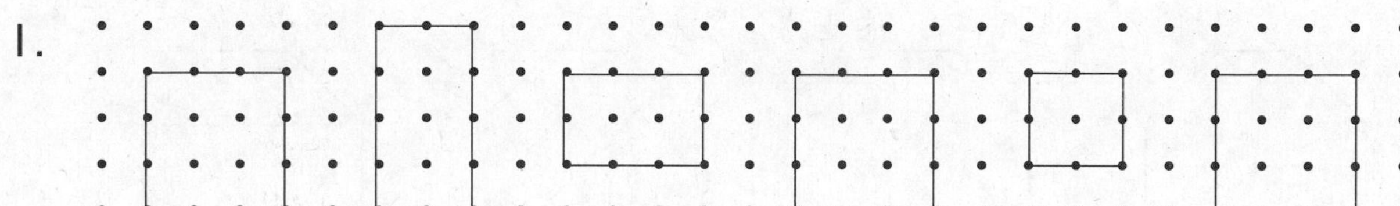

2. 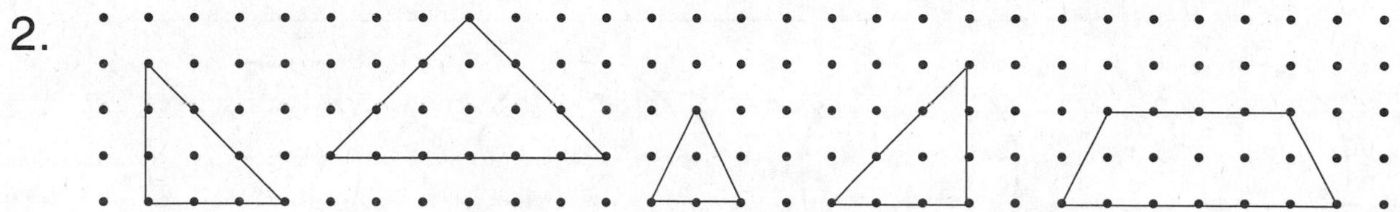

3. 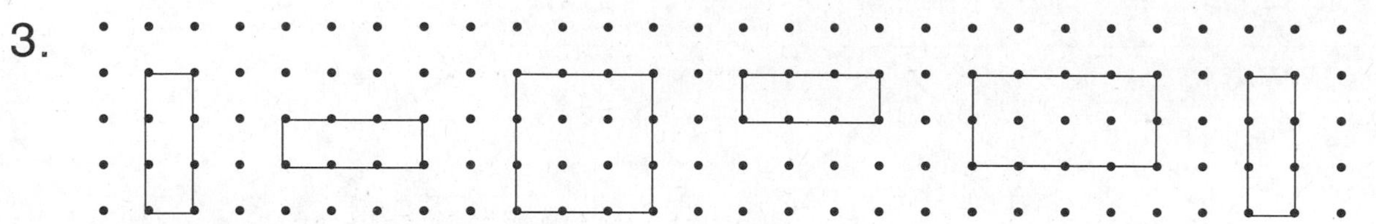

4. 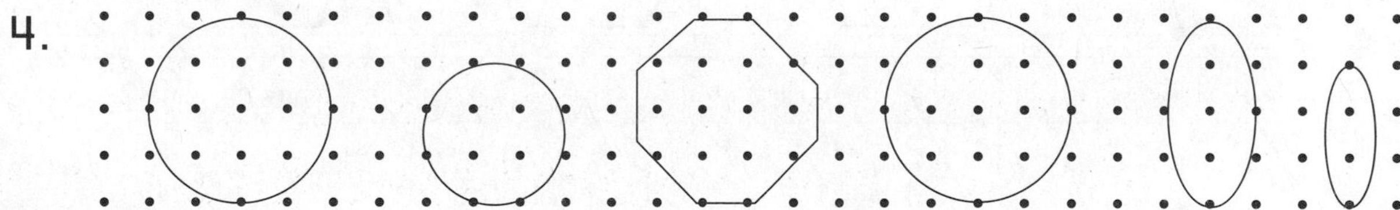

Write About It

5. Draw a shape. Now draw another one that is the same size and shape.

Notes for Home Your child identified figures that have the same sizes and shapes. *Home Activity:* Ask your child to draw shapes with 3, 4, and 5 sides.

Name ______________________________

Symmetry

Circle the shapes if the parts match when you fold on the line.

1.

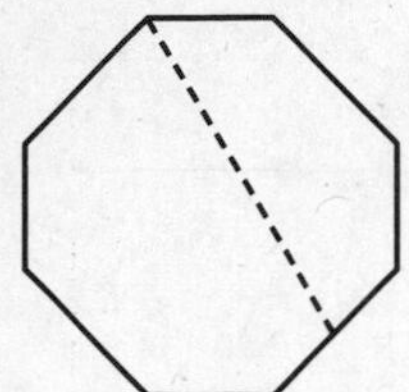 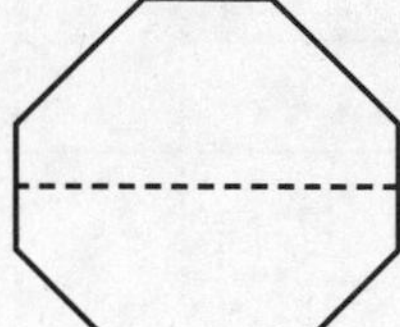 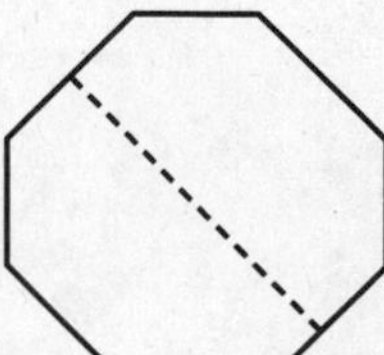 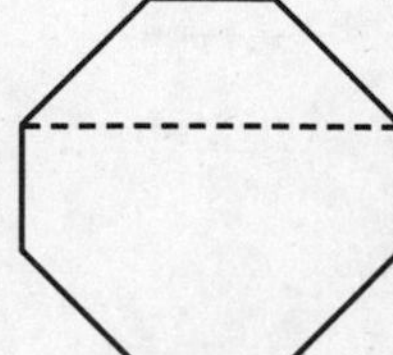

2.

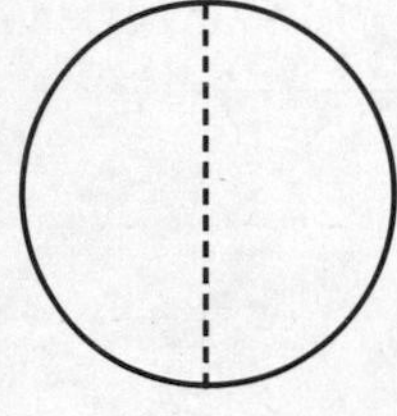 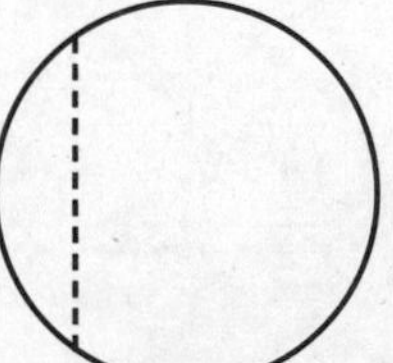 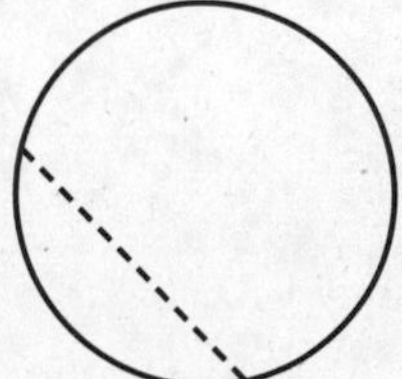 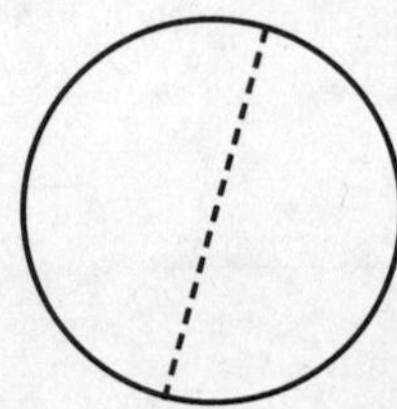

3.

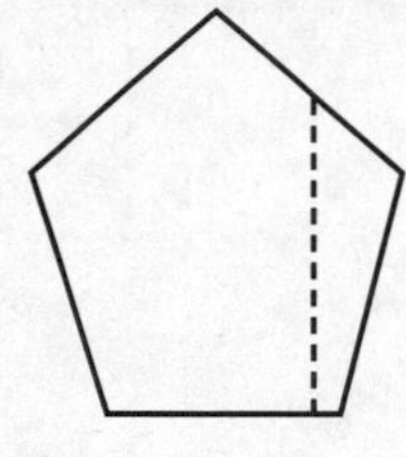 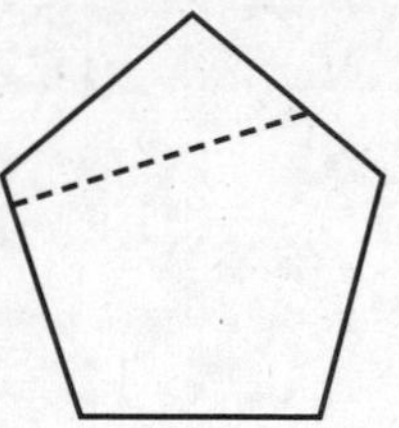 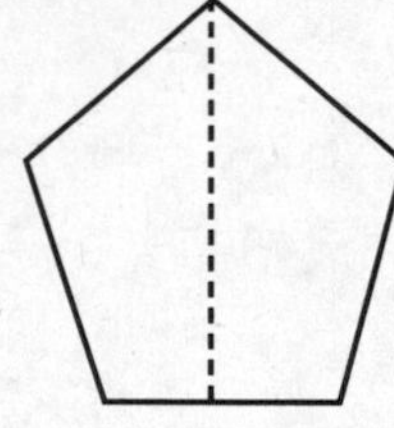 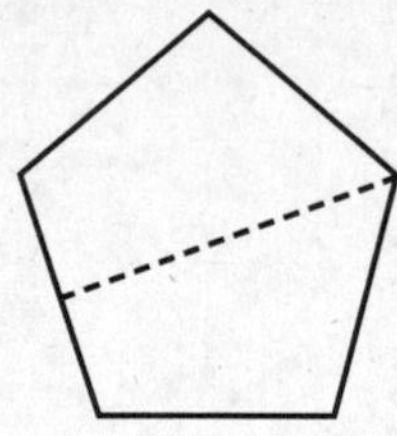

4.

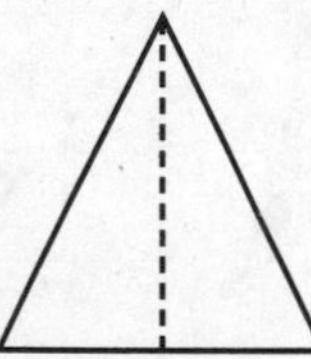 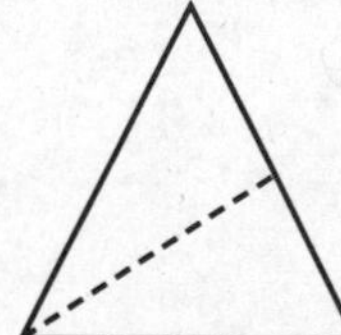 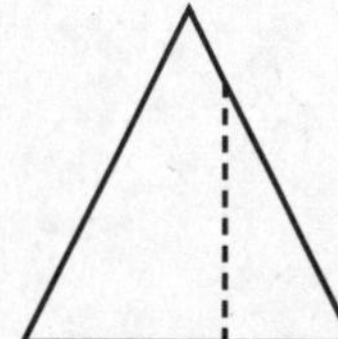 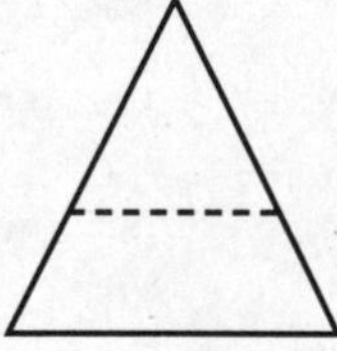

Problem Solving Visual Thinking

5. Draw to make two parts that match.

Notes for Home Your child identified lines of symmetry. *Home Activity:* Point to different symmetrical objects in your home such as doors, plates, or windows. Ask your child to draw the object and to add a line to each drawing to create two parts that match.

Name ______________________________

Practice 5-6

Problem Solving: Make a Table

Use pattern blocks.
How many ways
can you make this shape?

Record the blocks
you used.

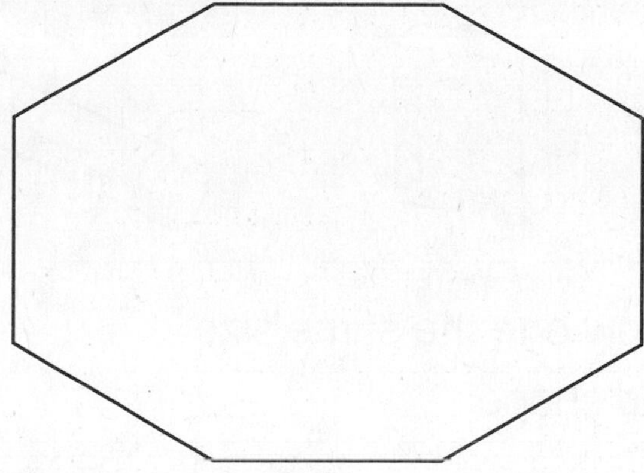

Shapes I used	trapezoid	square	triangle	rhombus
1st way	2	2	0	0
2nd way				
3rd way				
4th way				
5th way				

Patterns

Draw what comes next.

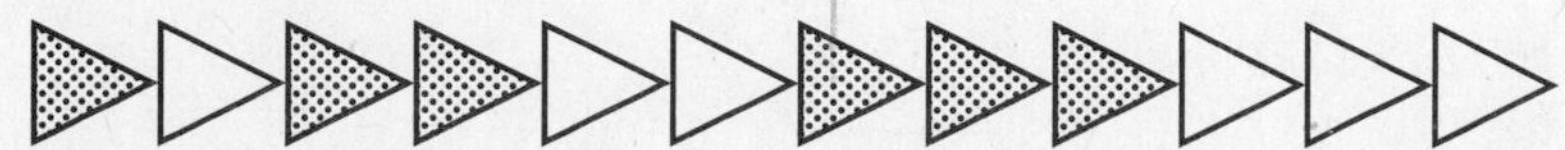

Notes for Home Your child used pattern blocks to find different ways to make a shape, and recorded the ways in a table. *Home Activity:* Ask your child to choose 2 or 3 shapes and draw a pattern using only those shapes.

Name ______________________________

Mixed Practice: Lessons 1–6

Practice
Chapter 5
A

1. Circle the things that can roll.

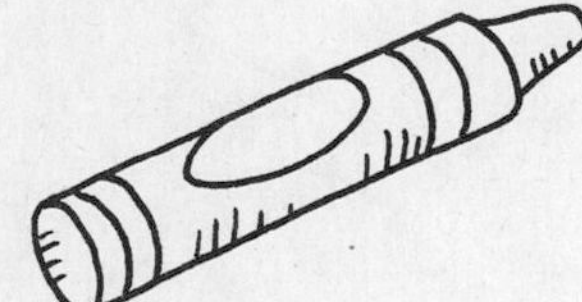

2. Draw one the same size and shape.

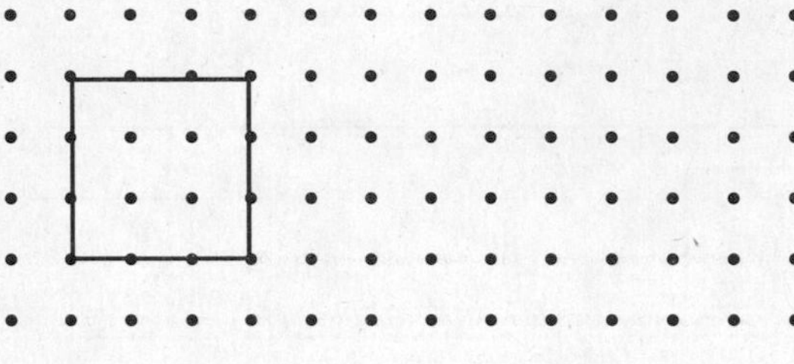

3. Circle the shape if both parts match when you fold on the line.

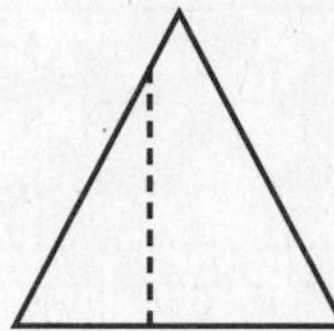

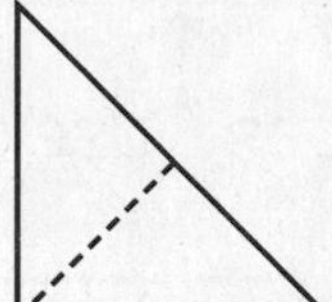

Problem Solving

4. How many of each shape are there? Record the numbers in the table.

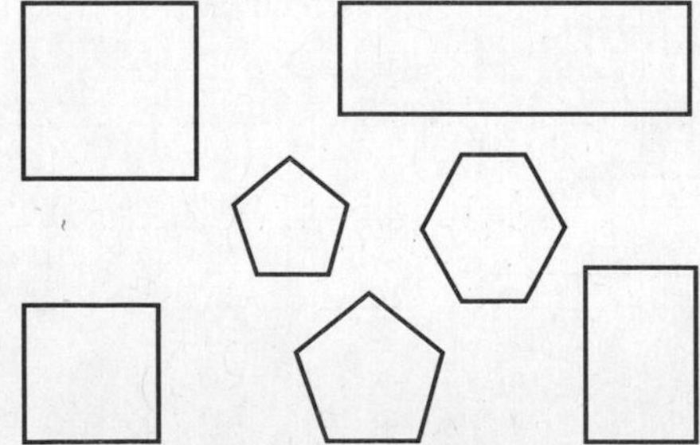

	4 sides	5 sides	6 sides
Number of Shapes			

Journal

5. Write about the shape of a box.

Notes for Home Your child identified shapes. *Home Activity:* Ask your child to count the number of objects in the kitchen that have 4 or more sides.

 Use with page 189.

Name ______________________

Practice
Chapters 1-5
A

Cumulative Review

Count on to add.

1. $2 + 5 =$ ____
   $5 + 2 =$ ____

2. $1 + 8 =$ ____
   $8 + 1 =$ ____

Subtract.

3. $\begin{array}{r} 6 \\ -2 \\ \hline \end{array}$ $\begin{array}{r} 8 \\ -1 \\ \hline \end{array}$ $\begin{array}{r} 9 \\ -6 \\ \hline \end{array}$ $\begin{array}{r} 10 \\ -8 \\ \hline \end{array}$ $\begin{array}{r} 7 \\ -2 \\ \hline \end{array}$ $\begin{array}{r} 5 \\ -4 \\ \hline \end{array}$ $\begin{array}{r} 4 \\ -4 \\ \hline \end{array}$

Problem Solving

4. Draw a picture to match the number sentence.
   Write how many in all.

$2 + 7 =$ ____	$9 - 7 =$ ____

Test Prep

Fill in the ○ for the correct answer.
Add or subtract.

5. $\begin{array}{r} 8 \\ -8 \\ \hline \end{array}$ ○ 8 ○ 1 ○ 12 ○ 0

6. $\begin{array}{r} 3 \\ +2 \\ \hline \end{array}$ ○ 3 ○ 4 ○ 5 ○ 6

7. $\begin{array}{r} 1 \\ +0 \\ \hline \end{array}$ ○ 0 ○ 1 ○ 2 ○ 10

Notes for Home Your child reviewed the concepts learned in Chapters 1–5. *Home Activity:* Ask your child to draw a picture to match the number sentence in Exercise 6.

Name ______________________

Practice 5-7

Fair Shares

Draw lines to show fair shares.

1. 

2. 

3. 

4. 

5. 

6. 

Problem Solving

Solve.

7. Jon, Pablo, and Tania want to share some pie. There are 6 pieces of pie. How can they make fair shares?

____

Notes for Home Your child made fair shares of items. *Home Activity:* Ask your child to explain his or her reasoning.

Name ______________________________

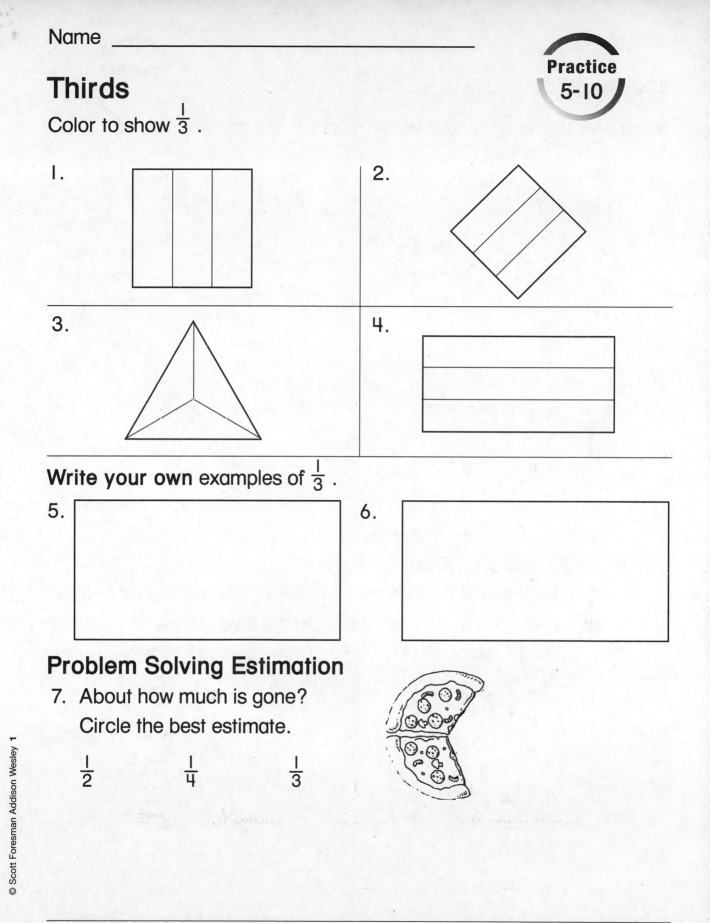

Thirds

Color to show $\frac{1}{3}$.

1. 

2. 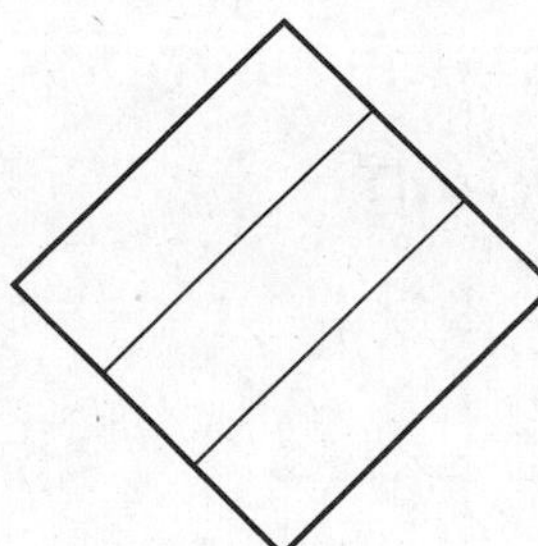

3. 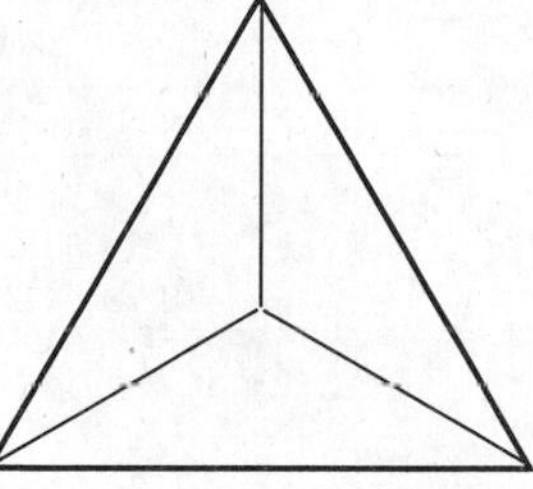

4. 

Write your own examples of $\frac{1}{3}$.

5. 

6. 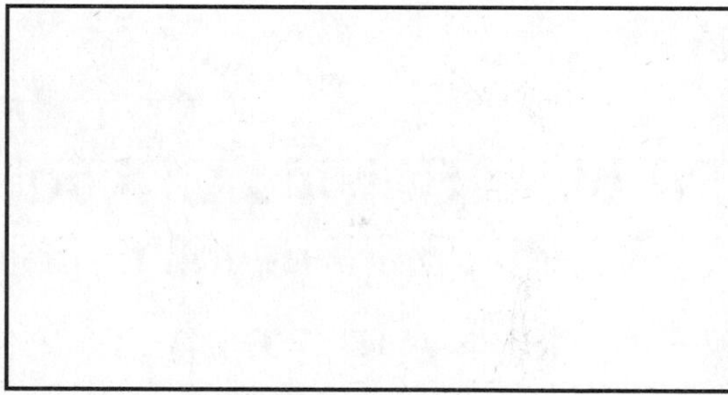

Problem Solving Estimation

7. About how much is gone?
   Circle the best estimate.

   $\frac{1}{2}$ $\frac{1}{4}$ $\frac{1}{3}$

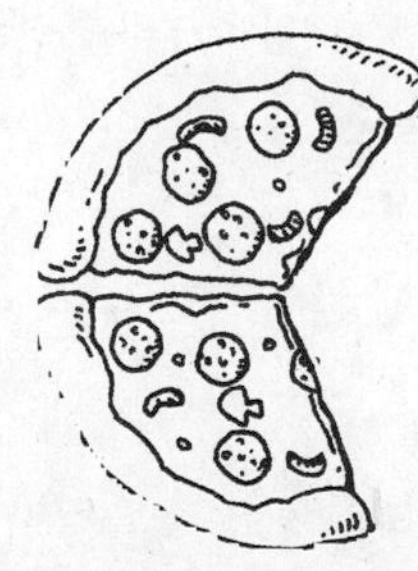

Notes for Home Your child colored thirds of whole shapes. *Home Activity:* Ask your child to cut a piece of bread to show thirds.

Name ______________________________

Practice 5-11

Explore Probability

What will happen if you use the spinner? Circle the word.

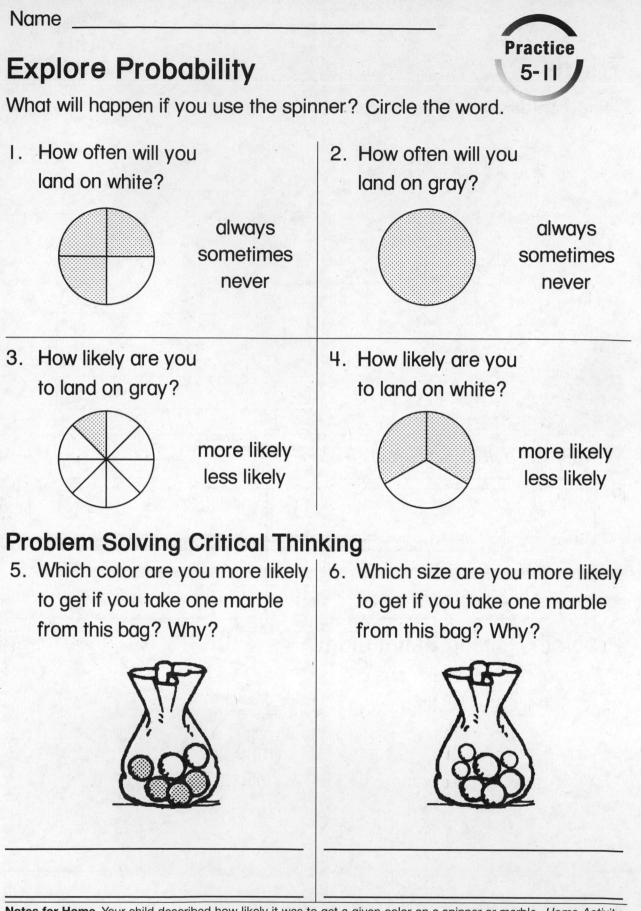

1. How often will you land on white?

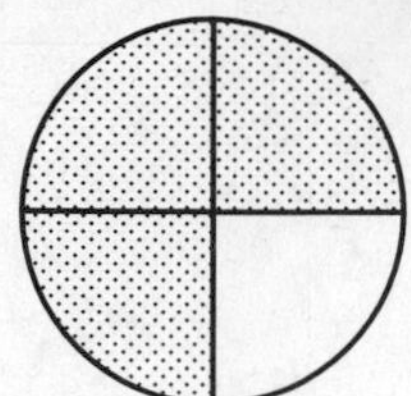

always
sometimes
never

2. How often will you land on gray?

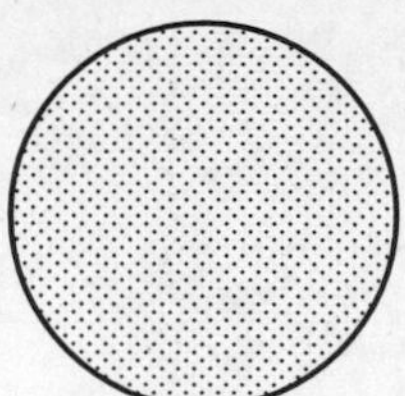

always
sometimes
never

3. How likely are you to land on gray?

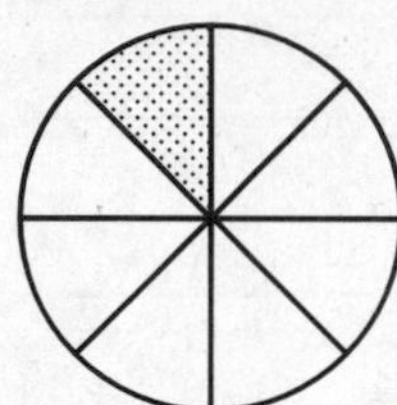

more likely
less likely

4. How likely are you to land on white?

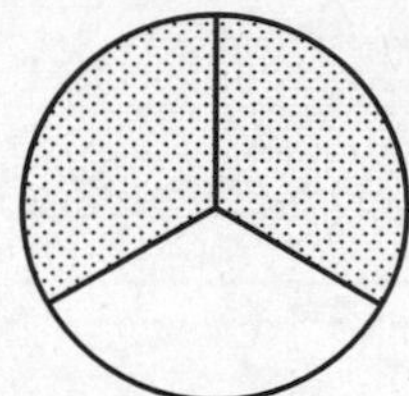

more likely
less likely

Problem Solving Critical Thinking

5. Which color are you more likely to get if you take one marble from this bag? Why?

____

____

6. Which size are you more likely to get if you take one marble from this bag? Why?

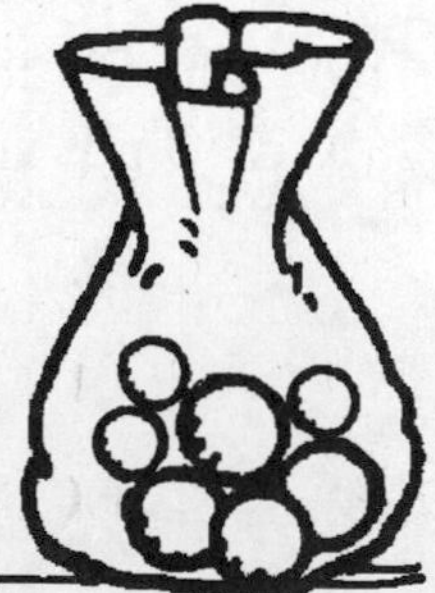

____

____

Notes for Home Your child described how likely it was to get a given color on a spinner or marble. *Home Activity:* Flip a coin several times and ask your child to tell you whether you are more likely to flip heads or tails. (Neither is more likely than the other.)

 Use with pages 201–202.

Name ________________________________

Practice 5-12

Fractions and Probability

1. Make your own spinner. Use 3 colors.

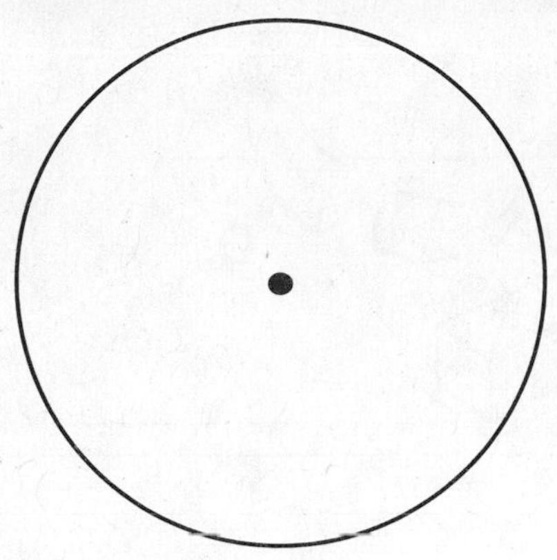

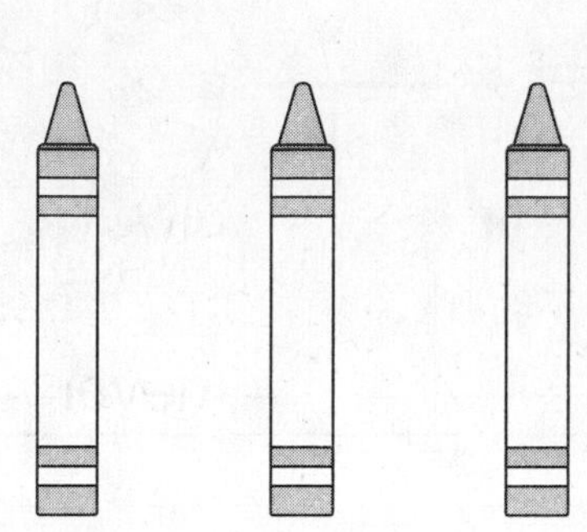

Is your spinner fair? ________

2. Make 20 spins.
   Color to show what you get.

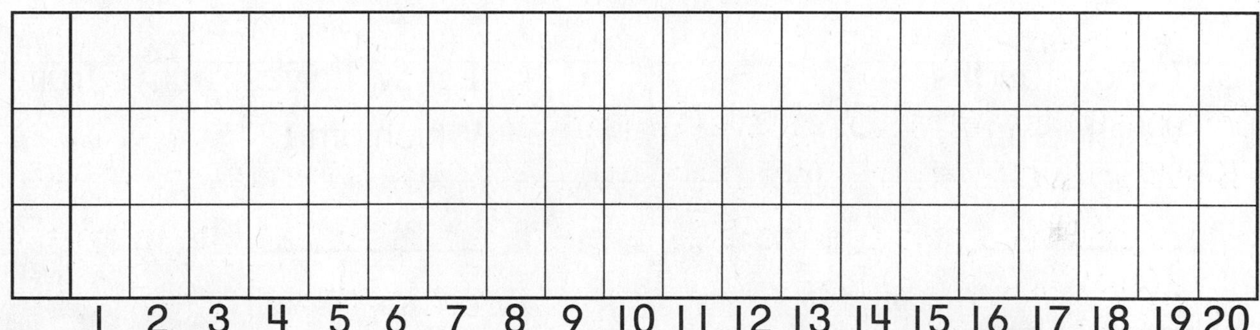

Problem Solving

Solve.

3. Tad got 3 blue, 1 red, and 2 green. How many times did he spin?

   ____

4. Anne got 5 red and 3 green. How many times did she spin?

   ____

Notes for Home Your child colored spinners in thirds and made a table to show the results of 20 spins.
Home Activity: Hide a small object, such as a button or paper clip, in one hand. Ask your child to guess the hand. Repeat several times and record the number of correct guesses.

Name ______________________________

Problem Solving:
Use Data from a Picture

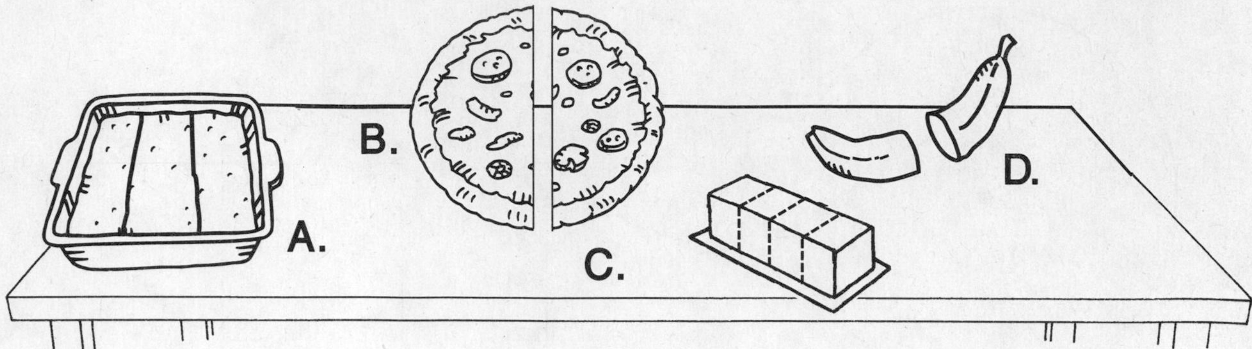

Answer the riddles.

1. I show halves. I am round.
   Which am I?

   ____

2. I show thirds.
   Which am I?
   ____

3. I show fourths.
   Which am I?
   ____

4. I show halves. I am a fruit.
   Which am I?
   ____

Mental Math

5. The girls are going to eat the 🍎.

   Kendra has $\frac{1}{4}$ of the 🍎. Rhea has $\frac{1}{4}$ of the 🍎.

   Is there any of the 🍎 left for Alicia? Why or why not?

   ____

   ____

Notes for Home Your child used a picture to answer riddles about fractions. *Home Activity:* Cut a fruit (or vegetable) into 2, 3, or 4 equal pieces. Ask your child to tell if the fruit has been cut into halves (2 pieces), thirds (3 pieces), or fourths (4 pieces).

Name ______________________________

Mixed Practice: Lessons 7–13

Draw a line to show 2 fair shares.

1.    

2. 

Color to show the fraction.

3. 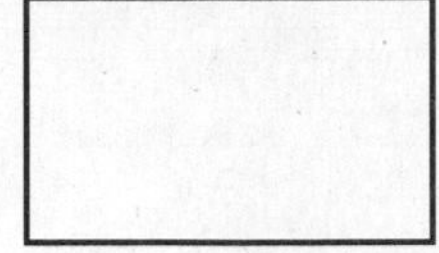

$\frac{1}{3}$

4. 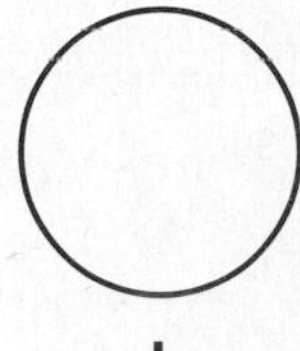

$\frac{1}{2}$

5. 

$\frac{1}{2}$

Circle the answer.

6. Pick a frog.

certain
impossible

7. Pick a coin.

certain
impossible

Problem Solving

8. Look at the animals. Circle the correct answer.

I show fourths. Which animals am I?

Journal

9. Draw objects you see that show fourths.

Notes for Home Your child used fractions and probability concepts. *Home Activity:* Ask your child to design 2 different spinners, one that is fair and one that is not fair.

Use with page 207.

Name ______________________________

Cumulative Review

Practice Chapters 1–5 B

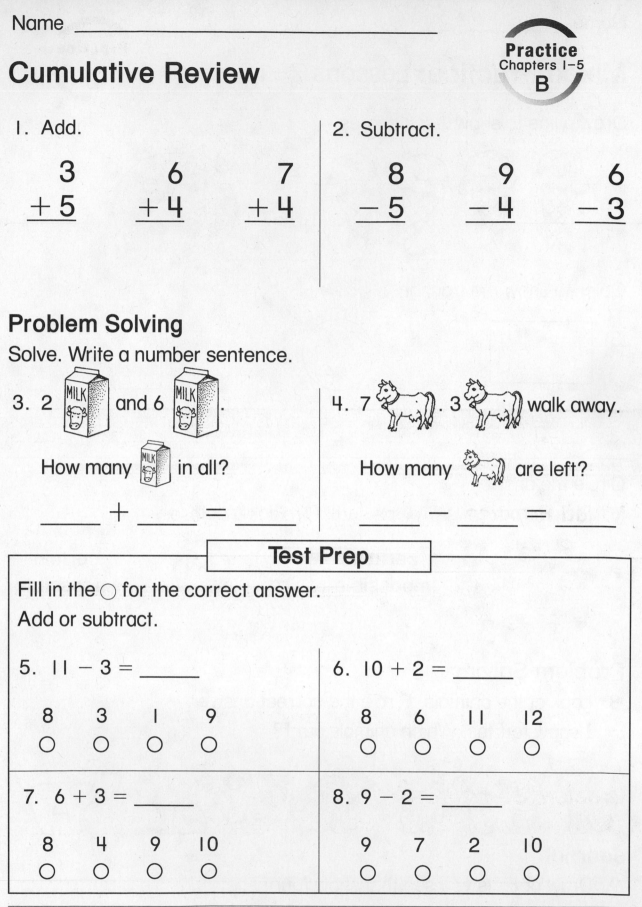

1. Add.

$$\begin{array}{r} 3 \\ +5 \\ \hline \end{array} \quad \begin{array}{r} 6 \\ +4 \\ \hline \end{array} \quad \begin{array}{r} 7 \\ +4 \\ \hline \end{array}$$

2. Subtract.

$$\begin{array}{r} 8 \\ -5 \\ \hline \end{array} \quad \begin{array}{r} 9 \\ -4 \\ \hline \end{array} \quad \begin{array}{r} 6 \\ -3 \\ \hline \end{array}$$

Problem Solving

Solve. Write a number sentence.

3. 2 

and 6 

.

How many 

in all?

_____ + _____ = _____

4. 7 . 3 walk away.

How many  are left?

_____ − _____ = _____

Test Prep

Fill in the ○ for the correct answer.

Add or subtract.

5. 11 − 3 = _____

○ 8 ○ 3 ○ 1 ○ 9

6. 10 + 2 = _____

○ 8 ○ 6 ○ 11 ○ 12

7. 6 + 3 = _____

○ 8 ○ 4 ○ 9 ○ 10

8. 9 − 2 = _____

○ 9 ○ 7 ○ 2 ○ 10

Notes for Home Your child reviewed the concepts taught in Chapters 1– 5. *Home Activity:* Ask your child to draw pictures to show 4 + 1 = 5 and 5 − 1 = 4.

Name ______________________________

Practice 6-1

Add with Doubles

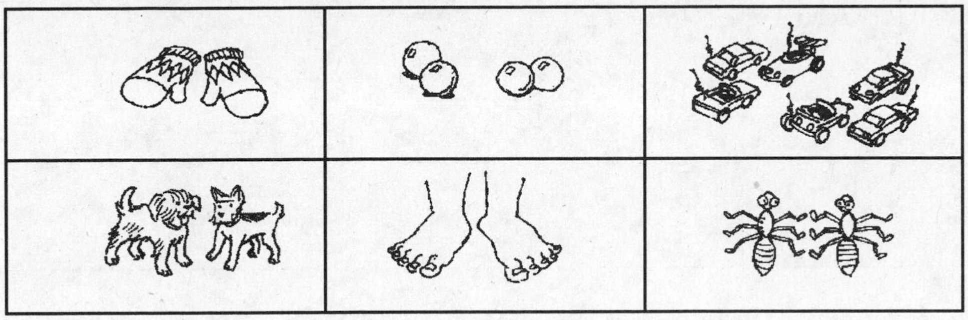

Write the sum. Use the doubles to help.

1. $6 + 6 = \underline{12}$ $2 + 2 = \_\_\_$ $0 + 0 = \_\_\_$

2. $3 + 3$ $6 + 6$ $0 + 0$ $5 + 5$ $4 + 4$ $1 + 1$ $3 + 3$

Mixed Practice Write the sum. Circle the doubles.

3. $3 + 3$ $7 + 3$ $2 + 3$ $5 + 5$ $2 + 4$ $9 + 2$ $2 + 2$

4. $4 + 4$ $3 + 1$ $3 + 4$ $5 + 2$ $9 + 1$ $6 + 6$ $5 + 6$

Problem Solving Critical Thinking

5. Can you use doubles to make 11? Why not? ______________________

____

Notes for Home Your child solved addition facts to 12. *Home Activity:* Write these facts on a piece of paper: 3 + 4, 4 + 4, 0 + 0, 5 + 4. Ask your child to solve the problems and to identify the doubles. (3 + 4 = 7, 4 + 4 = 8 is a doubles fact, 0 + 0 = 0 is a doubles fact, 5 + 4 = 9)

Name ___________________________

Explore Adding Doubles Plus One

Practice 6-2

Use a doubles fact to add other facts.

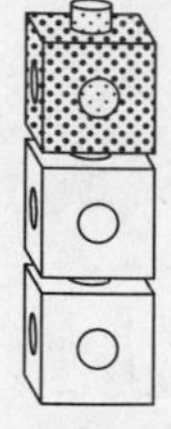

2 + 3 = 5

Write the doubles fact that helps.
Add.

1. 1 + 2 = 3   1 + 1 = 2

2. 6 + 5 = ___   ___ + ___ = ___

3. 3 + 4 = ___   ___ + ___ = ___

Add.

4. 5 + 6 = ___   5 + 5 = ___   4 + 5 = ___

5. 4 + 4   6 + 3   1 + 2   3 + 5   7 + 4   6 + 4   2 + 3

Tell a Math Story

6. Use doubles to make up a math story about these dogs. Retell the story using doubles plus one.

Notes for Home Your child learned that facts like 3 + 4 = 7 are 1 more than a doubles fact (3 + 3 = 6). *Home Activity:* Say a doubles fact like 5 + 5 = 10 and ask your child to name a fact that is 1 more. (5 + 6 = 11 or 6 + 5 = 11)

Name ______________________

Practice 6-3

Add with Doubles Plus One

Add.

1. $5 + 5 = \underline{10}$ $5 + 6 = \_\_\_$ $6 + 5 = \_\_\_$

2. $3 + 3 = \_\_\_$ $3 + 4 = \_\_\_$ $4 + 3 = \_\_\_$

3. $\begin{array}{r} 2 \\ +2 \\ \hline \end{array}$ $\begin{array}{r} 2 \\ +3 \\ \hline \end{array}$ $\begin{array}{r} 3 \\ +2 \\ \hline \end{array}$

4. $\begin{array}{r} 0 \\ +0 \\ \hline \end{array}$ $\begin{array}{r} 0 \\ +1 \\ \hline \end{array}$ $\begin{array}{r} 1 \\ +0 \\ \hline \end{array}$

5. $\begin{array}{r} 3 \\ +3 \\ \hline \end{array}$ $\begin{array}{r} 0 \\ +0 \\ \hline \end{array}$ $\begin{array}{r} 5 \\ +5 \\ \hline \end{array}$ $\begin{array}{r} 6 \\ +6 \\ \hline \end{array}$ $\begin{array}{r} 4 \\ +4 \\ \hline \end{array}$ $\begin{array}{r} 2 \\ +2 \\ \hline \end{array}$ $\begin{array}{r} 1 \\ +1 \\ \hline \end{array}$

6. $\begin{array}{r} 4 \\ +5 \\ \hline \end{array}$ $\begin{array}{r} 3 \\ +2 \\ \hline \end{array}$ $\begin{array}{r} 1 \\ +0 \\ \hline \end{array}$ $\begin{array}{r} 5 \\ +6 \\ \hline \end{array}$ $\begin{array}{r} 1 \\ +2 \\ \hline \end{array}$ $\begin{array}{r} 6 \\ +5 \\ \hline \end{array}$ $\begin{array}{r} 4 \\ +3 \\ \hline \end{array}$

Problem Solving Critical Thinking

7. Billy Bee threw 3 darts.
   His total score was 9.
   Circle the 3 numbers he scored.

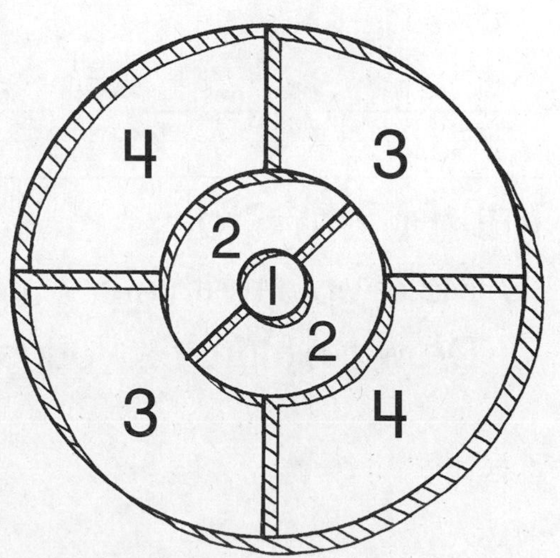

Notes for Home Your child used doubles plus one. *Home Activity:* Ask your child to find 5 numbers on the dart board that equal 11 when added. (3 + 3 + 2 + 2 + 1)

Name ______________________

Practice 6-4

Use Doubles to Subtract

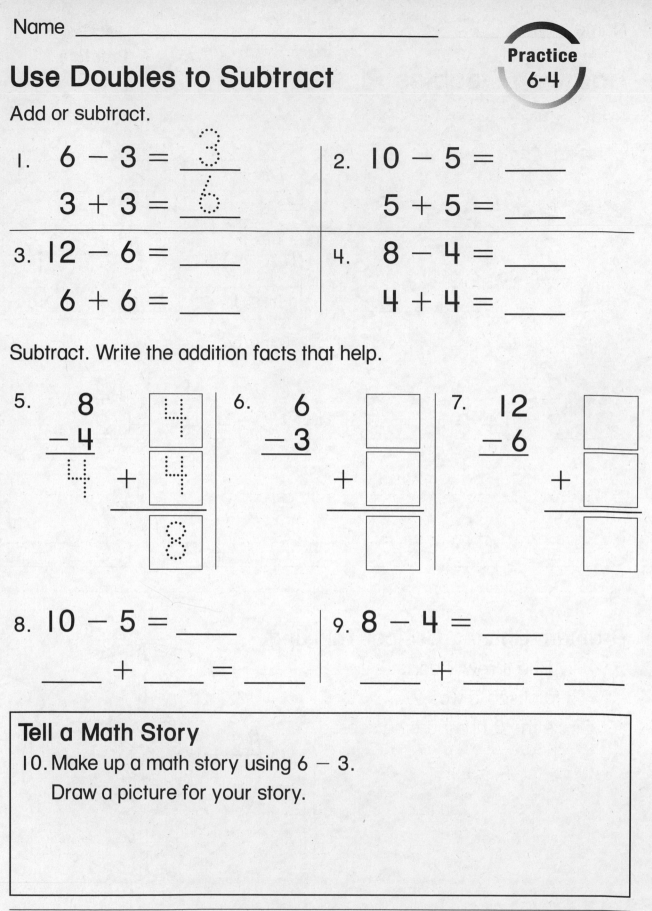

Add or subtract.

1. $6 - 3 = \underline{3}$
   $3 + 3 = \underline{6}$

2. $10 - 5 = \_\_\_\_$
   $5 + 5 = \_\_\_\_$

3. $12 - 6 = \_\_\_\_$
   $6 + 6 = \_\_\_\_$

4. $8 - 4 = \_\_\_\_$
   $4 + 4 = \_\_\_\_$

Subtract. Write the addition facts that help.

5. $8 - 4 = 4$ $\quad$ $4 + 4 = 8$

6. $6 - 3 = \_\_$ $\quad$ $\square + \square = \square$

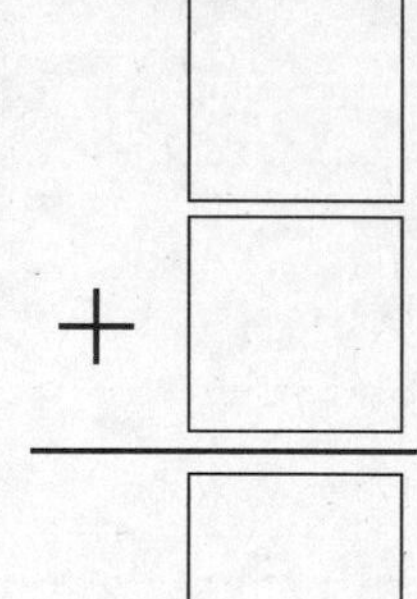

7. $12 - 6 = \_\_$ $\quad$ $\square + \square = \square$

8. $10 - 5 = \_\_\_\_$
   $\_\_\_\_ + \_\_\_\_ = \_\_\_\_$

9. $8 - 4 = \_\_\_\_$
   $\_\_\_\_ + \_\_\_\_ = \_\_\_\_$

Tell a Math Story

10. Make up a math story using $6 - 3$.
    Draw a picture for your story.

Notes for Home Your child used addition and subtraction to find answers. *Home Activity:* Ask your child to say a subtraction fact for things found around your home that come in doubles, such as 4 windowpanes minus 2 windowpanes is 2 windowpanes.

Name ________________________________

Practice 6-5

Problem Solving: Collect and Use Data

Mrs. Shah's class went for a walk outside. Here is what they saw.

Critters	Tally	Total
Dogs	||||	4
Cats	|||	3
Birds	卌 |||	8
Worms	卌 ||	7
Insects	卌 卌	10

Write your own questions.
Use the chart to write 3 questions.
Trade papers. Answer each other's questions.

1. ________________________________

____

2. ________________________________

____

3. ________________________________

____

Patterns Algebra Readiness

4. Complete the pattern.
Draw the towers.
Write the number.

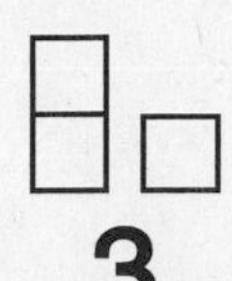
3

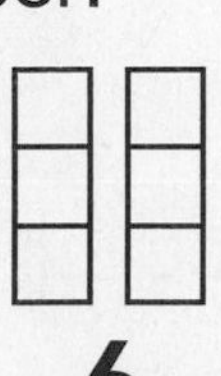
6

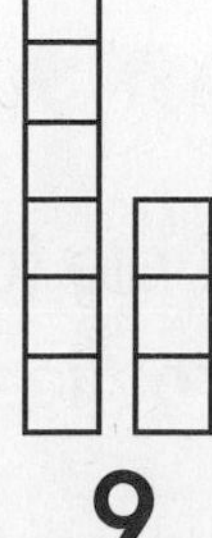
9

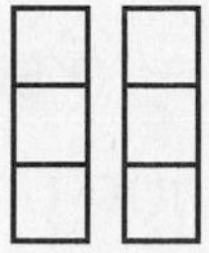
____

____

Notes for Home Your child used a tally chart to answer questions. *Home Activity:* Ask your child to show you how to make a tally chart. You may wish to count the number of forks, spoons, and knives in a drawer. Then ask *"Which do we have the fewest of?" "Which do we have the most of?"*

Name ______________________

Practice Chapter 6 A

Mixed Practice: Lessons 1-5

Add. Use doubles when you can.

1. $\begin{array}{r}2\\+2\\\hline\end{array}$ $\begin{array}{r}2\\+3\\\hline\end{array}$ $\begin{array}{r}5\\+5\\\hline\end{array}$ $\begin{array}{r}5\\+6\\\hline\end{array}$ $\begin{array}{r}0\\+0\\\hline\end{array}$ $\begin{array}{r}0\\+1\\\hline\end{array}$ $\begin{array}{r}1\\+1\\\hline\end{array}$

2. $3 + 3 =$ ___ $3 + 4 =$ ___ $5 + 6 =$ ___

Subtract.

3. $\begin{array}{r}8\\-4\\\hline\end{array}$ $\begin{array}{r}0\\-0\\\hline\end{array}$ $\begin{array}{r}2\\-1\\\hline\end{array}$ $\begin{array}{r}12\\-6\\\hline\end{array}$ $\begin{array}{r}10\\-5\\\hline\end{array}$ $\begin{array}{r}6\\-3\\\hline\end{array}$ $\begin{array}{r}4\\-2\\\hline\end{array}$

Problem Solving

Write the totals.
Use the chart to solve.

4. How many chose green? ______
5. Which one did the most children choose? ________

Favorite Colors		
Color	Tally	Total
Green	卌 I	____
Blue	卌 IIII	____
Yellow	III	____

Journal

6. Draw a picture to show a double for 3.
Write an addition and a subtraction sentence for the picture.

Notes for Home Your child added and subtracted through 12. *Home Activity:* Ask your child to circle all the problems on this page that use doubles to add or subtract, such as 3 + 3 and 8 – 4. Then have him or her write and solve two more different doubles problems.

Name ______________________________

Practice
Chapters 1–6
A

Cumulative Review

Add or subtract.

1.

8	6	7	5	3	9	12
− 4	+ 6	+ 2	− 2	+ 5	− 2	− 7

2.

0	10	6	4	3	9	10
+ 1	− 5	− 4	+ 5	+ 3	− 6	+ 2

Problem Solving

Write a number sentence. Solve.

3. Martin has 5 stickers.
Josh gives him 6 more.
How many stickers
does he have?

______________ stickers

4. Ellen has 11 marbles.
She gives 6 to her brother.
How many marbles
are left?

______________ marbles

Test Prep

Fill in the ○ for the correct answer.

Choose the fraction for the shaded part shown.

5. $\frac{1}{3}$ ○ $\frac{1}{5}$ ○ $\frac{1}{4}$ ○

6. $\frac{1}{3}$ ○ $\frac{1}{5}$ ○ $\frac{1}{4}$ ○

7. $\frac{1}{3}$ ○ $\frac{1}{2}$ ○ $\frac{1}{4}$ ○

Notes for Home Your child reviewed adding 1, 2, and 3 and subtracting 1 and 2; and identifying fractions. *Home Activity:* Ask your child to explain how he or she determined the fraction for the shaded parts shown in Exercises 5 – 7.

Name ______________________

Practice 6-6

Relate Addition and Subtraction

Add or subtract. You can use [counters].

1. $\begin{array}{r} 3 \\ +4 \\ \hline 7 \end{array}$ $\begin{array}{r} 7 \\ -3 \\ \hline \end{array}$

2. $\begin{array}{r} 5 \\ +6 \\ \hline \end{array}$ $\begin{array}{r} 11 \\ -5 \\ \hline \end{array}$

3. $\begin{array}{r} 6 \\ +3 \\ \hline \end{array}$ $\begin{array}{r} 9 \\ -3 \\ \hline \end{array}$

4. $\begin{array}{r} 7 \\ +5 \\ \hline \end{array}$ $\begin{array}{r} 12 \\ -5 \\ \hline \end{array}$

5. $\begin{array}{r} 4 \\ +1 \\ \hline \end{array}$ $\begin{array}{r} 5 \\ -1 \\ \hline \end{array}$

6. $\begin{array}{r} 2 \\ +5 \\ \hline \end{array}$ $\begin{array}{r} 7 \\ -5 \\ \hline \end{array}$

7. $\begin{array}{r} 4 \\ +5 \\ \hline \end{array}$ $\begin{array}{r} 9 \\ -5 \\ \hline \end{array}$

8. $\begin{array}{r} 6 \\ +4 \\ \hline \end{array}$ $\begin{array}{r} 10 \\ -4 \\ \hline \end{array}$

9. $3 + 7 =$ ____ $10 - 7 =$ ____

10. $6 + 1 =$ ____ $7 - 1 =$ ____

11. $6 + 3 =$ ____ $9 - 3 =$ ____

Problem Solving

Solve.

12. Mark had 5 peas on his plate. He took 7 more. How many peas does Mark have on his plate?

____ peas

13. Mark had 12 peas on his plate. He ate 7 peas. How many peas does Mark have on his plate?

____ peas

Notes for Home Your child used addition facts to help solve subtraction facts. *Home Activity:* Ask your child to explain how he or she can use the fact 3 + 4 = 7 to find 7 - 3 and 7 - 4. (Possible answer: since 3 + 4 = 7, I can subtract either 3 or 4 from 7 and get the other number for the answer.)

Name ______________________

Practice 6-7

Fact Families

Complete the fact family. You can use 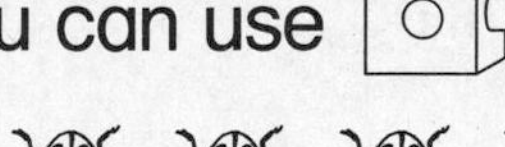.

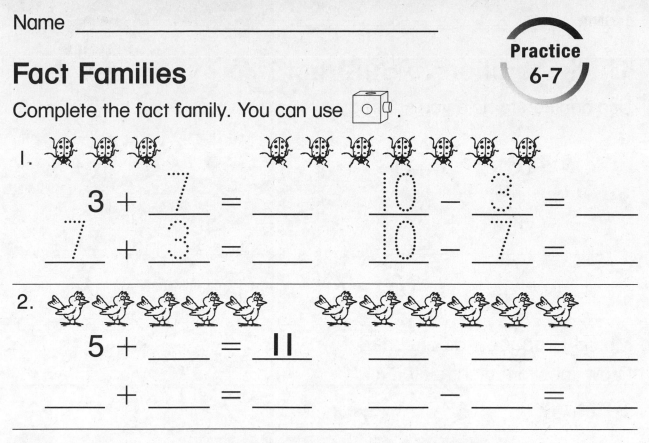

1.

3 + 7 = ____   10 − 3 = ____

7 + 3 = ____   10 − 7 = ____

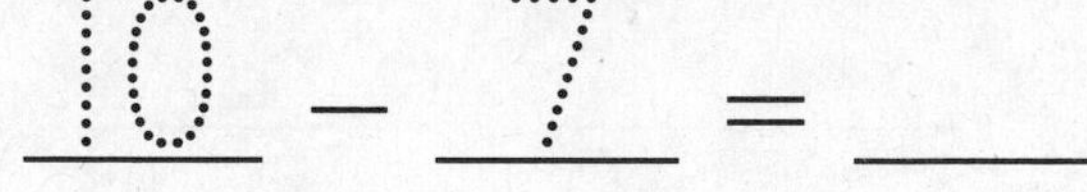

2.

5 + ____ = 11   ____ − ____ = ____

____ + ____ = ____   ____ − ____ = ____

Write your own fact family. Draw a picture to go with it.

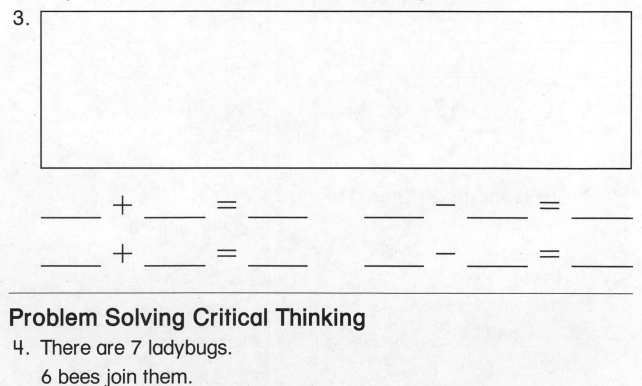

3.

____ + ____ = ____   ____ − ____ = ____

____ + ____ = ____   ____ − ____ = ____

Problem Solving Critical Thinking

4. There are 7 ladybugs.
   6 bees join them.
   How many ladybugs are there? ____

Notes for Home Your child wrote number sentences to show the number relationships in addition and subtraction. *Home Activity:* Ask your child to use objects such as 5 dry beans and 6 dry macaroni to show the four related number sentences for 5 + 6, 6 + 5, 11 − 5, and 11 − 6.

Name ______________________________

Think Addition to Subtract

Practice 6-8

Use addition to help you subtract.

1.
$$\begin{array}{r} 10 \\ -\ 6 \\ \hline 4 \end{array} \qquad \begin{array}{r} 6 \\ +\ 4 \\ \hline 10 \end{array}$$

2.
$$\begin{array}{r} 9 \\ -\ 3 \\ \hline \square \end{array} \qquad \begin{array}{r} 3 \\ +\ \square \\ \hline 9 \end{array}$$

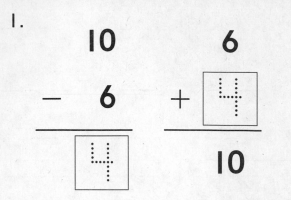

Mixed Practice Add or subtract.

Draw lines to match related facts.

3.
$$\begin{array}{r} 3 \\ +\ 8 \\ \hline 11 \end{array} \qquad \begin{array}{r} 3 \\ +\ 6 \\ \hline \end{array} \qquad \begin{array}{r} 7 \\ +\ 4 \\ \hline \end{array}$$

$$\begin{array}{r} 11 \\ -\ 4 \\ \hline \end{array} \qquad \begin{array}{r} 11 \\ -\ 3 \\ \hline \end{array} \qquad \begin{array}{r} 9 \\ -\ 6 \\ \hline \end{array}$$

4.
$$\begin{array}{r} 2 \\ +\ 9 \\ \hline 11 \end{array} \qquad \begin{array}{r} 4 \\ +\ 3 \\ \hline \end{array} \qquad \begin{array}{r} 7 \\ +\ 1 \\ \hline \end{array}$$

$$\begin{array}{r} 7 \\ -\ 3 \\ \hline \end{array} \qquad \begin{array}{r} 8 \\ -\ 1 \\ \hline \end{array} \qquad \begin{array}{r} 11 \\ -\ 9 \\ \hline \end{array}$$

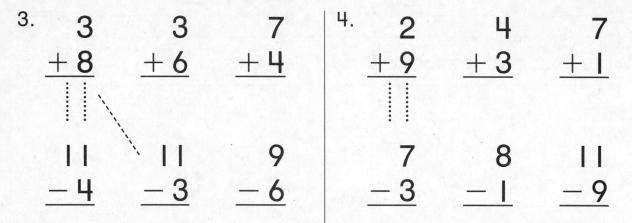

Problem Solving Critical Thinking

Solve the riddle.

5. First double me.
Then subtract 4.
You will get 8.
What number am I? ______

Write your own riddle.

6. ______________________________

____

____

Notes for Home Your child used addition to check subtraction. *Home Activity:* Write a subtraction sentence such as 11 – 6 = ____. Ask your child to write the answer, then write an addition fact that can help check the subtraction. (Answers may include: 5 + 6 = 11 and 6 + 5 = 11.)

Name ______________________

Practice 6-9

Fact Families for 10

Complete the fact family for 10.

1.

3 + ____ = ____   ____ − ____ = ____

____ + ____ = ____   ____ − ____ = ____

Mixed Practice Add or subtract.
Draw lines to match related facts.

3.

2	4	7
+ 7	+ 6	+ 4

11	10	9
− 4	− 4	− 7

4.

2	3	6
+ 10	+ 6	+ 1

9	7	12
− 6	− 1	− 2

Problem Solving Visual Thinking

5. There are 7 frogs in all.

How many are in the water?

____ 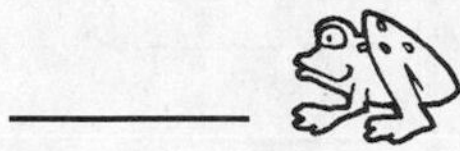

Notes for Home Your child added and subtracted with 10. *Home Activity:* Show your child 10 small objects, such as paper clips. Cover 7 of them. Have your child say an addition and a subtraction sentence to tell about the objects. (Answers may include: 7 + 3 = 10, 3 + 7 = 10, 10 − 7 = 3.)

Name ______________________

Practice 6-10

Problem Solving: Guess and Check

Use .

Guess. Then check to find the answer.

1. Try ____ 6 + ____ = ____

   Try ____ 6 + ____ = ____

15 in all

2. Try ____ 5 + ____ = ____

   Try ____ 5 + ____ = ____

9 in all

---

3. Try ____ 9 + ____ = ____

   Try ____ 9 + ____ = ____

11 in all

Mental Math

4. Circle numbers that are odd numbers less than 16.

12 15 17 14

3 10 4 1 8

9 6 7 11

Notes for Home Your child solved addition and subtraction problems by using the Guess and Check strategy.
Home Activity: Ask your child to find the even numbers in the Mental Math activity. (4, 6, 8, 10, 12, 14)

Name ______________________

Mixed Practice: Lessons 6–10

Use [cube]. Complete the fact family.

1. 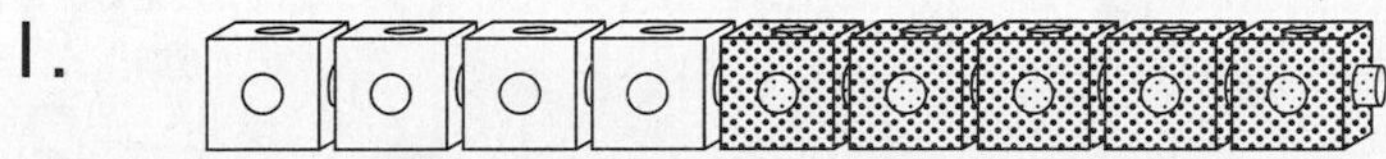

4 + ____ = ____   ____ − ____ = ____

____ + ____ = ____   ____ − ____ = ____

Add or subtract.

2.

4	9	5	12	2	9
+ 2	+ 3	− 5	− 8	+ 7	− 8

3.

2	6	12	5	9	6
+ 2	+ 2	− 3	+ 6	− 2	− 5

Problem Solving

4. Guess. Then check to find the answer. You can use  .

12 in all

Guess	Check
Try ____	7 + ____ = ____
Try ____	7 + ____ = ____

Journal

5. Take a total of 9 [cube] in two colors. Draw a picture of the cubes.
   Write the fact family.

Notes for Home Your child practiced addition and subtraction facts through 12 and problem solving.
Home Activity: Ask your child to make up one addition and one subtraction problem for you to solve. Work together to check your answers.

Name ______________________________

Cumulative Review

Add or subtract.

1.

8	8	7	4	3	4	10
+ 3	− 5	+ 0	+ 5	+ 5	+ 4	− 2

2.

5	6	6	5	3	9	3
− 1	+ 4	− 4	+ 2	− 0	− 5	+ 7

3. $7 + 4 =$ ____ $11 - 8 =$ ____ $12 - 4 =$ ____

Problem Solving

Write a number sentence.

4. Frank has 8 marbles.
Martha gives him 4 more.
How many does Frank have now?

____

5. Alice had 6 books.
She gave away 2.
How many are left?

____

Test Prep

Fill in the ○ for the correct answer.

6. Which shows a circle and a triangle?

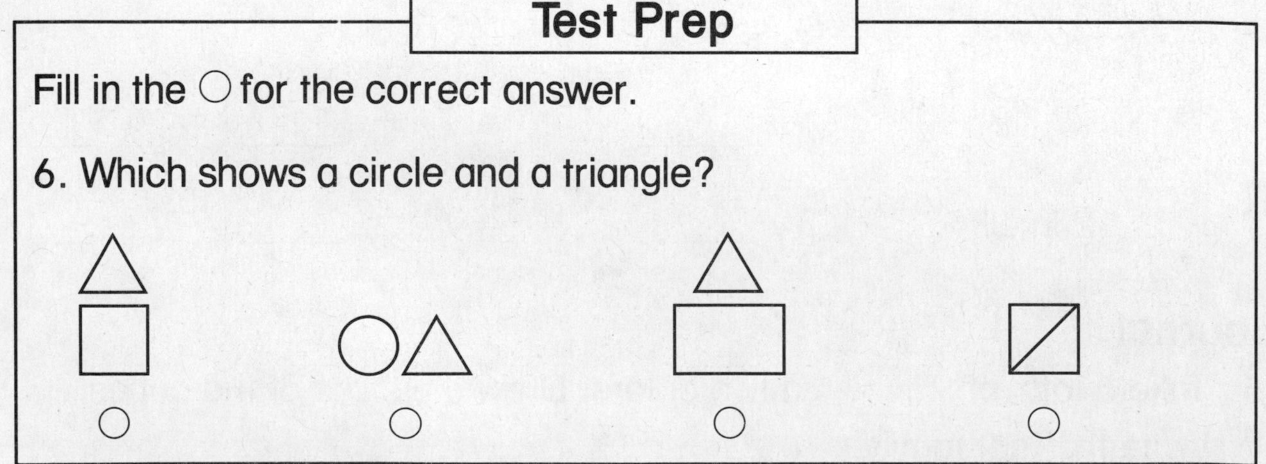

Notes for Home Your child reviewed addition and subtraction, writing number sentences, and identifying shapes.
Home Activity: Ask your child to tell you how he or she found the answer to Exercise 4.

Name ______________________________

Practice 7-1

Numbers to 19

Write the numbers.

1. 17 seventeen
   10 and 7 is 17.

2. 13 thirteen
   10 and ______ is ______.

3. 11 eleven
   10 and ______ is ______.

4. 19 nineteen
   10 and ______ is ______.

5. 15 fifteen
   10 and ______ is ______.

6. 12 twelve
   10 and ______ is ______.

7. 16 sixteen
   10 and ______ is ______.

8. 14 fourteen
   10 and ______ is ______.

Problem Solving

9. These are José's trucks.
   Tell how you found how many he has.

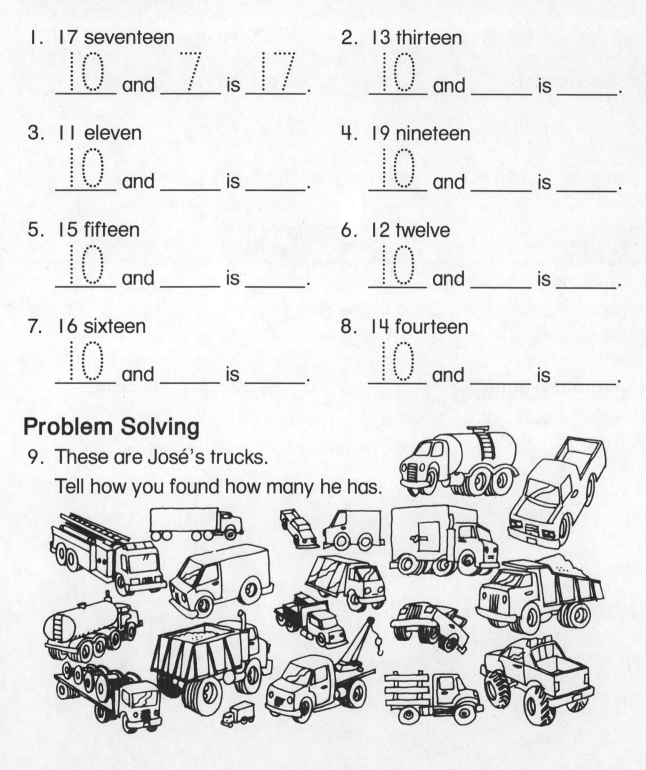

Notes for Home Your child wrote numbers 11–19 as 10 and ones. *Home Activity:* Ask your child to complete this sentence for 19: ____ and ____ is ____. (10 and 9 is 19.)

Name ____________________

Practice 7-2

Tens

Write the number.

1. 20 and 10 is 30.
2. 40 and 10 is ____.
3. 30 and 10 is ____.
4. 60 and 10 is ____.
5. 70 and 10 is ____.
6. 80 and 10 is ____.

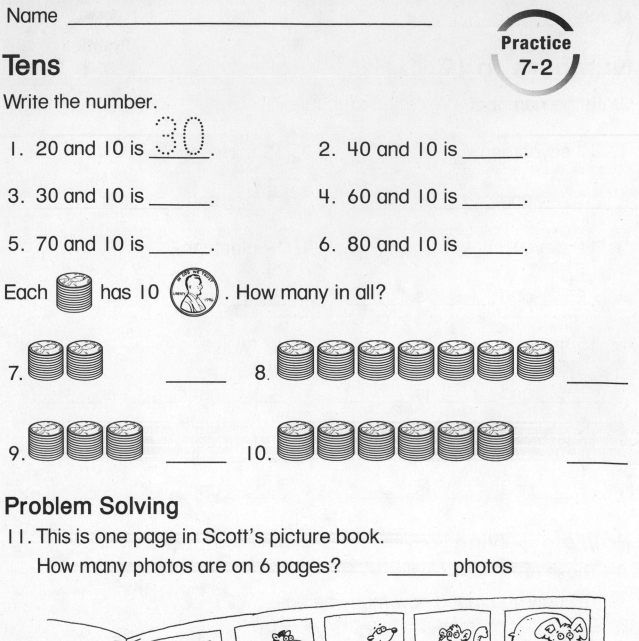

Each  has 10 . How many in all?

7. ____

8.  ____

9. ____

10. ____

Problem Solving

11. This is one page in Scott's picture book.
How many photos are on 6 pages? ____ photos

Notes for Home Your child counted groups of 10. *Home Activity:* Ask your child "*How many 10s are in 50?*" (5)

Name ______________________________

Practice 7-3

Numbers to 60

Circle groups of 10. Write the numbers.

1. ☆☆☆☆☆☆☆☆☆☆☆☆
☆☆☆☆☆☆☆☆☆☆☆☆
☆☆☆☆☆☆☆☆☆☆☆☆
☆☆☆☆☆☆☆☆☆☆☆

_____ tens and _____ extra is _____.

2. **Write your own** problem.
Draw a lot of things.
Circle groups of 10. Write the numbers.

_____ tens and _____ extra is _____.

Estimation

3. About how many are in the middle bowl?
Circle the number.

20 40 10

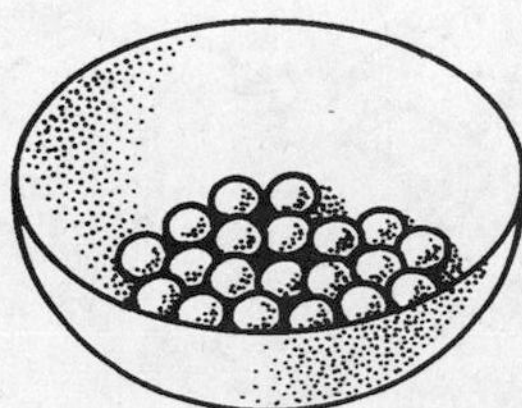
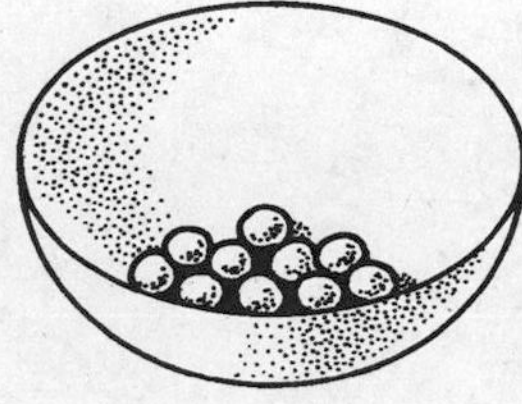
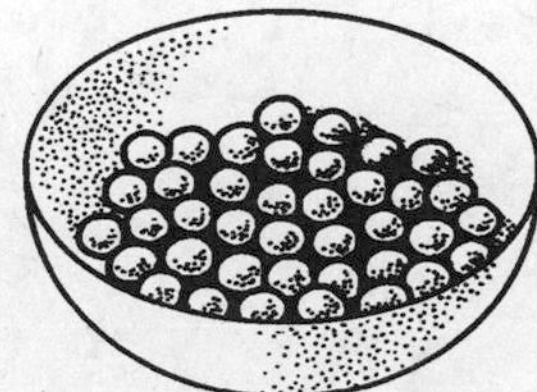

4. Why do you think so?

Notes for Home Your child put things into groups of ten and wrote the number. *Home Activity:* Have your child count a handful of pennies by putting them in groups of 10.

Name ________________________________

Practice 7-4

Explore Estimation

Take a lot of counters. Do not count yet.
Estimate how many there are.
Let your partner count how many.

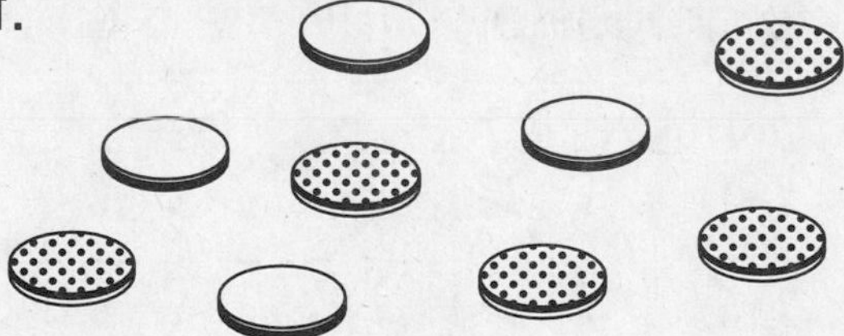

	Estimate.	Draw. Circle tens.	How many in all?
1.			
2.			
3.			

Journal

4. Look at cars in a parking lot.
   About how many cars are in the lot?

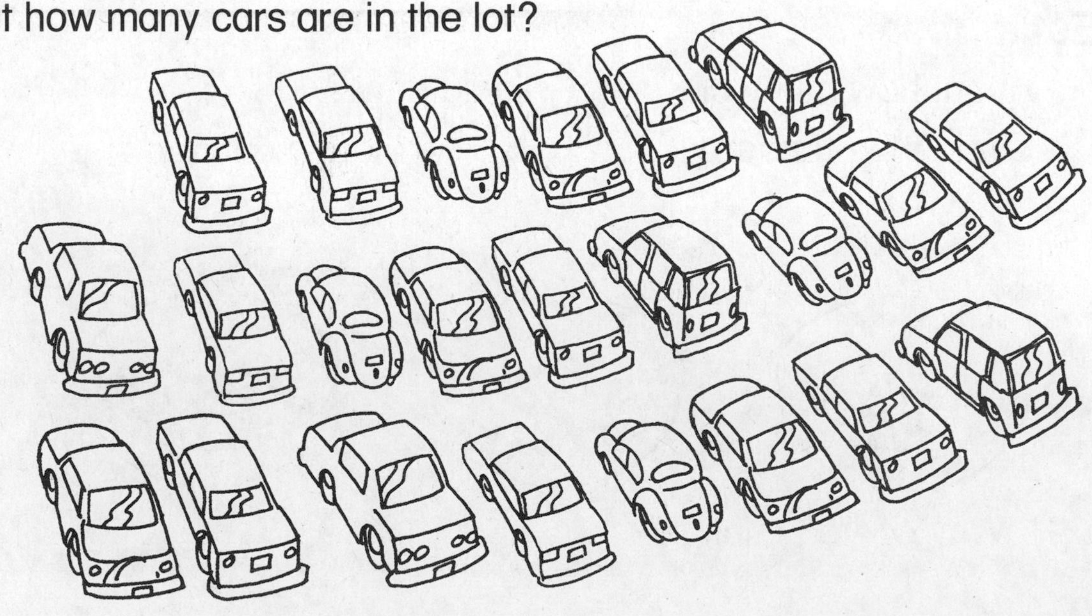

Notes for Home Your child worked with another child to estimate an amount and to check how good the estimate was. *Home Activity:* While in the grocery store, ask your child to count 10 cans on a shelf. Then ask him or her to estimate how many cans there are on the whole shelf.

Name ______________________________

Practice 7-5

Estimation

Estimate how many. Circle the number.

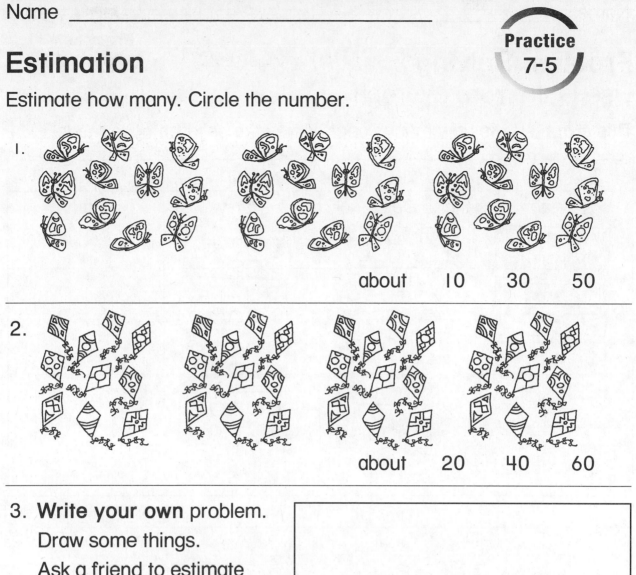

1.

about 10 30 50

2.

about 20 40 60

3. **Write your own** problem.
Draw some things.
Ask a friend to estimate how many.

Mental Math

Solve.

4. Chelsea has 40 stickers on one page.
She also has 10 stickers on another page.
How many stickers does she have on both pages? ______

Notes for Home Your child estimated numbers of objects. *Home Activity:* Ask your child to estimate the number of socks in his or her drawer.

Name ______________________________

Practice 7-6

Problem Solving: Use Data from a Graph

This graph shows how many paper apples the children have made.

Paper Apples We Made			
Sean	Della	Perry	Patty

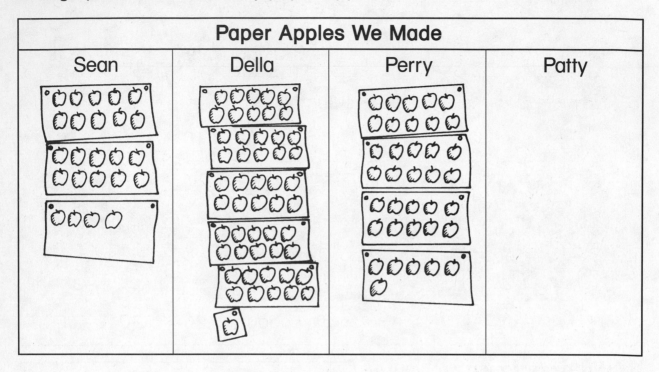

Read the graph.

1. Patty made 13 paper apples.
   Complete the graph to show this.

2. Who has more apples than Perry? ____________

3. How many more apples does Della have than Perry? ______

4. How many more apples does Sean need to have 30? ______

Tell a Math Story

5. Make up your own math story about paper apples.
   Tell it to a friend.

Notes for Home Your child practiced using a graph to find information. *Home Activity:* Ask your child to use the graph to answer "*Who has the most apples?*" (Della)

Name ______________________________

Mixed Practice: Lessons 1-6

Write the number.

1. 10 and 6 is _____.
2. 10 and 9 is _____.
3. 40 and 10 is _____.
4. 30 and 10 is _____.

---

5. Estimate how many. Circle the number.

about 10 20 40

Problem Solving

Read the graph.

Seashells collected	
Jennifer	
Bart	

---

6. How many does Jennifer have? _____

Journal

7. What are some things you might count by tens? Why?

Notes for Home Your child practiced counting groups of numbers to 60. *Home Activity:* Ask your child to tell how many toes three people have in all. (30)

Name ______________________________

Practice
Chapters 1–7
A

Cumulative Review

1. Circle the one that comes next in this pattern.

Problem Solving

Write the number sentence.

2. I had 9 stamps.
I got 3 more.
How many do I have now?

_____ + _____ = _____

3. Nell had 7 cards.
She gave away 3.
How many are left?

_____ − _____ = _____

Test Prep

Fill in the ◯ for the correct answer.

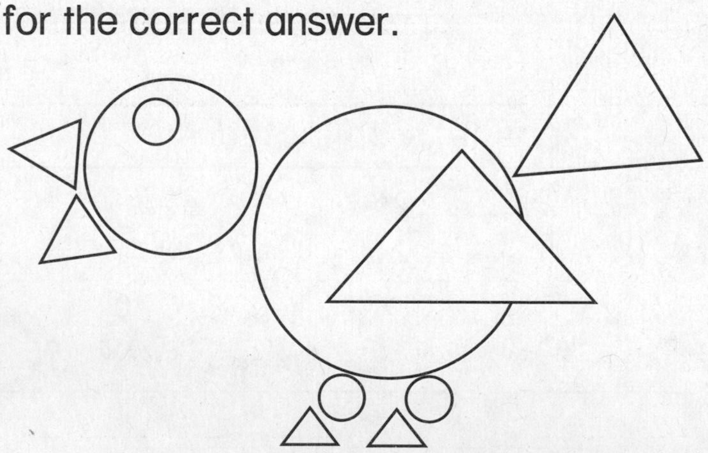

4. How many ◯ ?

◯ 3 ◯ 4 ◯ 5 ◯ 6

5. How many △ ?

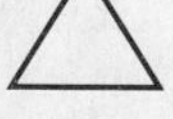

◯ 3 ◯ 4 ◯ 5 ◯ 6

Notes for Home Your child reviewed concepts taught in Chapters 1-7. *Home Activity:* Ask your child to tell you how he or she solved Exercise 3.

Name ______________________

Practice 7-7

Count by 2s and 10s

1. How many fingers? Count by 10s.

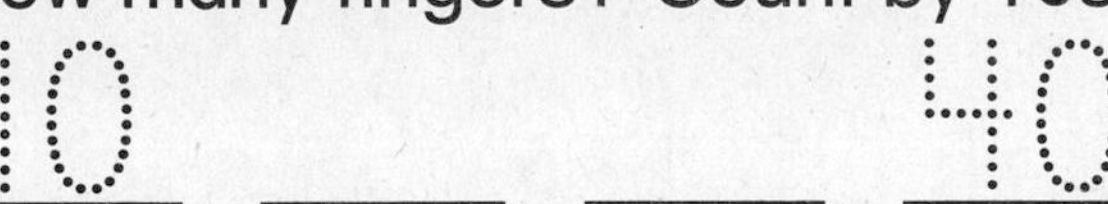

2. Count by 10s. You can use a .

Press	Display
	0
+ 1 0 =	
+ 1 0 =	
+ 1 0 =	

Press	Display
+ 1 0 =	
+ 1 0 =	
+ 1 0 =	
+ 1 0 =	

Problem Solving Patterns

Use a calculator. Press the buttons shown below.

3. Count by 2s.

+ 2 = = =

4. Count by 10s.

+ 1 0 = = =

5. What happens each time you press = ?

____

Notes for Home Your child counted by 2s and 10s. *Home Activity:* Ask your child to count how many ears there are in your family.

Name ________________________

Practice 7-8

Count by 2s, 5s, and 10s

Count by 5s.

1. 10, 15, 20, ______, ______, ______, ______, 45

2. 35, ______, ______, ______, 55, ______, 65, ______

3. 55, 60, ______, ______, 75, 80, ______, ______

Count by 2s.

4. 10, 12, ______, ______, 18, ______, 22, ______

5. 46, 48, 50, ______, ______, ______, ______, 60

6. 72, 74, ______, 78, 80, 82, ______, ______

Count by 10s.

7. 30, ______, 50, ______, ______, ______

Write your own counting pattern.

8. ______, ______, ______, ______, ______, ______

Problem Solving Visual Thinking

9. Look at the picture.
Count by 10s.
How many muffins
will be baked?

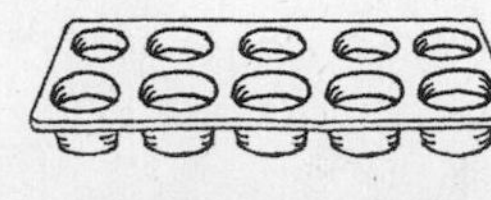

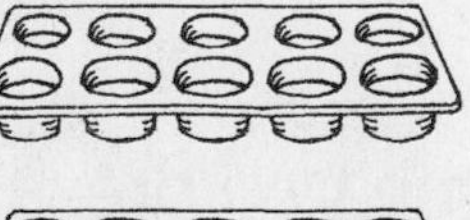

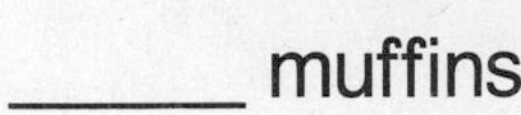
______ muffins

Notes for Home Your child practiced counting by 10s, 5s, and 2s. *Home Activity:* Ask your child to count by 2s from 8 to 20. (8, 10, 12, 14, 16, 18, 20)

Name ______________________________

Ordinals

1. Color the shelves.

second
third
fourth
fifth

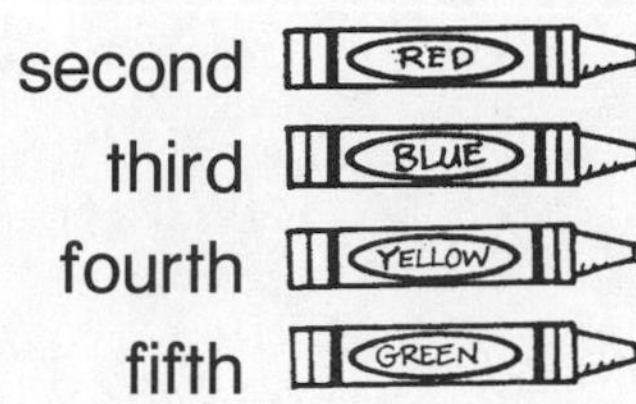

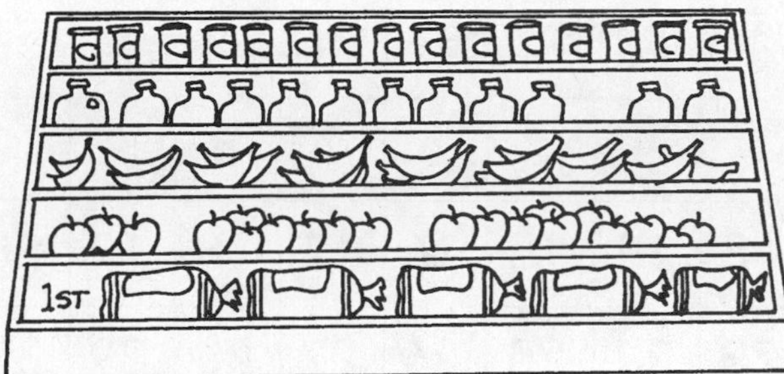

2. Color the cars.

fourth
fifth
sixth
seventh
eighth

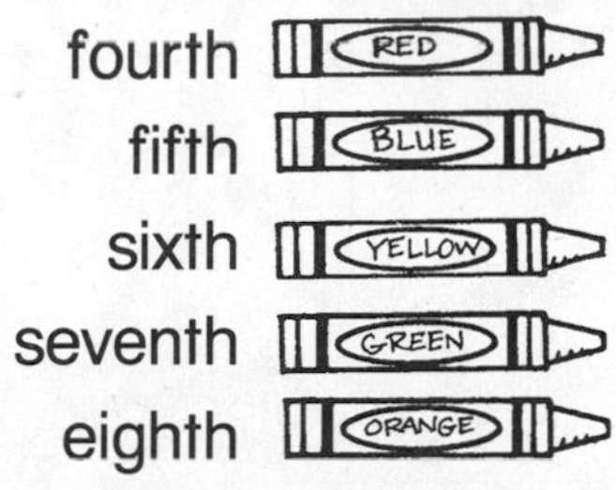

Problem Solving Visual Thinking

3. How many cars are in this tunnel?

Write how many. ______

Notes for Home Your child used number words from *first* through *tenth* to identify position. *Home Activity:* Ask your child to arrange 5 things in a line and show you the ones that are first, third, and fifth.

Name ______________________________

Practice 7-10

Problem Solving: Look for a Pattern

Color the charts to continue the pattern.

1. Start with 2. Count by 2s.

1	2	3	4	5	6	7	8	9	10
11	12	13	14	15	16	17	18	19	20
21	22	23	24	25	26	27	28	29	30

2. Start with 10. Count by 10s.

1	2	3	4	5	6	7	8	9	10
11	12	13	14	15	16	17	18	19	20
21	22	23	24	25	26	27	28	29	30
31	32	33	34	35	36	37	38	39	40
41	42	43	44	45	46	47	48	49	50
51	52	53	54	55	56	57	58	59	60
61	62	63	64	65	66	67	68	69	70
71	72	73	74	75	76	77	78	79	80

Write About It

3. Write about one of the patterns.
   You can use the words in the list.

   ____

   ____

odd	pattern
even	diagonal
row	chart
column	count

Notes for Home Your child continued patterns on a chart. *Home Activity:* Ask your child to tell you which numbers he or she would color if each chart had another row. (32, 34, 36, 38, 40; 90)

Name ________________________________

Mixed Practice: Lessons 7-10

1. Count by 2s. 6, _____, _____, 12, _____, _____, 18, _____

2. Count by 5s. 10, 15, 20, _____, _____, _____, _____, 45

3. Count by 10s. 20, _____, 40, _____, _____, _____

4. Color the tops.

fifth blue

sixth orange

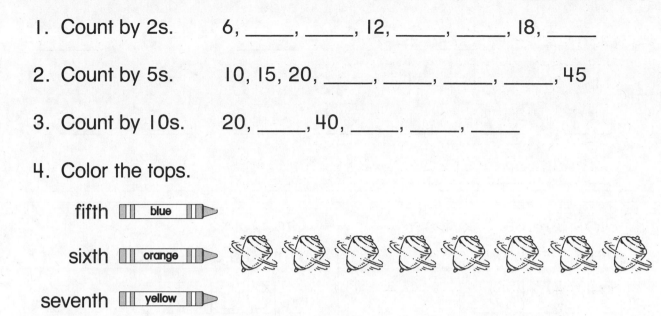

seventh yellow

Problem Solving

5. Color to continue the pattern.

1	2	3	4	5	6	7	8	9	10
11	12	13	14	15	16	17	18	19	20
21	22	23	24	25	26	27	28	29	30
31	32	33	34	35	36	37	38	39	40
41	42	43	44	45	46	47	48	49	50
51	52	53	54	55	56	57	58	59	60

Journal

6. Write about how you count by 2s, 5s, or 10s to find how much money is in a pile of nickels and dimes.

Notes for Home Your child practiced counting by 2s, 5s, and 10s, and matching numbers to positions in line.
Home Activity: Ask your child to count aloud by 2s from 10 to 30. (10, 12, 14, 16, 18, 20, 22, 24, 26, 28, 30)

Name ________________________

Practice
Chapters 1–7
B

Cumulative Review

Count on to add.

1. $8 + 2 =$ ____ $4 + 8 =$ ____ $6 + 3 =$ ____

2.

8	3	5	10	5	4	1
+ 1	+ 7	+ 4	+ 2	+ 3	+ 2	+ 9

3. Draw 3 more ⬭ ⬭.
Write the sum.

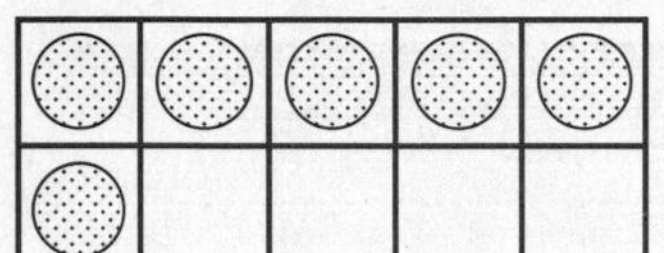

$6 + 3 =$ ____

4. Cross out 3 ⬭ ⬭.
Write the difference.

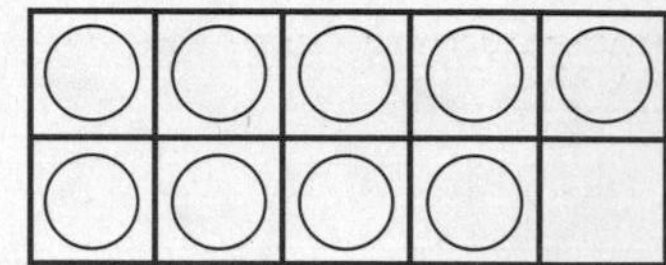

$9 - 3 =$ ____

Test Prep

Fill in the ○ for the correct answer.
Add or subtract.

5. 10
+ 0

○ 7 ○ 8 ○ 9 ○ 10

6. $7 - 0 =$ ____

○ 7 ○ 8 ○ 9 ○ 10

Notes for Home Your child reviewed basic addition and subtraction facts. *Home Activity:* Ask you child to explain how he or she used a ten frame to solve Exercise 3.

Name ______________________________

Practice 8-1

Explore Tens and Ones

Use [cube] and [tens | ones mat].

Take a lot of [cube].

Use the [tens | ones mat] to help make train of 10 [cube].
Record how many tens and ones.

1.

tens	ones

2.

tens	ones

3.

tens	ones

4.

tens	ones

5.

tens	ones

6.

tens	ones

Journal

Draw something that has more than 10 parts or pieces.
Write how many tens and ones.

Notes for Home Your child used snap cubes to make groups of tens and ones and recorded the number of tens and ones. *Home Activity:* Have your child use between 10 and 19 pennies to show you how to make a group of ten and ones.

Name ______________________________

Practice 8-2

Tens and Ones to 60

Use [tens rod] [ones cube] and [tens | ones mat].

Count how many tens and ones. Write the number.

1. 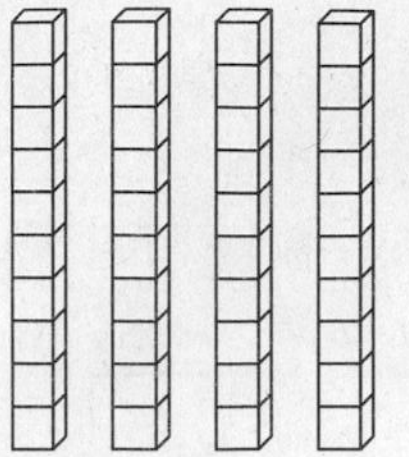

tens	ones
4	5

______

2. 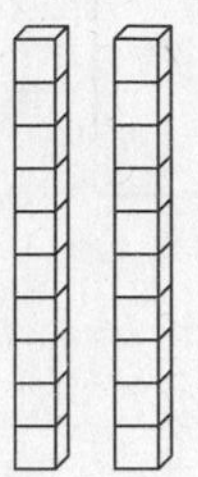

tens	ones

______

Write your own example. Show with [tens rod] [ones cube].

3.

tens	ones

______

4.

tens	ones

______

Problem Solving

5. Solve.

Sam has 34 carrots.
He buys 10 more.
How many does he have now?

______ 

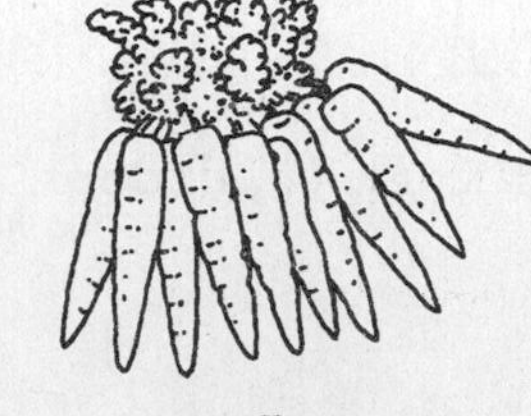

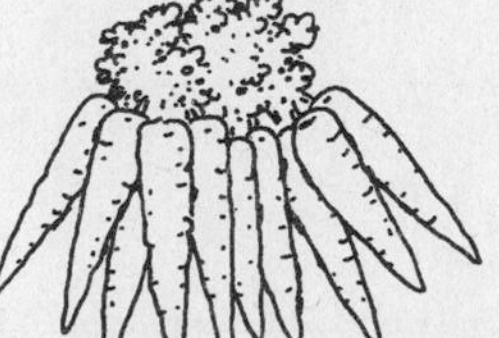
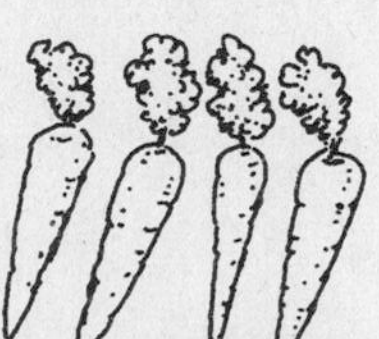

Notes for Home Your child modeled tens, then wrote the number. *Home Activity:* Have your child use objects such as pencils to represent tens and paper clips to represent ones to solve problems such as "*Ana has 25 stickers. She buys 10 more. How many does she have now?*" (25 + 10 = 35 stickers)

Name ______________________

Practice 8-5

10 Ones Make 1 Ten

Use [ten rod] [one cube] and [tens | ones mat].

Show this many.

Add 2 more. Do you need to make a trade? Circle yes or no.

Write how many tens and ones.

1. 4 tens 6 ones — yes / no

tens	ones
4	8

2. 6 tens 9 ones — yes / no

tens	ones

3. 9 tens 0 ones — yes / no

tens	ones

4. 8 tens 8 ones — yes / no

tens	ones

Problem Solving Estimate

4. Jake has these blocks. He needs 80. About how many more does he need?

______

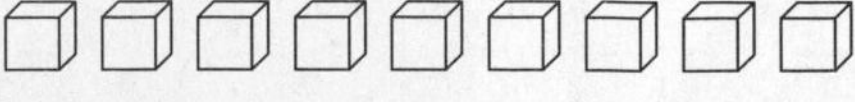

Notes for Home Your child traded 10 ones for 1 ten. *Home Activity:* Have your child explain how he or she solved Exercise 4. Then ask if a trade would be needed if 1 one were added to 8 tens and 8 ones, and to explain why or why not. (No, you would have 8 tens and 9 ones, and you do not trade 9 ones for 1 ten.)

Name ______________________________

Practice 8-6

Problem Solving: Use Objects

Use [tens and ones blocks] and [tens | ones chart].

Trade if you need to.

1. The Blues won these points in the spelling bee.
   What is their final score?

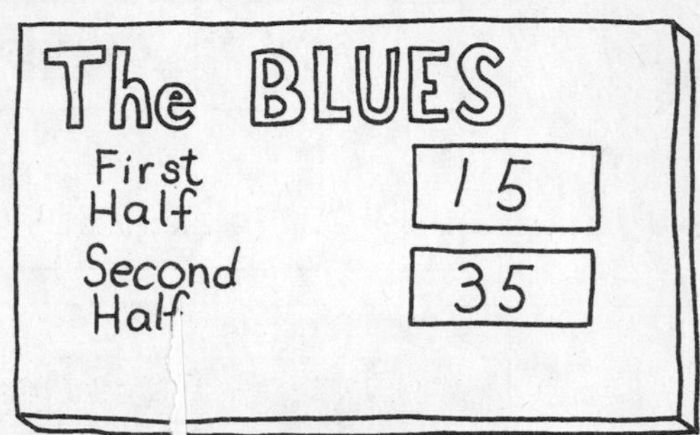

tens	ones
5	0

Final score: ______

2. The Re ds won these points in the spelling bee.
   What i their final score?

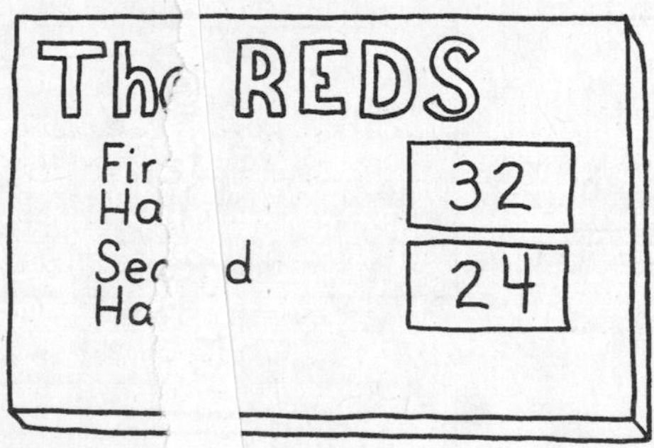

Final score: ______

3. Look a e team's scores.
   Circle t eam that won the spelling bee. The Blues The Reds

Tell a Mat tory

Tell a math st about this spelling bee.

How will it enc

Which team w in?

What will the fin score be?

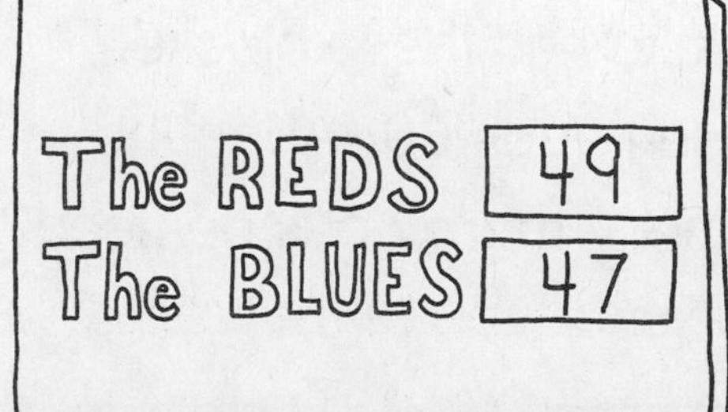

Notes for Home Your chil lved problems using place-value blocks. *Home Activity:* Point to the results of some game scores in a newspape sk your child to tell who won each game and to explain how they know. (Possible answer: The Knicks won. The ad 9 tens and 6 ones. The other team had 8 tens and 9 ones.)

Name ______________________________

Mixed Practice: Lessons 1–6

Write the number.

1. Estimate how many. Make groups of 10.

About **30** **50** **70** ______ tens ______ ones

2. Count how many.	Add 2 more. Do you need to make a trade? Circle yes or no.	Write how many tens and ones.
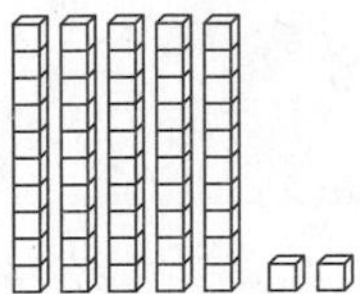	**yes** **no**	tens / ones

tens	ones

Problem Solving

Use and tens ones. Trade if you need to.

3. What is the Honey Bees final score?

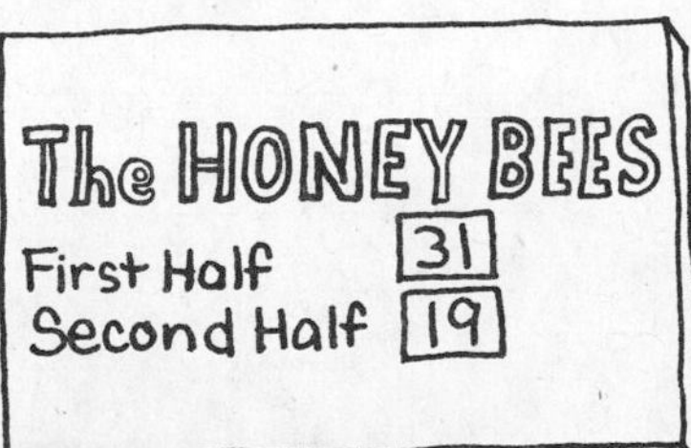

The HONEY BEES
First Half 31
Second Half 19

Final Score: ______

Journal

Draw a picture that shows 2 tens and 7 ones.
Write the number.

Notes for Home Your child practiced estimating, counting numbers to 99, and problem solving. *Home Activity:* Have your child look for numbers displayed on products in your home. Ask your child to explain what the numbers show. (Answer might include the dates of a month on a calendar, weights on food packaging, etc.)

Name ______________________

Practice
Chapters 1–8
A

Cumulative Review

Complete the fact family.

1. 8 + 3 = ____
   3 + 8 = ____
   11 − 8 = ____
   11 − 3 = ____

2. 6 + 7 = ____
   7 + 6 = ____
   13 − 6 = ____
   13 − 7 = ____

Write a number sentence.

3. 12 children played tag.
   3 left to play ball.
   How many play tag now?

   ____

4. Maya found 7 shells.
   Ellie found 5 shells.
   How many shells do they have all together?

   ____

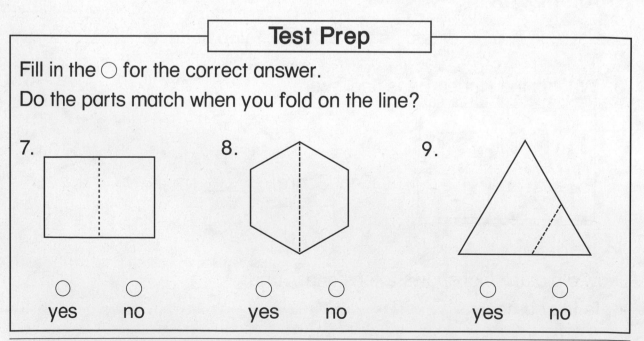

Test Prep

Fill in the ○ for the correct answer.
Do the parts match when you fold on the line?

7. 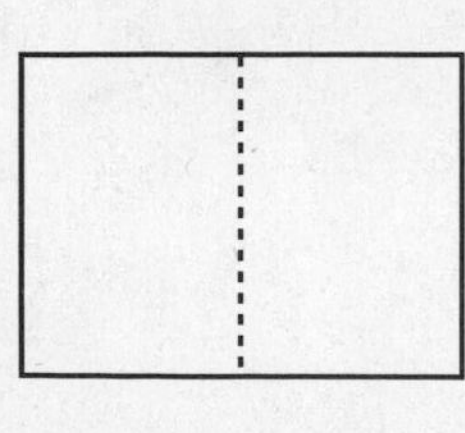

○ yes ○ no

8.

○ yes ○ no

9. 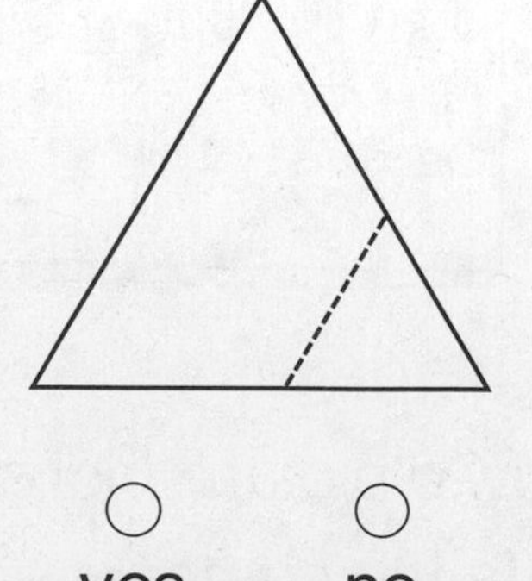

○ yes ○ no

Notes for Home Your child reviewed fact families and finding shapes with parts that match. *Home Activity:* Ask your child to use objects such as pennies to model an addition and a subtraction problem on the page.

Name ________________________________

Practice 8-7

Compare Numbers

Use [tens rod] [ones cube] and [tens | ones chart].

Write the tens and ones. Circle the number that is less.

1. 73	7 tens	3 ones	2. 24	____ tens	____ ones
48	4 tens	8 ones	49	____ tens	____ ones
3. 56	____ tens	____ ones	4. 90	____ tens	____ ones
85	____ tens	____ ones	67	____ tens	____ ones
5. 36	____ tens	____ ones	6. 17	____ tens	____ ones
63	____ tens	____ ones	71	____ tens	____ ones

Write your own numbers. Circle the number that is less.

7. ____	____ tens	____ ones	8. ____	____ tens	____ ones
____	____ tens	____ ones	____	____ tens	____ ones

Problem Solving Visual Thinking

Circle the one that is less.

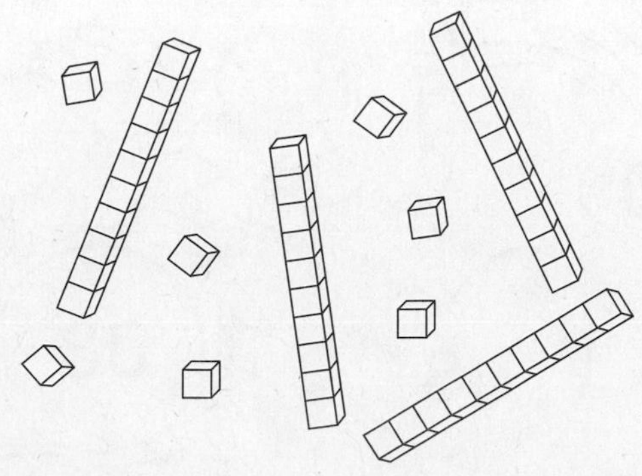

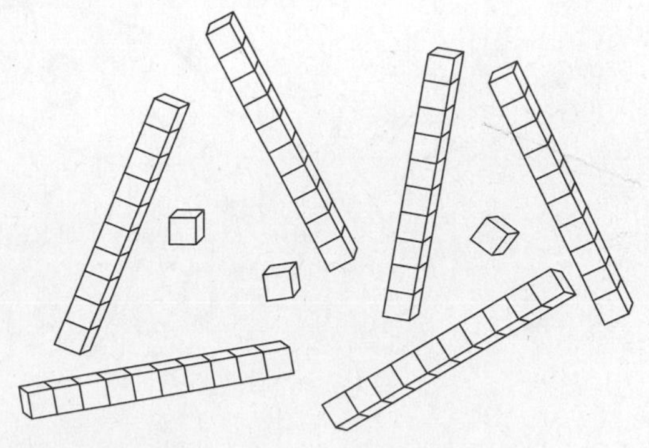

Notes for Home Your child compared two numbers to tell which is less. *Home Activity:* Show your child two page numbers from a newspaper. Ask him or her to tell you which number is less.

Name ________________________

Practice 8-8

Order Numbers to 100

Write the number that comes after.

1. 82 ____ | 2. 39 ____ | 3. 71 ____

4. 68 ____ | 5. 42 ____ | 6. 94 ____

Write the numbers that come before.

7. ____ 20 | 8. ____ 57 | 9. ____ 88

10. ____ 65 | 11. ____ 42 | 12. ____ 79

Write the numbers that come between.

13. 68, ____, ____, 71 | 14. 87, ____, ____, 90

15. 49, ____, ____, 52 | 16. 75, 76, ____, ____, 79

Problem Solving Critical Thinking

17. Al picked three of these stickers.
They were odd numbers between 77 and 85.
Circle the stickers he picked.

Notes for Home Your child learned about numbers that come before, after, and between. *Home Activity:* Point to different page numbers in a newspaper or magazine and ask your child to tell you the numbers before and after.

Name ______________________________

Patterns on the 100 Chart

Write the missing numbers.

1.

37	38	39
	48	49

2.

21	22	23
31	32	33

3.

	82	83
91		

4.

		54	55
	63	64	65

5.

11	12	
	22	

6.

64	65		
	75		77

7.

	46	
55	56	

8.

	78	79	
87			

Problem Solving Patterns

9. What comes next?

Circle the next shape in the pattern.

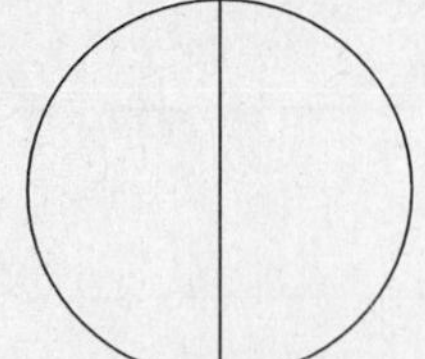 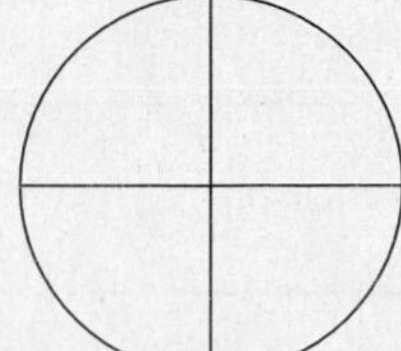   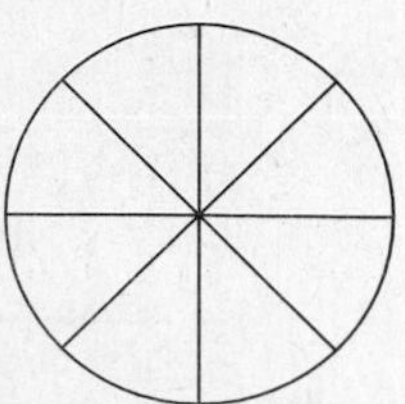

Notes for Home Your child used the patterns in a 100 chart to help find missing numbers. *Home Activity:* Ask your child to write 3 numbers to extend the following pattern: 5, 10, 15. (20, 25, 30)

Name ____________________

Practice 8-10

Problem Solving:
Collect and Use Data

1. Put your name where it belongs.
Ask 6 friends to put their names in the circles.

Write About It

2. Which children put their names in the left circle?

____

3. What do you know about the children whose names belong in both circles?

____

____

Notes for Home Your child made a diagram and answered questions about it. *Home Activity:* Have your child explain the diagram to you and other family members, and ask them to put their names in the circles where they belong.

Name ______________________________

Practice
Chapter 8
B

Mixed Practice: Lessons 7 - 10

1. Write the missing numbers.

71	72				76				80
			84	85			88		
91						97			100

Write the missing numbers.

2. 45, 46, ______
3. 29, ______, 31
4. ______, 50, 51
5. 92, ______, 94
6. ______, 61, 62
7. 18, 19, ______

Problem Solving

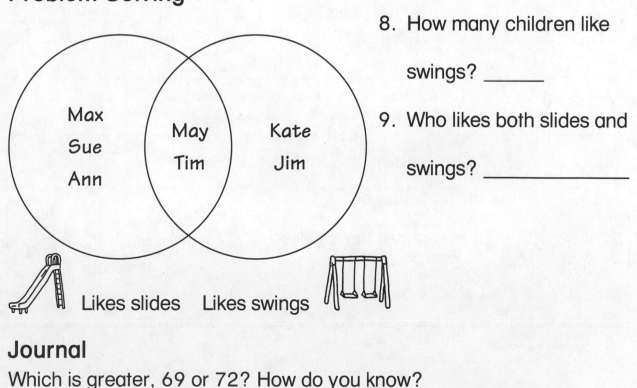

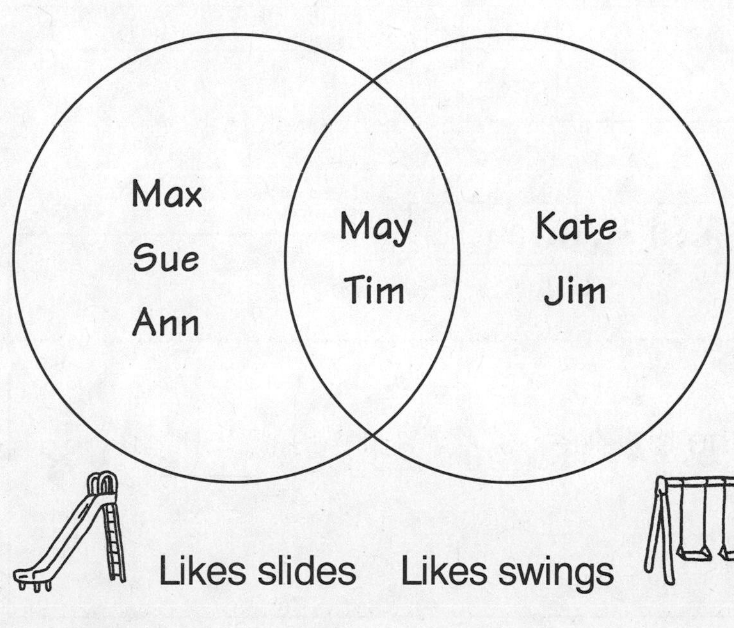

8. How many children like swings? ______

9. Who likes both slides and swings? ______________

Journal

Which is greater, 69 or 72? How do you know?

Notes for Home Your child practiced using numbers to 99 and reading a diagram to solve problems.
Home Activity: Ask your child to tell you whether more children like swings or slides. (More children like slides.)

Name ______________________________

Cumulative Review

Subtract.

1. $\begin{array}{r} 6 \\ +4 \\ \hline \end{array}$ $\begin{array}{r} 10 \\ -4 \\ \hline \end{array}$

2. $\begin{array}{r} 12 \\ -5 \\ \hline \end{array}$ $\begin{array}{r} 7 \\ +5 \\ \hline \end{array}$

3. $\begin{array}{r} 5 \\ +6 \\ \hline \end{array}$ $\begin{array}{r} 11 \\ -6 \\ \hline \end{array}$

---

4. 3 + 4 = ____
   7 − 4 = ____

5. 1 + 11 = ____
   12 − 1 = ____

6. 8 + 4 = ____
   12 − 4 = ____

Problem Solving

7. Circle the shape that shows $\frac{1}{3}$.

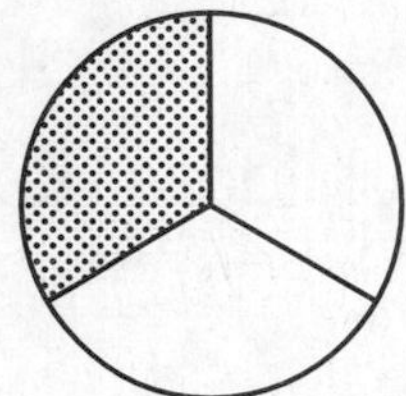

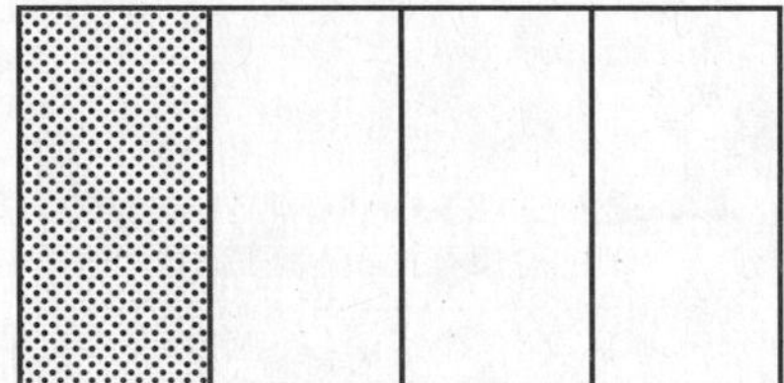

Test Prep

What number comes next?

Fill in ○ for the correct answer.

8. 3 6 9 12 ____ ○ 15 ○ 13

9. 15 20 25 30 ____ ○ 32 ○ 35

Notes for Home Your child reviewed basic addition and subtraction facts, problem solving, and skip counting.
Home Activity: Ask your child to find something in the kitchen that he or she can count by 2s.

 Use with page 322.

Name ______________________________

Nickels and Pennies

Circle the coins you need.

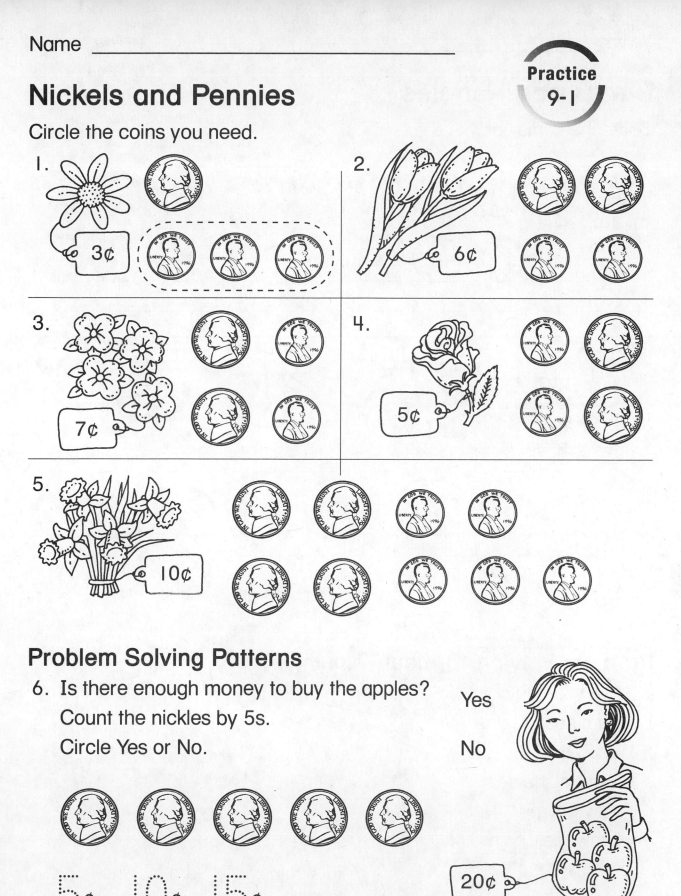

1. 

2. 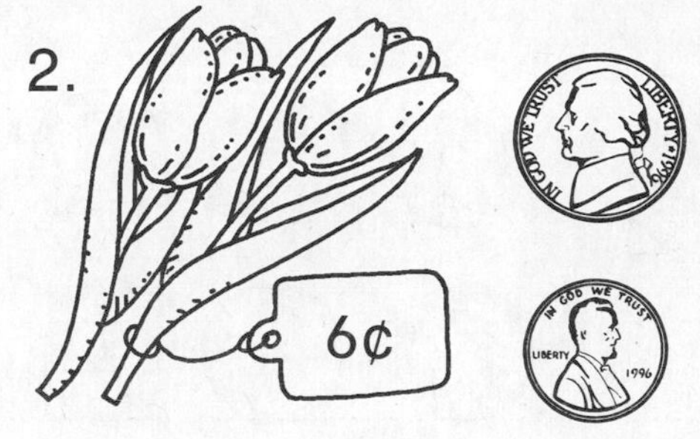

3. 

4. 

5. 

Problem Solving Patterns

6. Is there enough money to buy the apples?
Count the nickles by 5s.
Circle Yes or No.

Yes

No

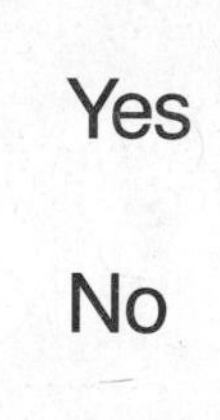

5¢ 10¢ 15¢ ______ ______

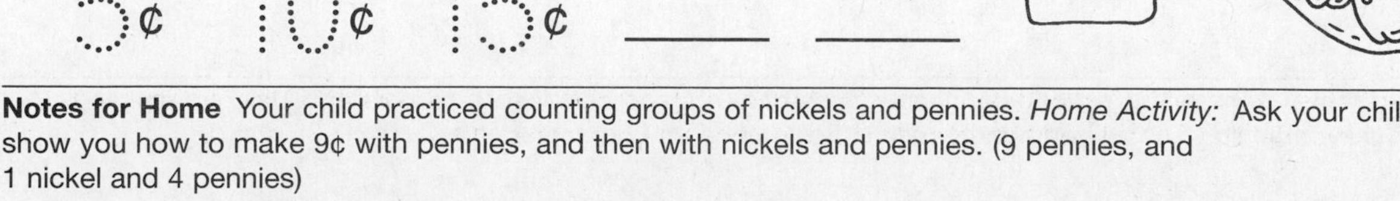

Notes for Home Your child practiced counting groups of nickels and pennies. *Home Activity:* Ask your child to show you how to make 9¢ with pennies, and then with nickels and pennies. (9 pennies, and 1 nickel and 4 pennies)

Name ______________________________

Dimes and Pennies

Practice 9-2

Circle the coins you need.

1.

2.

3.
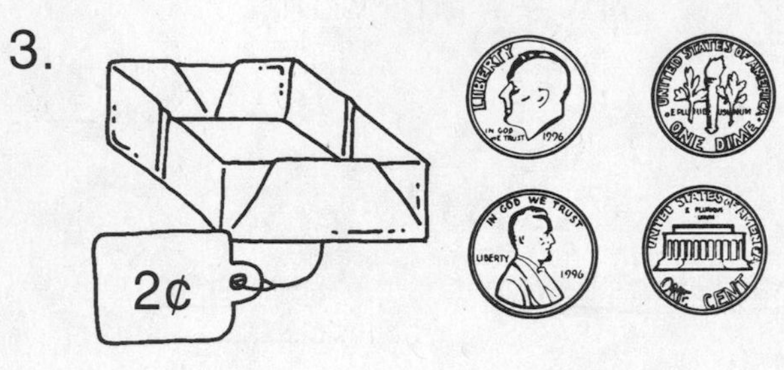

4.
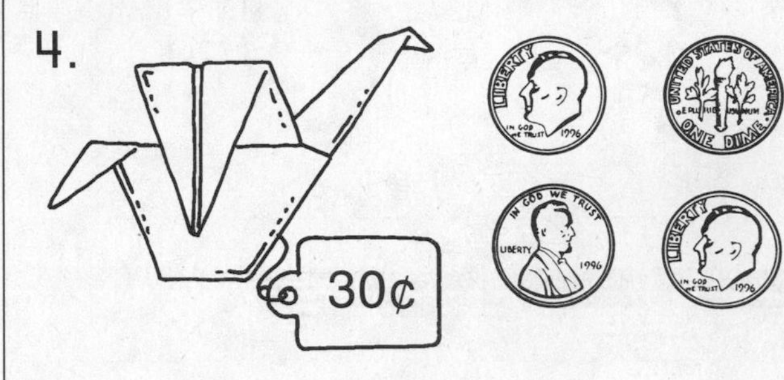

5.
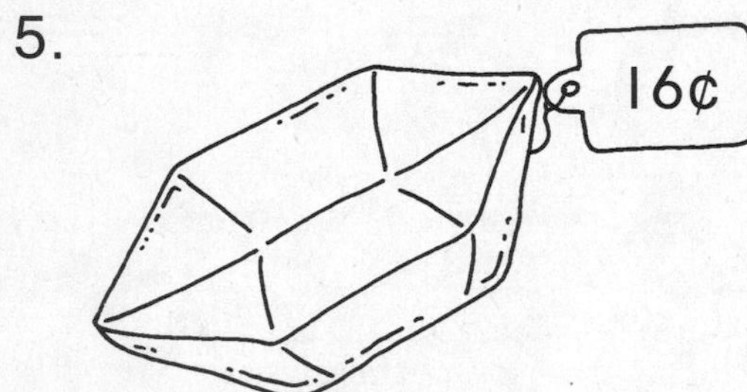

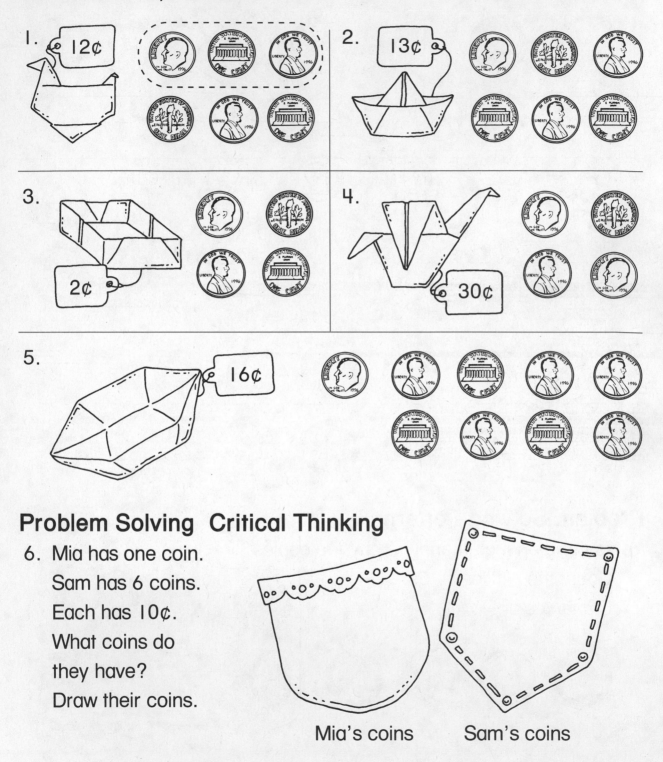

Problem Solving Critical Thinking

6. Mia has one coin.
Sam has 6 coins.
Each has 10¢.
What coins do
they have?
Draw their coins.

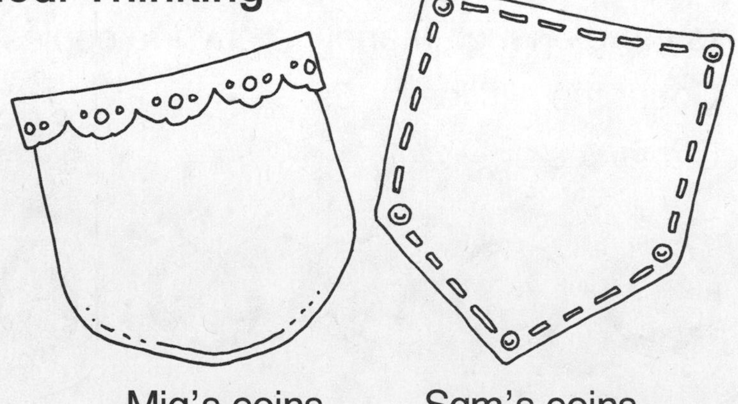

Notes for Home Your child practiced counting groups of dimes and pennies. *Home Activity:* Using dimes and pennies, ask your child to show you how to make 15¢. (1 dime and 5 pennies)

Name ______________________

Dimes, Nickels, and Pennies

Count. Write the amount.

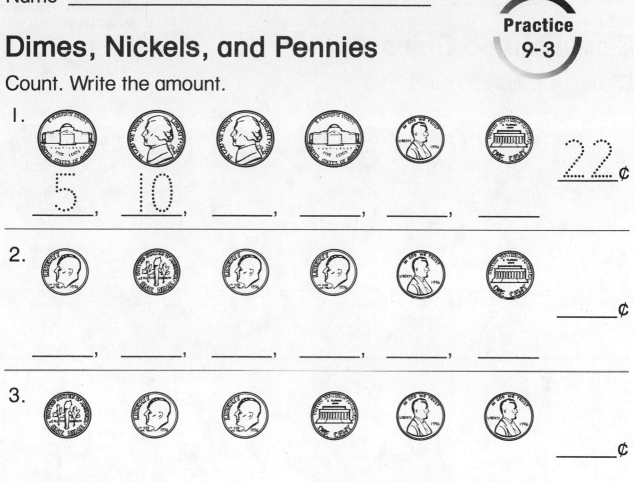

1.      

5, 10, ____, ____, ____, ____ 22¢

2.      

____, ____, ____, ____, ____, ____ ____¢

3.      

____, ____, ____, ____, ____, ____ ____¢

Problem Solving

4. Who has more money?
   Write the amount each child has.
   Circle the amount that is more.

____ ____

Notes for Home Your child counted groups of coins by 10s, 5s, and ones. *Home Activity:* Have your child show you how to make 23¢ with nickels and pennies, and again with dimes and pennies. (4 nickels and 3 pennies; 2 dimes and 3 pennies)

Name ___________________________

Practice 9-4

Count Mixed Coins

Circle the coins you need.

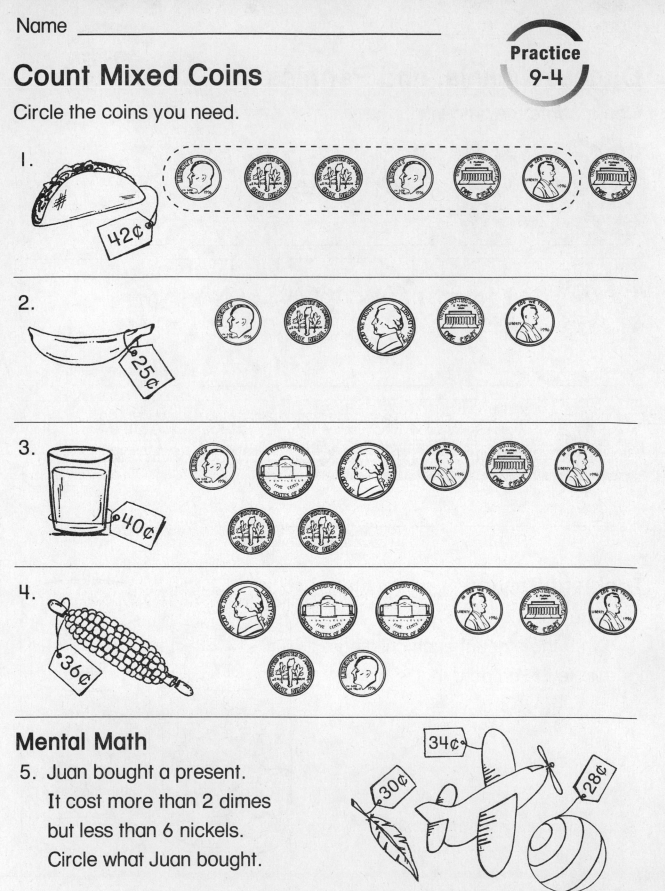

1.

2.

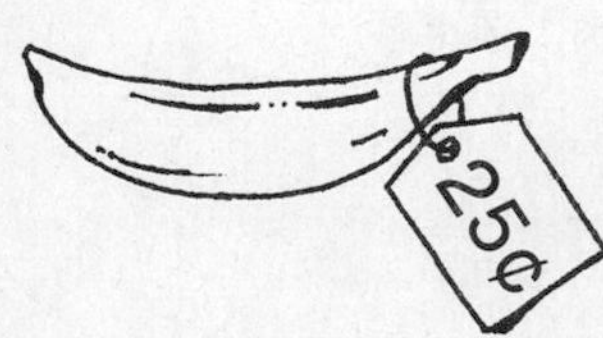

3.

4.

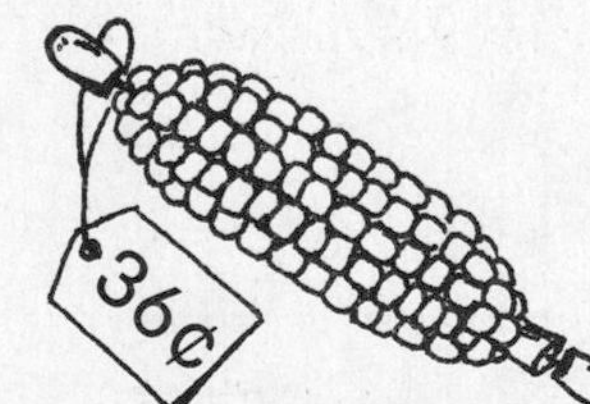

Mental Math

5. Juan bought a present.
   It cost more than 2 dimes
   but less than 6 nickels.
   Circle what Juan bought.

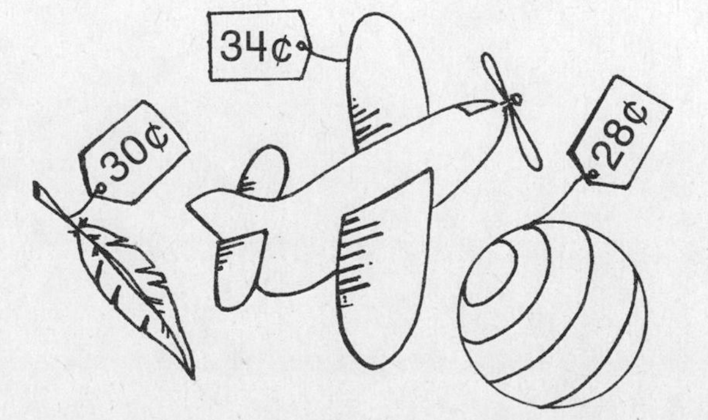

Notes for Home Your child decided which coins are needed to buy an item. *Home Activity:* Ask your child to show you how he or she counted the coins in Exercise 4. (10¢, 20¢, 25¢, 30¢, 35¢, 36¢)

Name ________________________________

Practice 9-5

Problem Solving: Use Data from a Picture

Use the picture of items at a yard sale. Count the money. Write the amount. Circle the item you can buy.

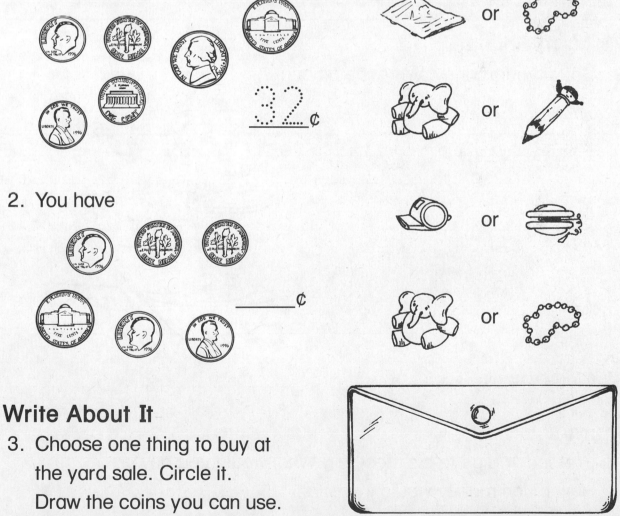

1. You have

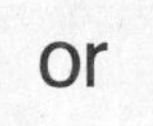

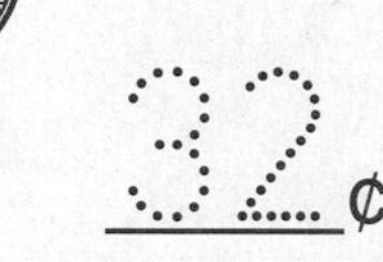

32 ¢

or

2. You have

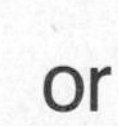

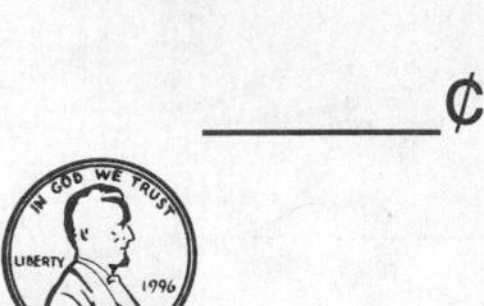

_____ ¢

or

Write About It

3. Choose one thing to buy at the yard sale. Circle it. Draw the coins you can use.

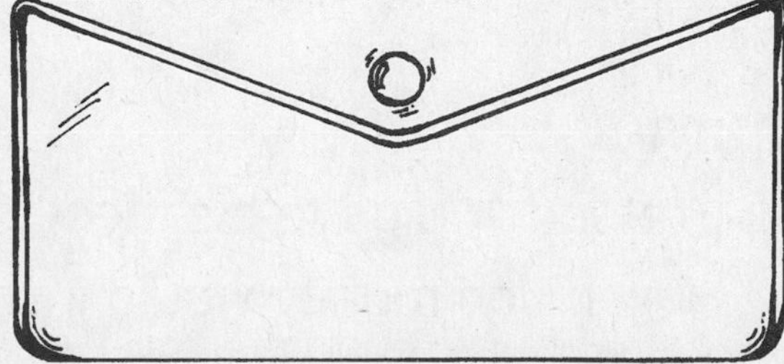

Notes for Home Your child practiced solving problems using information in a picture. *Home Activity:* With your child, look at the prices on grocery items that cost less than 50¢. Ask your child how many dimes, nickels, and pennies he or she would need to buy each one.

Name ____________________

Mixed Practice: Lessons 1–5

Count the money. Write the amount.

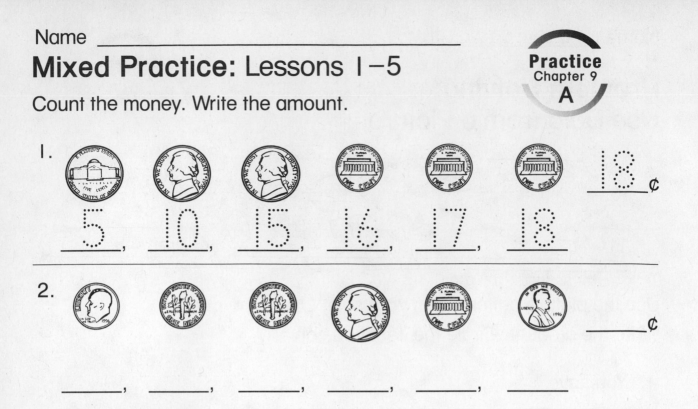

1.  18 ¢

5, 10, 15, 16, 17, 18

2.       ____ ¢

____, ____, ____, ____, ____, ____

Problem Solving

3. Count your money. Write the amount.

____ ¢

Circle what you can buy.

Journal

4. Pretend you go to a school fair. What would you buy?
How much money would it cost?

Notes for Home Your child practiced counting groups of dimes, nickels, and pennies. *Home Activity:* Arrange an assortment of dimes, nickels, and pennies on a table. Ask your child to use some of the coins to show you how to sort and count them.

Name ____________________

Cumulative Review

Write the number.

1. 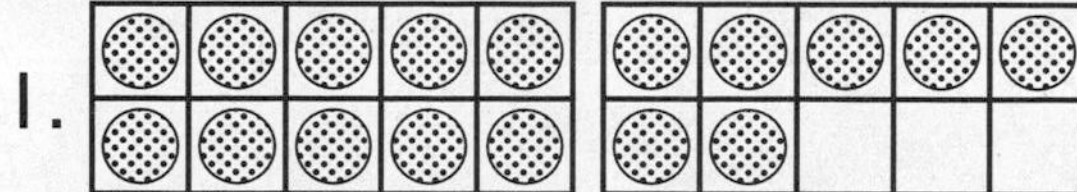

______

2.

______

Add or Subtract.

3.

4	3	12	5	9	8	10
+ 6	− 2	− 9	+ 7	− 6	+ 0	− 7

Problem Solving

Complete the number sentence.

4. Jamie made 12 snacks.
He gave 3 to Ben.
How many snacks are left?

12 − ____ = ____

5. Sarah baked four pies.
Then she baked 7 pies.
How many pies did she bake?

4 + ____ = ____

Test Prep

Fill in the ○ for the correct answer.

6. Which number is less than 32?

○ 38 ○ 63 ○ 35 ○ 23

7. Which number is greater than 89?

○ 39 ○ 88 ○ 94 ○ 72

Notes for Home Your child reviewed counting to 50, using addition and subtraction, and comparing numbers.
Home Activity: Ask your child to name another number that is less than 32 and another that is greater than 89.

Name ________________________________

Explore Quarters

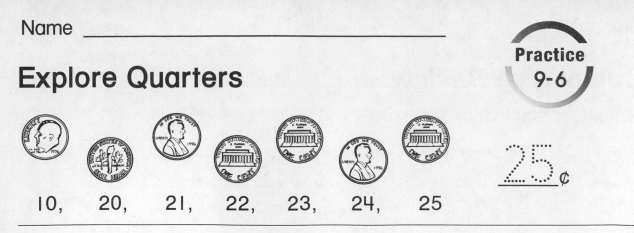

Practice 9-6

10, 20, 21, 22, 23, 24, 25

Circle the coins that show 25¢.

1.

2.

3.

Problem Solving

4. You have 25¢ to spend.
   You have 4 coins.
   Draw the coins you have.

Notes for Home Your child practiced counting groups of coins that equal 25¢. *Home Activity:* Give your child 2 dimes, 5 nickels, and 5 pennies. Ask him or her to show you different ways to make 25¢.

Name ______________________________

Practice 9-7

Quarter, Dimes, Nickels, and Pennies

Count the money. Write the amount.

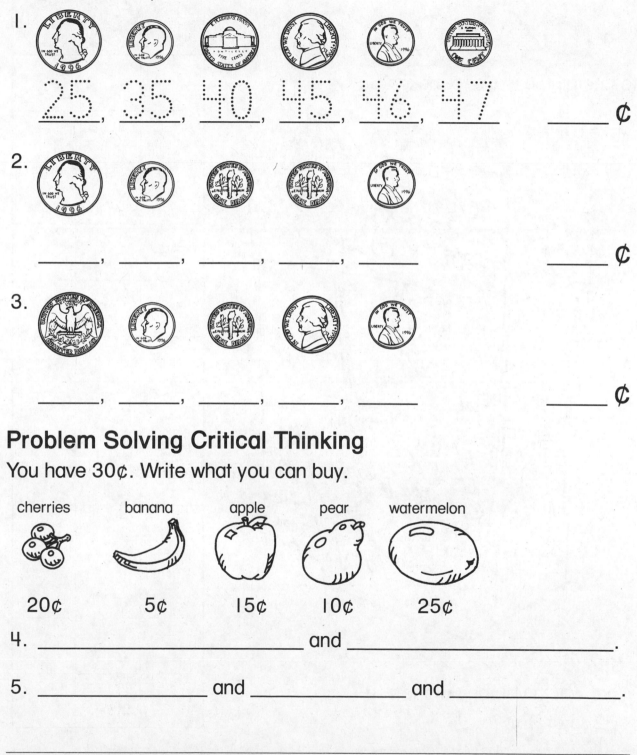

1.     

25, 35, 40, 45, 46, 47 ______ ¢

2.     

______, ______, ______, ______, ______ ______ ¢

3.     

______, ______, ______, ______, ______ ______ ¢

Problem Solving Critical Thinking

You have 30¢. Write what you can buy.

cherries	banana	apple	pear	watermelon
		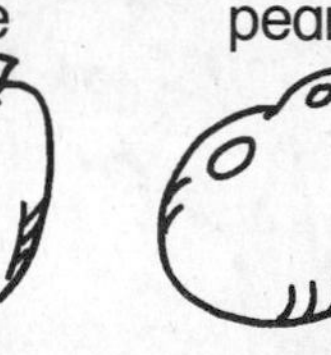		
20¢	5¢	15¢	10¢	25¢

4. ______________________ and ______________________.

5. ________________ and ________________ and ________________.

Notes for Home Your child counted mixed groups of coins. *Home Activity:* Ask your child to name 2 fruits he or she could buy and spend exactly one quarter. (grapes and banana, or apple and pear)

Name ____________________

Practice 9-8

Problem Solving: Make a List

Susie gets 25¢ to spend at the zoo.
What coins might Susie get?

Use   

to find all the ways to make 25¢.

Make a list.

Journal

What would you buy at the zoo
for 20¢ or 25¢?

Notes for Home Your child made a list of all the ways to make 25¢ with dimes, nickels, and pennies.
Home Activity: Ask your child to solve this riddle: *What coins do I use to make the same amount with 25 coins or 1 coin?* (25 pennies and 1 quarter)

Name ______________________________

Practice
Chapter 9
B

Mixed Practice: Lessons 6–8

1. Circle the coins that show 30¢.

2. Count the money. Write the amount.

      ______¢

Problem Solving

3. Amy buys a toy for 25¢.
   She has no pennies.
   Find the ways she can pay 25¢.
   Make a list.

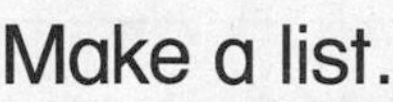

Journal

4. Do you think it is easier to pay for a toy with 25 pennies or 5 nickels? Why?

Notes for Home Your child practiced counting groups of coins and solving a problem by making a list.
Home Activity: Ask your child what is the fewest number of coins needed to buy something for 30¢. (1 quarter and 1 nickel)

Name ______________________

Practice
Chapters 1–9
B

Cumulative Review

Add or subtract.

1.

9	10	12	7	5	11	8
+ 3	− 3	− 6	+ 7	+ 4	− 7	− 5

Problem Solving

2. Read the graph.
How many birthdays are in July? ______

How many more birthdays does August need to match July? ______

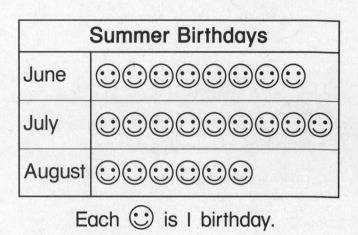

Summer Birthdays	
June	☺☺☺☺☺☺☺☺
July	☺☺☺☺☺☺☺☺☺
August	☺☺☺☺☺☺

Each ☺ is 1 birthday.

Test Prep

Fill in the ○ for the correct answer.
Which number sentence is not part of the fact family?

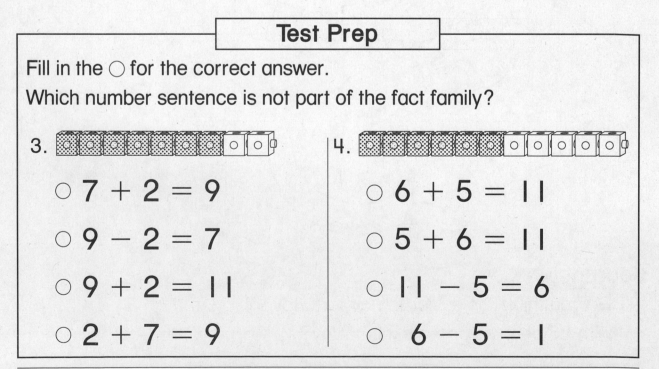

3.

○ 7 + 2 = 9

○ 9 − 2 = 7

○ 9 + 2 = 11

○ 2 + 7 = 9

4.

○ 6 + 5 = 11

○ 5 + 6 = 11

○ 11 − 5 = 6

○ 6 − 5 = 1

Notes for Home Your child reviewed addition and subtraction facts, reading a graph, and finding facts in a fact family. *Home Activity:* Ask your child how many birthdays there are in the months of July and August. (15)

Name ____________________

Practice 10-1

Explore Time

A clock shows time. Where can you see a clock?

Here are places you could see a clock.

Draw a clock you could see in each place.

in the kitchen	at home	outside
in a bedroom		in another room

Talk About It

Name three places you think a clock would be useful.

Explain your choices.

Notes for Home Your child talked about and drew pictures of clocks. *Home Activity:* Ask your child to point out clocks inside or outside the home.

Name ______________________________

Practice 10-2

Clocks

Write the time.

1. 

12 o'clock

2. 

______ o'clock

3. 

______ o'clock

4. 

______ o'clock

5. 

______ o'clock

6. 

______ o'clock

Problem Solving Visual Thinking

Write the time.

7. 

______ o'clock

8. 

______ o'clock

9. 

______ o'clock

Notes for Home Your child read a clock and wrote the time to the hour. *Home Activity:* Ask your child to tell you the time on the next hour. What time will it be on the following hour?

Name ___________________________________

Mixed Practice: Lessons 1-6

Write the time.

1. 

_____ o'clock

2. 

_____ o'clock

3. 

_____ o'clock

4. 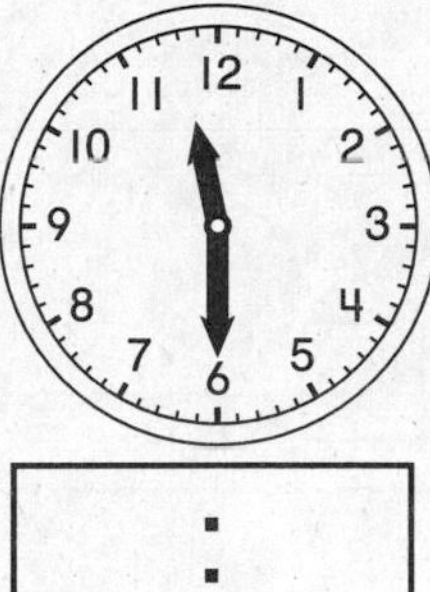

[:]

5. 

[:]

6. 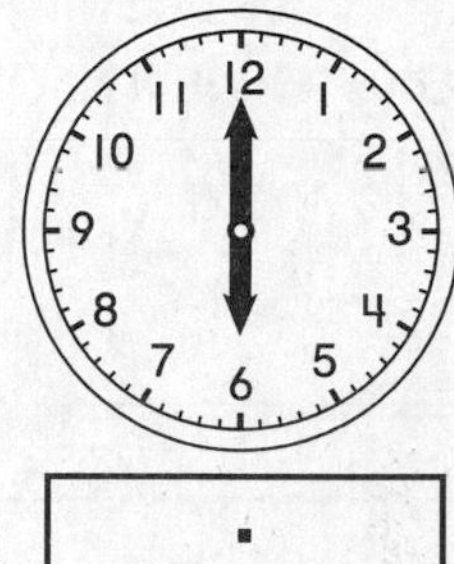

[:]

7. 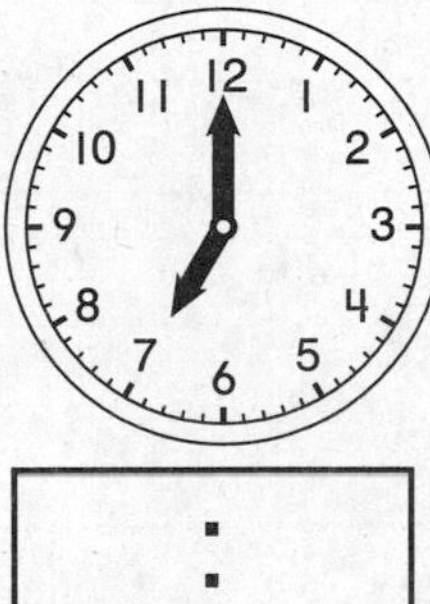

[:]

8. 

[:]

9. 

[:]

Problem Solving

10. Solve.

Anya has a flute lesson at 4:30. Her sister Laryssa has a lesson at 5:30. Joseph has a lesson before Anya. Who has the last lesson? _____________

Journal

11. Draw something you do at 12:00. Add a clock to your picture.

Notes for Home Your child practiced telling time to the hour and half hour and solved problems about time. *Home Activity:* Ask your child to read the time on a face clock and write the time as it would appear on a digital clock.

Name ______________________

Practice
Chapters 1-10
A

Cumulative Review

1. Add or subtract.

$$\begin{array}{r}10\\-4\\\hline\end{array}\quad\begin{array}{r}11\\-6\\\hline\end{array}\quad\begin{array}{r}7\\+4\\\hline\end{array}\quad\begin{array}{r}8\\+2\\\hline\end{array}\quad\begin{array}{r}6\\+6\\\hline\end{array}\quad\begin{array}{r}10\\-3\\\hline\end{array}\quad\begin{array}{r}5\\+4\\\hline\end{array}$$

Problem Solving

2. Make a picture graph. Color a picture for each □ and △.

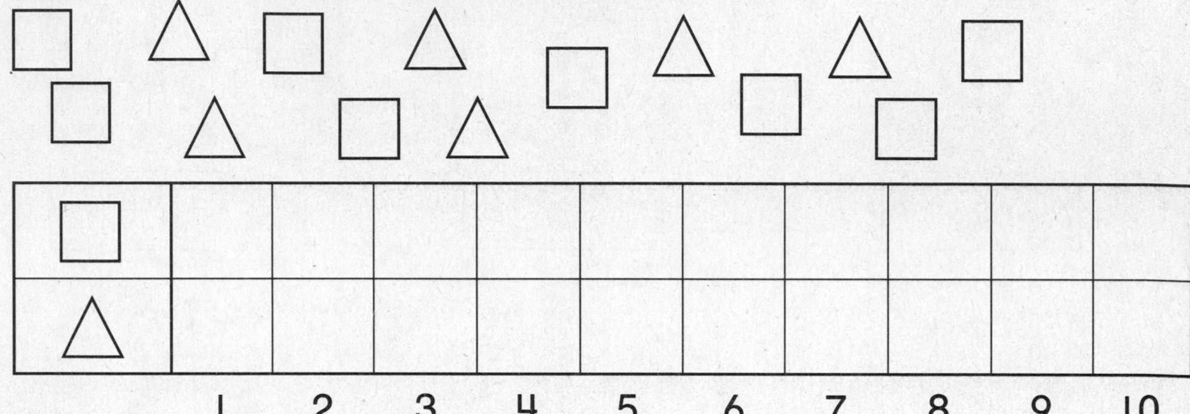

□										
△										
	1	2	3	4	5	6	7	8	9	10

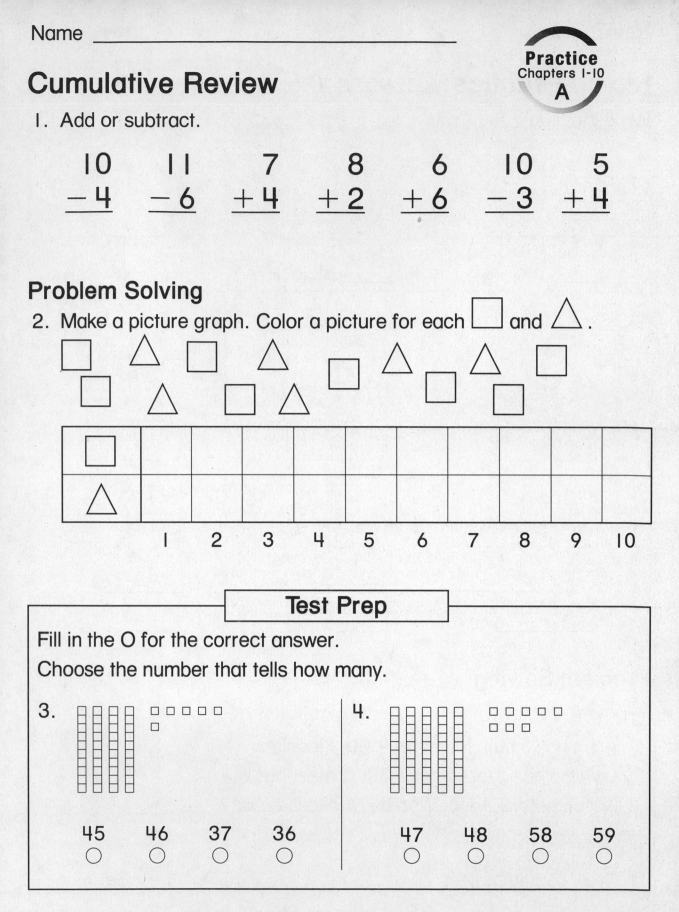

Test Prep

Fill in the O for the correct answer.

Choose the number that tells how many.

3. 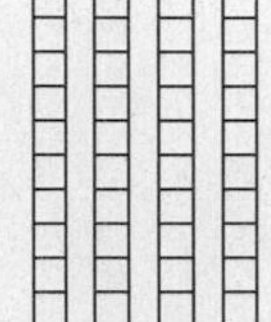

45 ○ 46 ○ 37 ○ 36 ○

4. 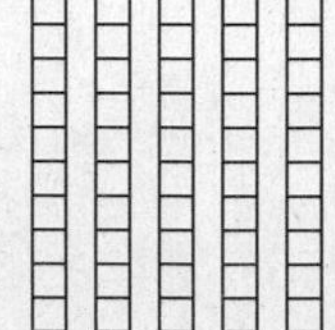

47 ○ 48 ○ 58 ○ 59 ○

Notes for Home Your child reviewed addition and subtraction, graphing, and tens and ones. *Home Activity:* Ask your child to explain how he or she solved Exercise 4.

Name ______________________________

Practice 10-7

Order Events

Write 1st, 2nd, 3rd to put the pictures in order.

1.

2.

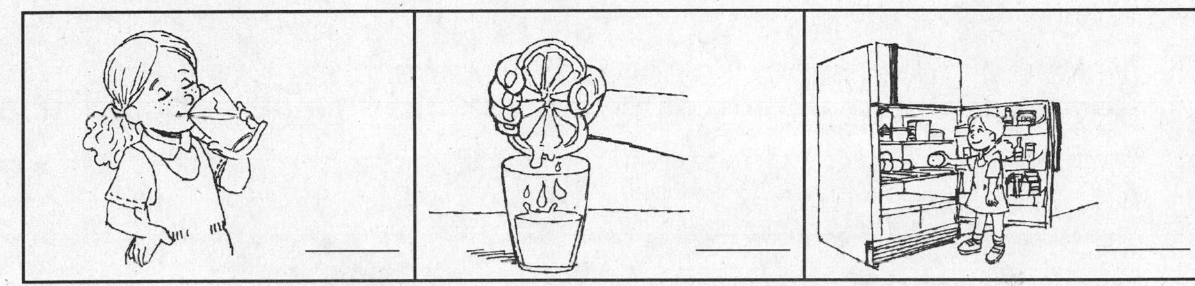

Write your own order problem.

3.

Problem Solving Critical Thinking

4. Write 1st, 2nd, and 3rd to show the order the students arrived.

The children arrive at Taft School
at different times in the morning.
The bus dropped Kisha off on time.
Jonathan arrived before Kisha.
Pablo arrived late.

Kisha ______

Jonathan ______

Pablo ______

Notes for Home Your child reordered events into the correct sequence using 1st, 2nd, and 3rd. *Home Activity:* Ask your child to write or draw pictures in order to show the events of a special day.

Name ______________________________

Practice 10-8

Estimate Time

Circle the time it takes.

1.

about 1 minute   about 1 hour

2.

about 1 minute   about 1 hour

3.

about 1 minute   about 1 hour

4.

about 1 minute   about 1 hour

5. **Draw your own** time problem.

Tell a Math Story

6. Tell about something you did yesterday.
   Tell what time you started and what time you stopped.

Notes for Home Your child estimated times for familiar activities. *Home Activity:* Do one of the activities shown in Exercises 1–5 with your child and time how long it takes.

Name ______________________

Practice 10-9

Calendar

1. Make a calendar for this month.

Month: ______						
Sunday	Monday	Tuesday	Wednesday	Thursday	Friday	Saturday

Use your calendar.

2. Today is ______________________.

3. The day before yesterday was ______________________.

4. In five more days it will be ______________________.

5. The day after tomorrow is ______________________.

Problem Solving Patterns

6. What is the number date of the Monday of next week? ________

Notes for Home Your child completed a calendar for the current month. *Home Activity:* Mark your family calendar with special days of family members and friends. Ask your child to tell you the month, date, and day of the week for each event.

Name ______________________________

Practice 10-10

Problem Solving: Too Much Information

Cross out what you do not need. Solve.

1. Stacy bought 9 stickers on Monday.
   She likes those with animals.
   Stacy gave away 3 stickers on Tuesday.
   How many stickers does Stacy have now? ______

2. Mark collected 11 soup can labels.
   Debbie collected 5 labels. The school
   will buy a new computer with the labels.
   How many labels do they have in all? ______

3. There are 14 children in Peggy's
   music class. There are 5 boys and 9 girls.
   6 of the children also take a dance class.
   How many children in the music class
   do not take a dance class? ______

Problem Solving Visual Thinking

What does each clock show? Write the time.

4.

___ : ___

5.

___ : ___

6.

___ : ___

Notes for Home Your child solved problems that give too much information. *Home Activity:* Ask your child to tell you about a time when he or she had more information than was needed to solve a problem or perform an activity.

Name ______________________________

Mixed Practice: Lessons 7-10

Write 1st, 2nd, and 3rd to put the pictures in order.

1.

Use the calendar to answer the question.

2.

July

Thursday	Friday	Saturday
4	5	6
11	12	13
18	19	20

Circle the correct day.

July 20	Saturday	Sunday
July 4	Wednesday	Thursday
July 19	Friday	Saturday
July 13	Friday	Saturday

Problem Solving

Cross out what you do not need.

Solve.

3. Jack went to the store at 3:30 with his brother.
   They bought 4 apples.
   Jack bought 6 bananas.
   His brother bought 5 oranges.
   How many pieces of fruit did they buy? ______

Journal

Write about something you do that takes less time than it takes to brush your teeth.

Notes for Home Your child practiced ordering events, reading a calendar, and solving problems. *Home Activity:* Ask your child to look at the calendar on this page and tell you the date of the first Sunday. (7)

Name ______________________________

Cumulative Review

1. Circle the shape that belongs.

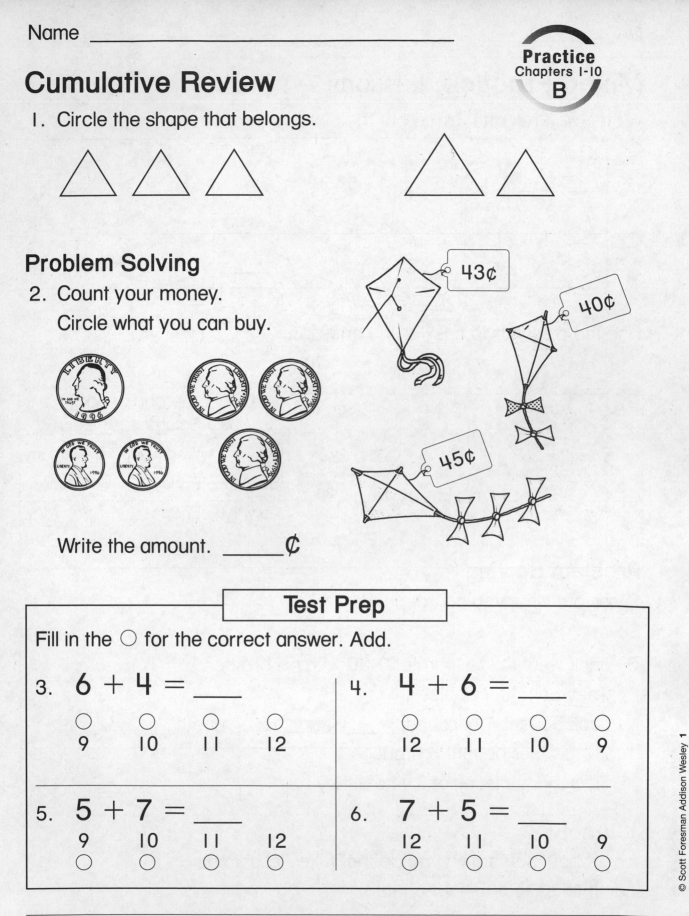

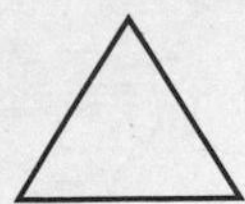  

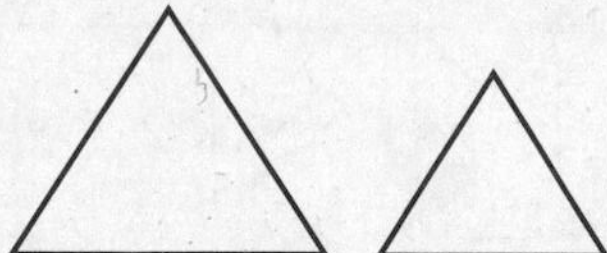

Problem Solving

2. Count your money.
   Circle what you can buy.

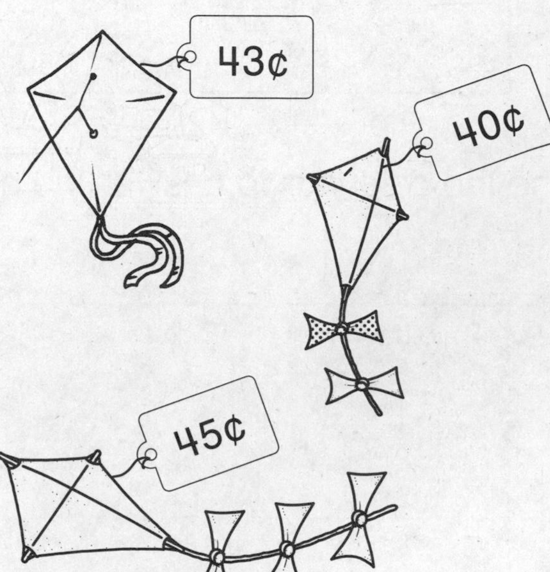

Write the amount. _____¢

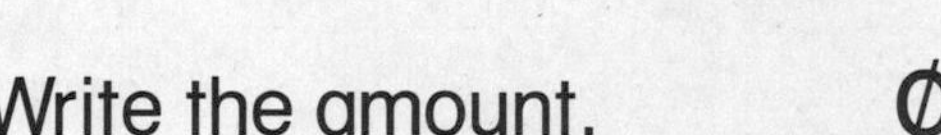

Test Prep

Fill in the ○ for the correct answer. Add.

3. 6 + 4 = ___

○ 9 ○ 10 ○ 11 ○ 12

4. 4 + 6 = ___

○ 12 ○ 11 ○ 10 ○ 9

5. 5 + 7 = ___

9 ○ 10 ○ 11 ○ 12 ○

6. 7 + 5 = ___

12 ○ 11 ○ 10 ○ 9 ○

Notes for Home Your child reviewed sorting, using money, and addition. *Home Activity:* Ask your child how much more money is needed to buy the 45¢ kite in exercise 2. (3¢)

Name ______________________________

Practice 11-1

Explore Measuring with Nonstandard Units

How wide is your desk?

Estimate. Then use a book and a pencil to measure.

How wide?

Use.	Estimate.	Measure.
1. book	about ____ book	about ____ book
2. pencil	about ____ pencil	about ____ pencil

How tall is your desk?

Use.	Estimate.	Measure.
1. book	about ____ book	about ____ book
2. pencil	about ____ pencil	about ____ pencil

Talk About It Did you use fewer 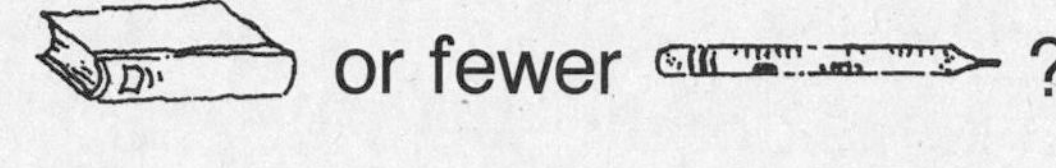 or fewer ?
Why do you think that happened?

Notes for Home Your child estimated and measured length using books and pencils. *Home Activity:* Ask your child to choose an object from his or her room, and measure three different objects or areas in that room.

Name ______________________________

Practice 11-2

Estimate, Measure, and Compare Lengths

Make a train of 10 [cube]. Use it to estimate the length.

Measure with [cube].	Does it look longer than 10 [cube] ?	How many [cube] long?
1.	yes no	about _____ [cube]
2.	yes no	about _____ [cube]
3.	yes no	about _____ [cube]

4. Choose an object.
   Draw it.
   Estimate its length.
   Measure its length.

Problem Solving Estimate

Circle the best answer.

5. Sarah and Susan are partners for folk dancing
   Sarah is about 45 [cube] tall. How tall is Susan?

   Susan is about 40 45 50 55 [cube] tall.

Notes for Home Your child used Snap Cubes to measure lengths of classroom objects. *Home Activity:* Give your child an object such as a spoon. Then ask your child to think of some things that are longer than 10 spoons and shorter than 10 spoons. Measure with the spoon to check.

Name ______________________________

Practice 11-3

Estimate and Measure with Inches

About how long? Estimate. Measure. Use your [ruler 1 2 3 4 5 6].

1.

Estimate. ______ inches

Measure. ______ inches

2. 

Estimate. ______ inches

Measure. ______ inches

3. 

Estimate. ______ inches

Measure. ______ inch

Start at the dot.

4. Draw a line that is about 3 inches long.

•

5. Draw another line.
Make it longer than 3 inches and shorter than 6 inches.

•

Problem Solving Visual Thinking

6. Circle the best answer.
Joan is putting books on the bookshelf.
Which book will fit on the top shelf?

Notes for Home Your child estimated and measured lengths of objects on the page with an inch ruler. *Home Activity:* Show your child three different objects. Ask your child to use a ruler to measure the length of the objects in inches.

Name ______________________________

Practice 11-4

Compare to One Foot

How long would each object be? Circle the best answer.

1.

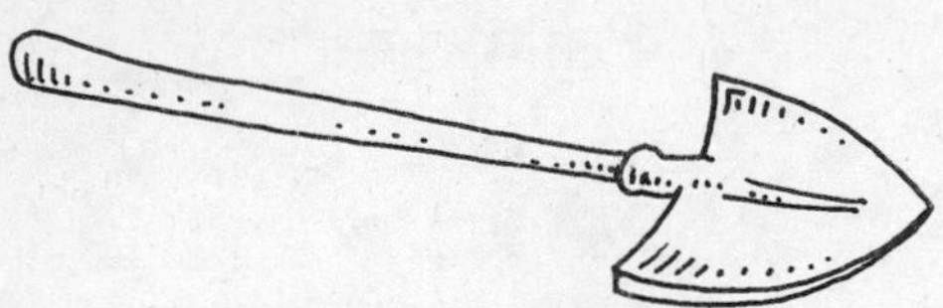

shorter than 1 foot
about 1 foot
longer than 1 foot

2.

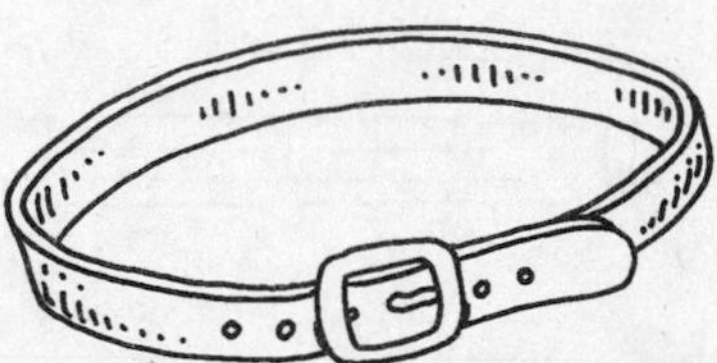

shorter than 1 foot
about 1 foot
longer than 1 foot

3.

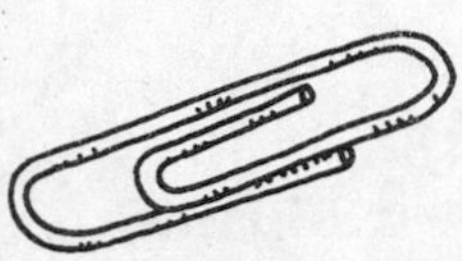

shorter than 1 foot
about 1 foot
longer than 1 foot

4.

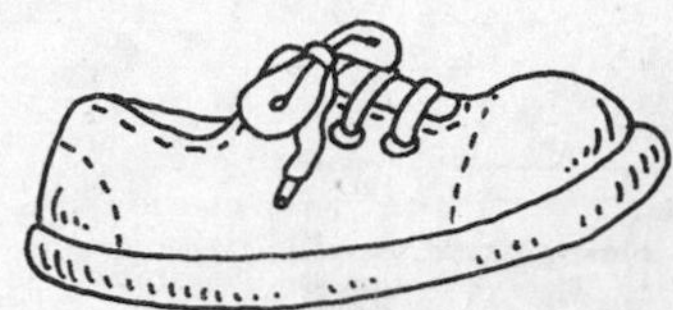

shorter than 1 foot
about 1 foot
longer than 1 foot

5.

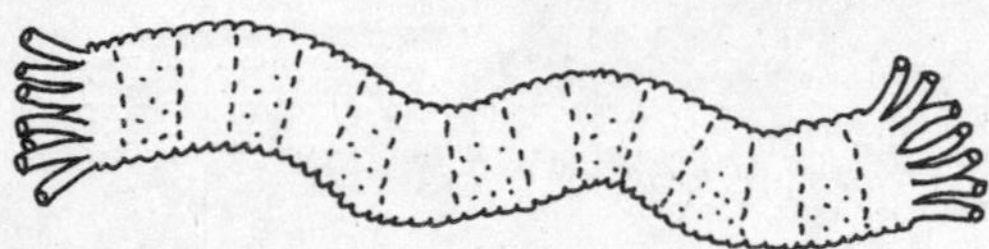

shorter than 1 foot
about 1 foot
longer than 1 foot

6.

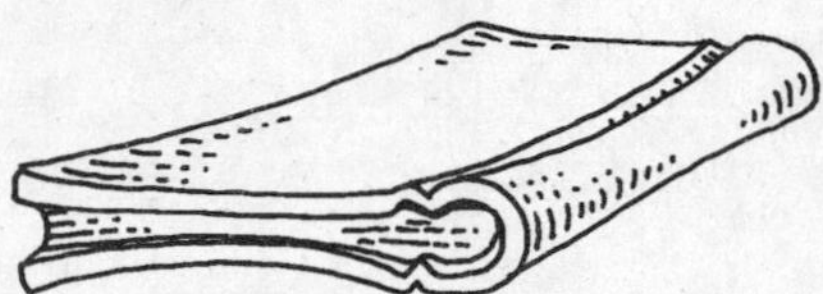

shorter than 1 foot
about 1 foot
longer than 1 foot

Problem Solving

7. Albert measured the longest watermelon in his garden. He found that it was about one foot and five inches long.

How many inches long was the watermelon? _____ inches

Notes for Home Your child identified whether an object is about 1 foot, shorter than 1 foot, or longer than 1 foot. *Home Activity:* Ask your child to find objects in your home that are longer than 1 foot and shorter than 1 foot. Measure them and compare your measurements.

Name ______________________________

Practice 11-5

Estimate and Measure with Centimeters

About how long? Estimate. Measure. Use your [ruler 1 2 3 4 5 6 7 8 9 10].

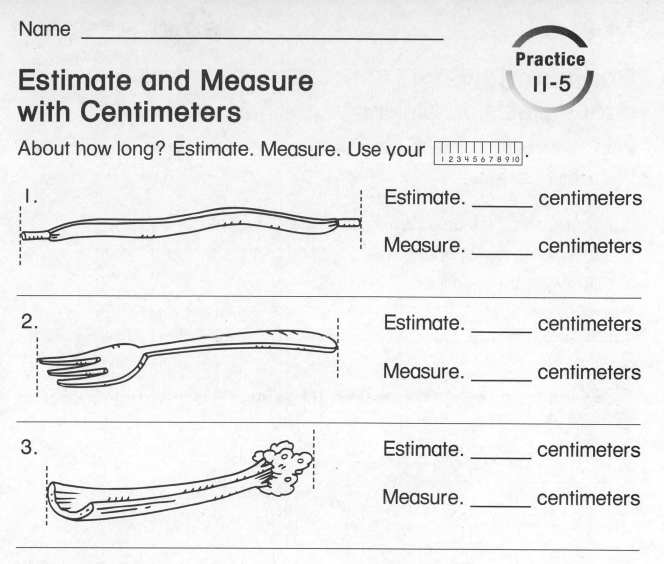

1.

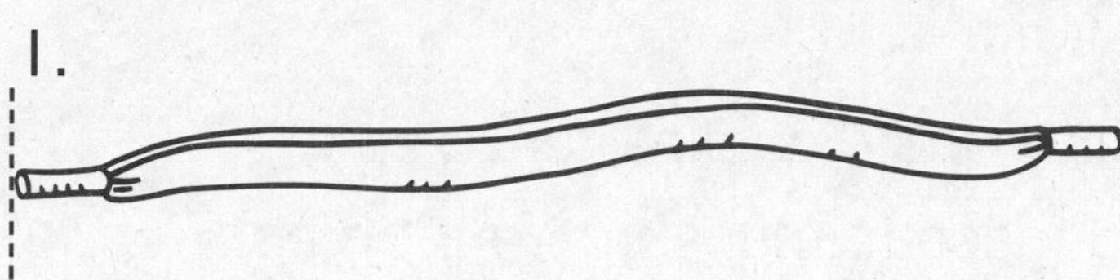

Estimate. ______ centimeters

Measure. ______ centimeters

2.

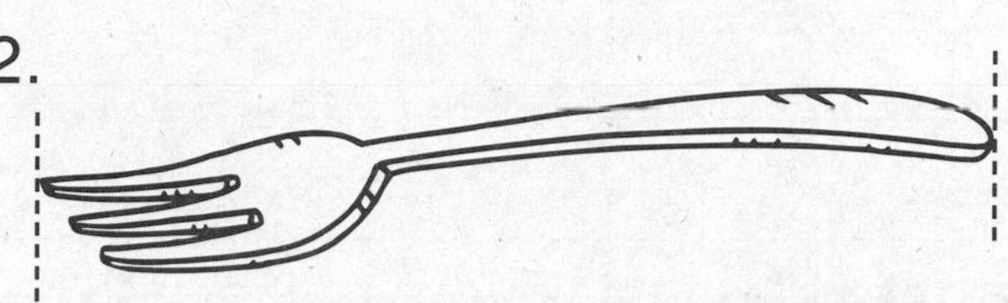

Estimate. ______ centimeters

Measure. ______ centimeters

3.

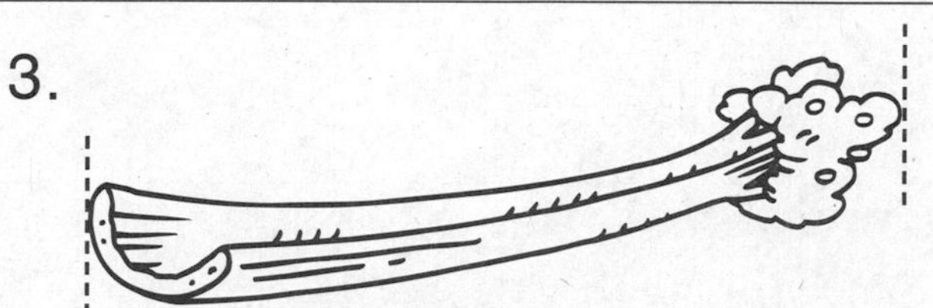

Estimate. ______ centimeters

Measure. ______ centimeters

Start at the dot.

4. Draw a line. Make it longer than 10 centimeters and shorter than 15 centimeters.

•

Problem Solving Critical Thinking

5. Solve.

Rover is taller than Rex.

Princess is taller than Rover.

Spot is shorter than Rex.

Who is the shortest? ____________

Notes for Home Your child estimated and measured lengths of objects with a centimeter ruler.
Home Activity: Have your child select 4 small kitchen utensils. Ask your child to guess and then measure the length of these objects in centimeters.

Name ___________________________

Practice 11-6

Problem Solving: Group Decision Making

Work with your group. Choose an object in the classroom to measure. Write the answers.

1. Your group has only paper clips and a centimeter ruler. Talk about how you can used these to measure your object. Draw what you will do.

2. Estimate. How big around does the group think your object is?

3. Measure. How big around is it?

4. Talk it over. Were paper clips a good thing to use? Why or why not?

Journal

Write about your group. How did you work together?
Would you do something differently the next time? Why or why not?
If you would change something, what would it be?

Notes for Home Your child worked with a group to choose tools and carry out a measurement project. *Home Activity:* Work with your child to measure around some large things in your home, such as the refrigerator, a bookcase, or a television set.

Name ______________________________

Practice
Chapter 11
A

Mixed Practice: Lessons 1–6

Use the rulers to measure length. Write the answer.

1.

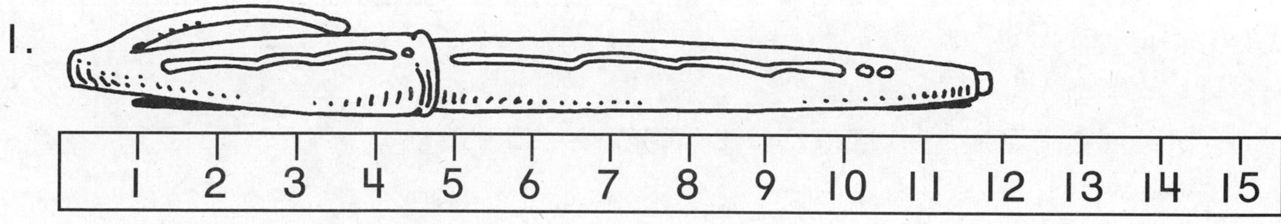

about ______ centimeters

2.

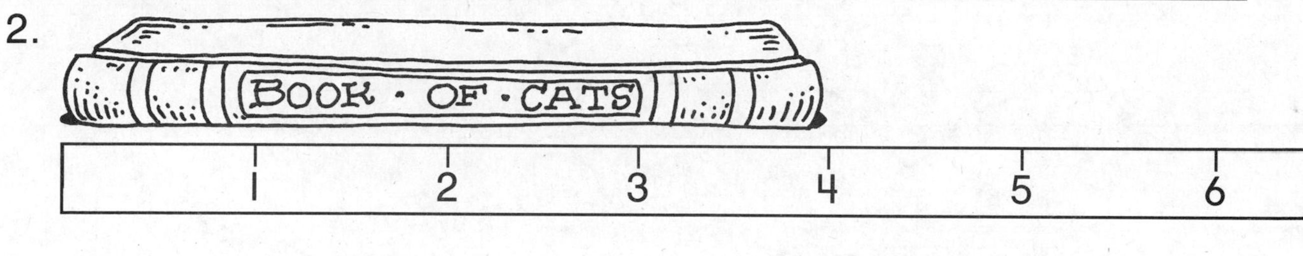

about ______ inches

How long would the wagon be? Circle the best answer.

3.

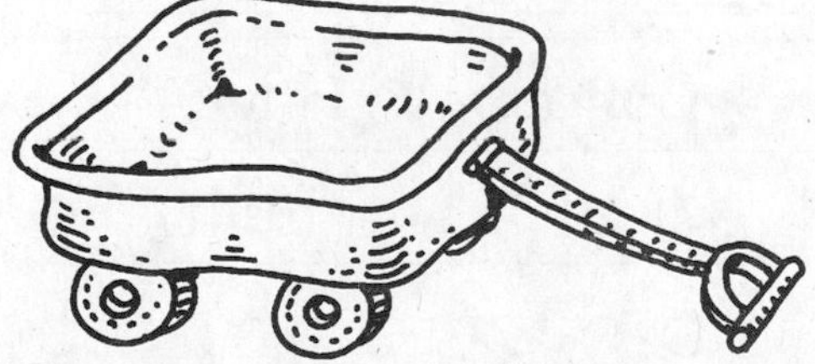

shorter than 1 foot

about 1 foot

longer than 1 foot

Problem Solving

4. Susie's mother needs to know how big the living room is. She wants to buy new carpeting. Should she measure the room in inches or feet?

____

Journal

What is something you would measure in feet?
Draw a picture of it.
Estimate how long it is.

Notes for Home Your child worked with centimeters, inches and feet. *Home Activity:* Ask your child to find something in your home that you would measure in inches. Measure it together.

Name ______________________________

Practice
Chapters 1–11
A

Cumulative Review

1. Add or subtract.

5	9	7	8	12	3	11
+ 6	− 5	+ 3	+ 4	− 9	+ 3	− 9

2. Circle the correct estimate.

about

10 20 30

Test Prep

Fill in the O for the correct answer.

Read the graph.

3. How many buttons does Mike have?

20 ○ 40 ○ 50 ○

4. How many fewer buttons does Kathy have than Mike?

5 ○ 10 ○ 15 ○

Buttons We Have

Mike	Kathy
○ ○ ○ ○ ○	○ ○ ○ ○ ○
○ ○ ○ ○ ○	○ ○ ○ ○ ○
○ ○ ○ ○ ○	○ ○ ○ ○ ○
○ ○ ○ ○ ○	○ ○ ○ ○ ○
○ ○ ○ ○ ○	○ ○ ○ ○ ○
○ ○ ○ ○ ○	
○ ○ ○ ○ ○	
○ ○ ○ ○ ○	

Notes for Home Your child reviewed addition and subtraction, estimation, and graphing. *Home Activity:* Ask your child to solve 7 + 2 = (9) and 12 − 5 = (7).

Name ______________________________

Practice 11-7

Explore Weight

Compare these weights. Write **more**, **less**, or **same**.

1.

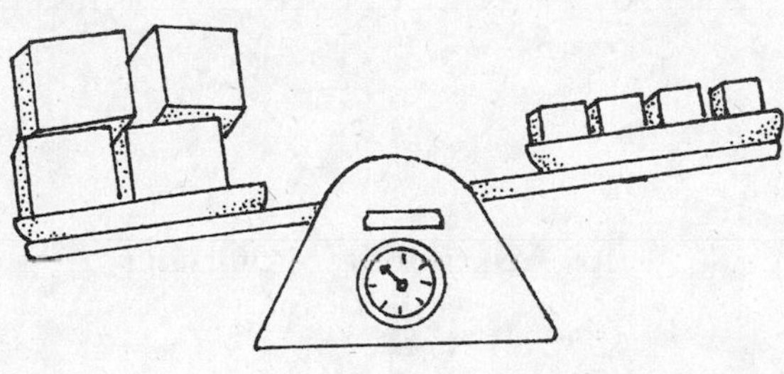

__________ __________

2.

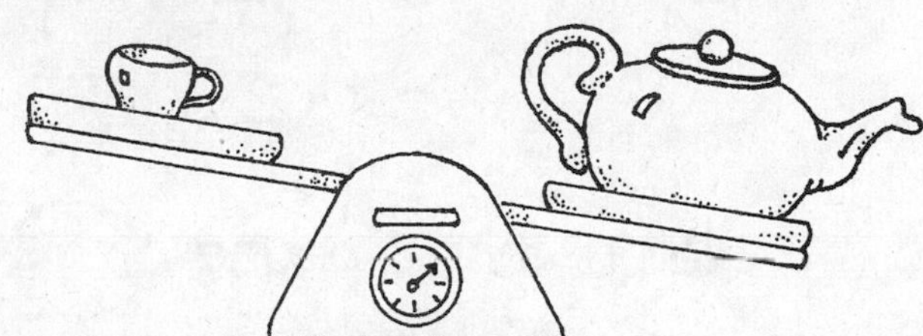

__________ __________

3.

__________ __________

4.

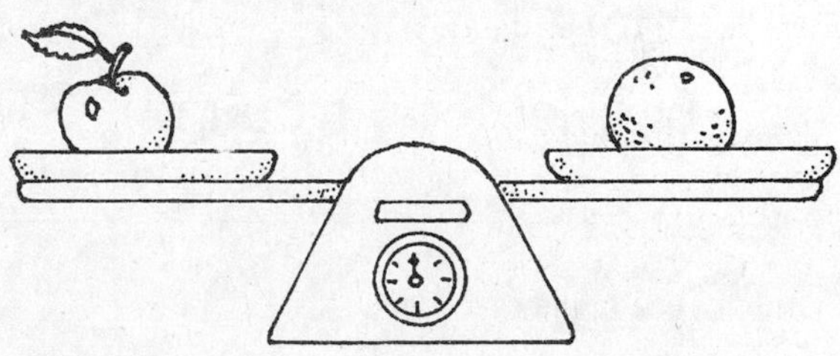

__________ __________

Talk About It What are some other ways you compare how heavy two things are?

Notes for Home Your child compared the weights of objects. *Home Activity:* Have your child select two objects and hold one in each hand. Ask him or her to tell which one weighs more and which one weighs less.

Name ________________________________

Practice 11-8

Compare to One Pound

How heavy would each be?
Circle the best answer.

1. 

lighter than 1 pound
about 1 pound
heavier than 1 pound

2. 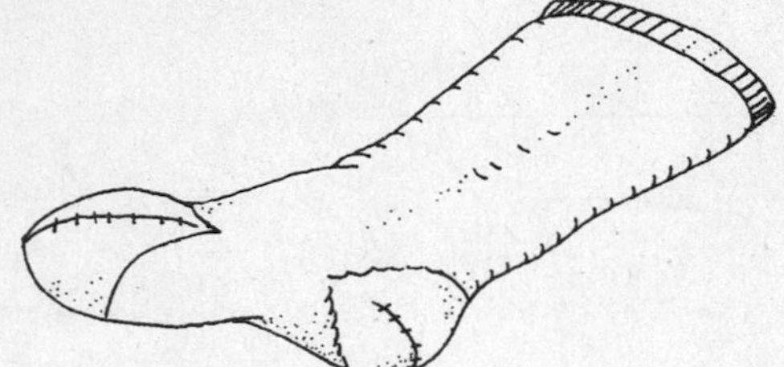

lighter than 1 pound
about 1 pound
heavier than 1 pound

3. 

lighter than 1 pound
about 1 pound
heavier than 1 pound

4. 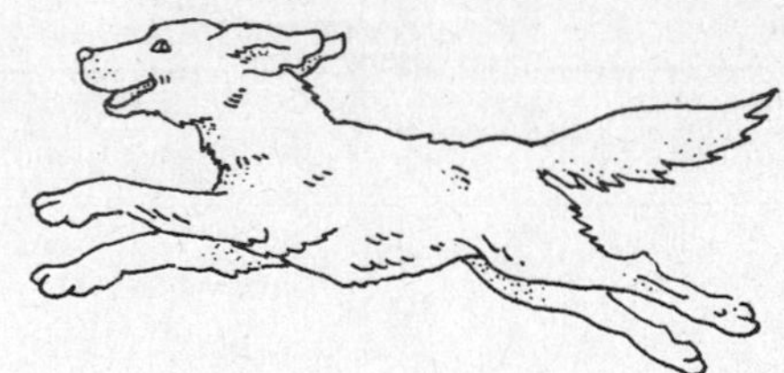

lighter than 1 pound
about 1 pound
heavier than 1 pound

Mental Math

5. Count by tens to solve.
Elana is buying green apples for her grandmother.
The apples costs 10¢ a pound.
Grandma needs 9 pounds of apples for her pies.
How much will the apples cost?

_______ ¢

Notes for Home Your child compared the weights of objects to one pound. *Home Activity:* Find a food product, such as a box of crackers or a bag of fruit, that weighs one pound. Have your child compare other objects to it. Which weighs more? Which weighs less?

Name ______________________________

Compare to One Kilogram

How heavy would each object be?
Circle the best answer.

1.

lighter than 1 kilogram
about 1 kilogram
heavier than 1 kilogram

2.

lighter than 1 kilogram
about 1 kilogram
heavier than 1 kilogram

3.

lighter than 1 kilogram
about 1 kilogram
heavier than 1 kilogram

4.

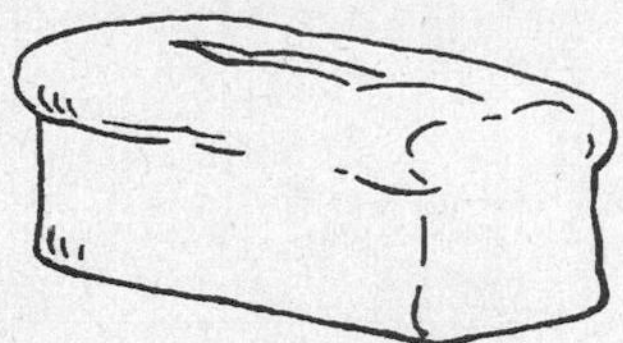

lighter than 1 kilogram
about 1 kilogram
heavier than 1 kilogram

Problem Solving Critical Thinking

5. Is a kilogram of playground sand heavier than a kilogram of marbles? Explain.

____

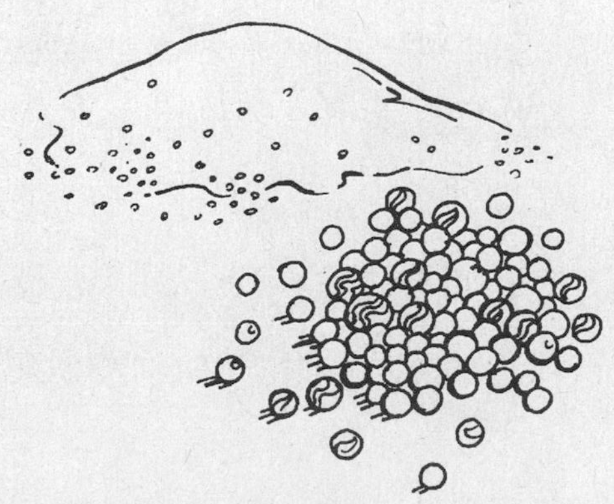

Notes for Home Your child estimated whether things are heavier or lighter than one kilogram. *Home Activity:* Ask your child to make a list of things in your home or neighborhood that are heavier than one kilogram.

Name ______________________________

Practice 11-10

Compare Cups, Pints, and Quarts

Circle the things that could hold less than 1 cup.
Mark an X on the things that hold more than 1 cup.

1.

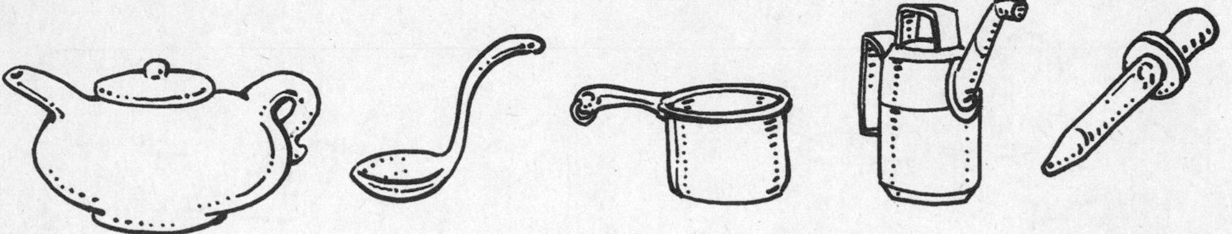

2.

Circle the things that could hold less than 1 quart.
Mark an X on the things that hold more than 1 quart.

3.

Tell a Math Story

Tell about a time you needed to measure using a cup, pint, or quart.

Notes for Home Your child identified containers that hold more or less than 1 cup, 1 pint, and 1 quart.
Home Activity: Ask your child to find some containers in your kitchen that hold more than a quart. Use a measuring cup to check.

Name ______________________________

Compare to One Liter

Check how much each container could hold.

Container	Less than 1 liter	About 1 liter	More than 1 liter
1. 			
2. 			
3. 			
4. 			
5. 			

Mental Math

6. Tanya went to the store to buy juice for a party. She bought 6 bottles of juice. Each bottle holds two liters. How many liters of juice did she buy? ______

Notes for Home Your child checked whether various containers hold more or less than 1 liter. *Home Activity:* Ask your child to explore the capacity of your kitchen containers. Often containers have capacities marked on the container, like a measuring cup. Show these markings to your child. Discuss how it might make it easier to choose a container to store leftovers.

Name ___________________________________

Practice 11-12

Use a Thermometer

Look at the [thermometer icon].

Draw a picture to show how it looks outside.

1.

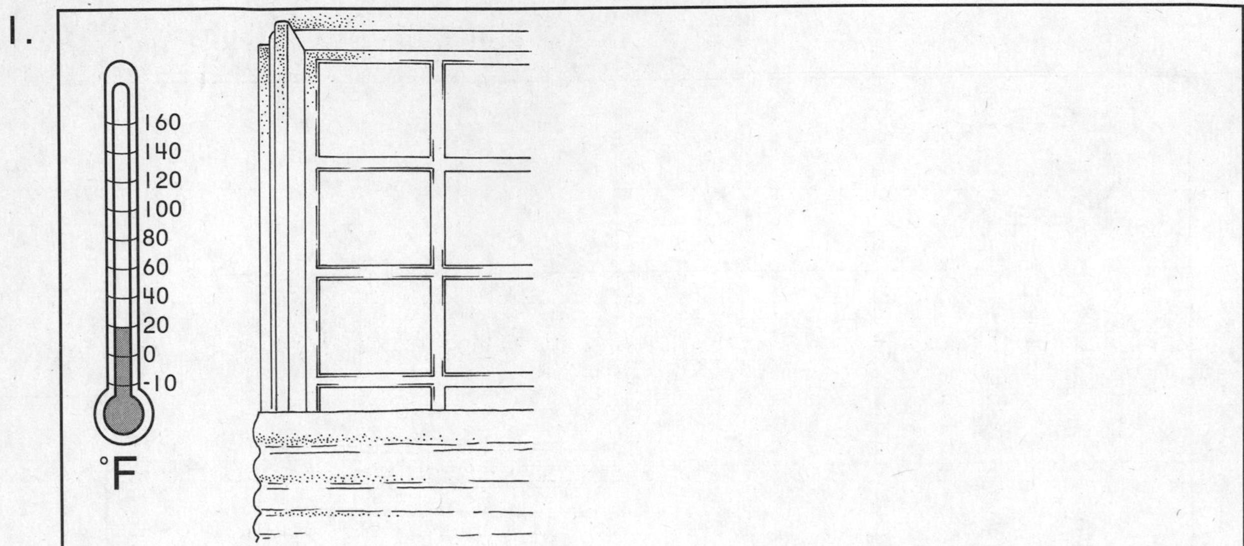

2.

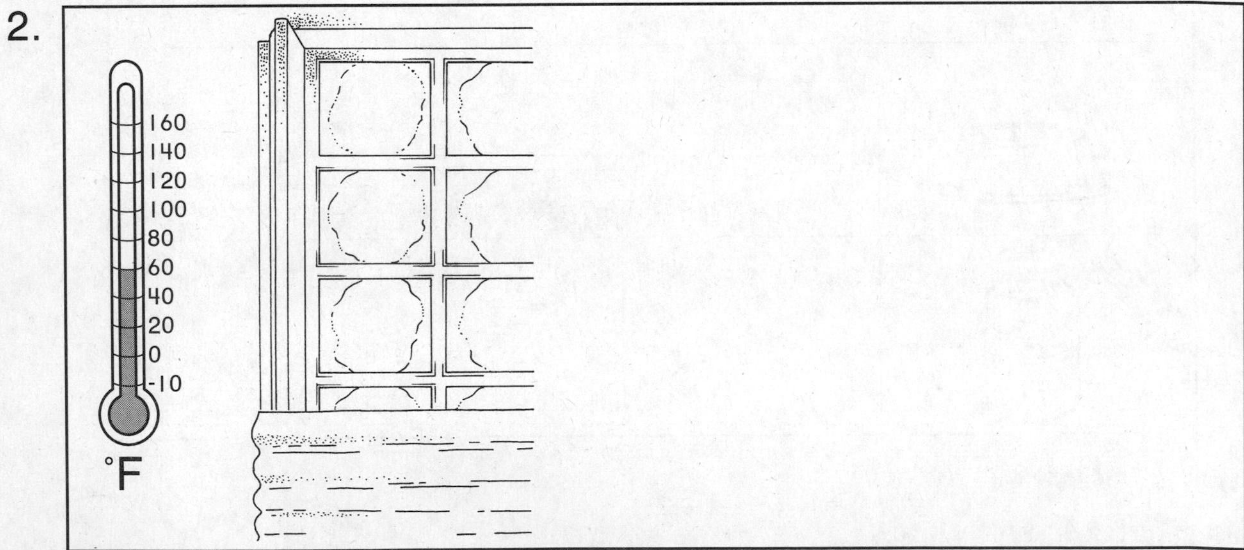

Journal

Write about some things you like to do outside when it is warm.

Write about some things you like to do outside when it is cool.

Notes for Home Your child drew pictures to show understanding of the temperature shown on a thermometer. *Home Activity:* Help your child look in the newspaper for today's high temperature. Have your child draw a picture of a thermometer showing the correct temperature.

Name ______________________________

Problem Solving: Logical Reasoning

Practice 11-13

Circle the tool that you need to answer each question.

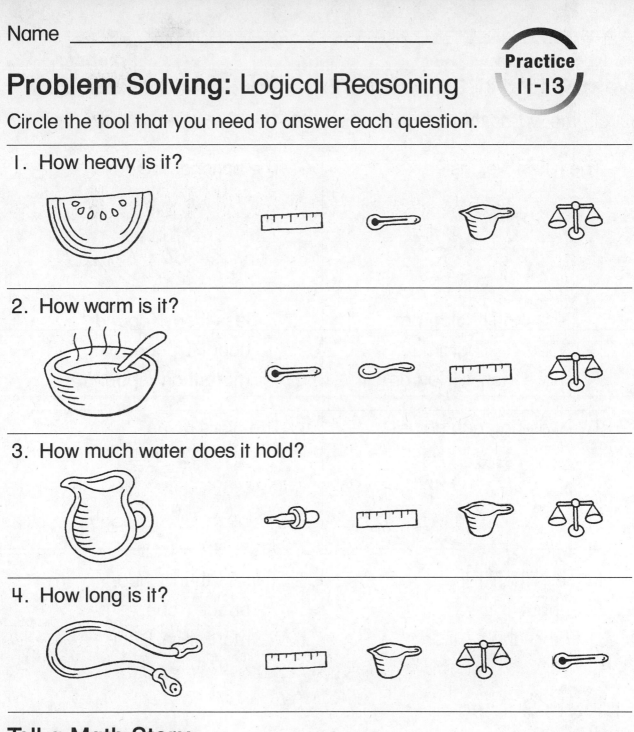

1. How heavy is it?

 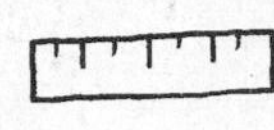   

2. How warm is it?

 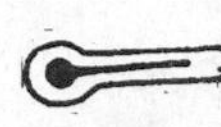 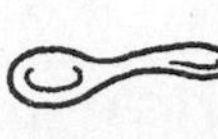 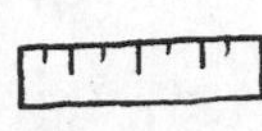 

3. How much water does it hold?

 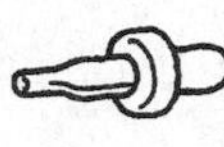 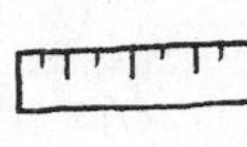  

4. How long is it?

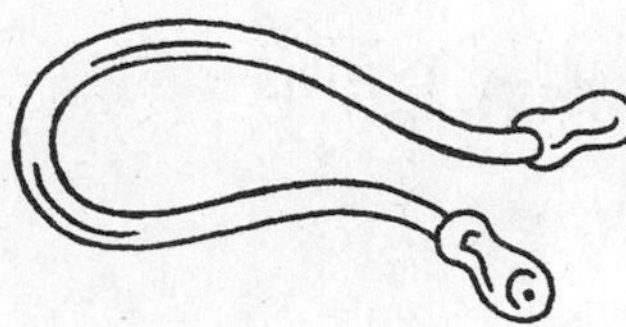    

Tell a Math Story

5. Richard is baking a cake with his father.
   Tell a story about how they follow the recipe.
   Talk about measuring the ingredients.
   Tell about choosing a container for mixing and baking.
   Tell about baking the cake.

Notes for Home Your child chose tools of measurement to measure length, weight, and capacity.
Home Activity: Ask your child to find objects in his or her bedroom to measure. Help your child identify the correct tool to measure each object and tell why he or she chose it.

Name ______________________________

Practice
Chapter 11
B

Mixed Practice: Lessons 7–13

Circle the words that tell about the object.

1. The kitten weighs

less than 1 kilogram.
about 1 kilogram.
more than 1 kilogram.

2. The bananas weigh

less than 1 pound.
about 1 pound.
more than 1 pound.

3. The watering can holds

less than 1 liter.
about 1 liter.
more than 1 liter.

4. The glass holds

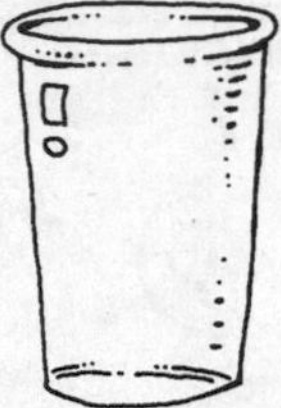

less than 1 cup.
about 1 cup.
more than 1 cup.

Problem Solving

Circle the tool you need to answer the question.

5. Is your dog heavier than your cat?

Journal

Choose an object and record as many things as you can about it.

Notes for Home Your child estimated weight and capacity measures. *Home Activity:* Ask your child to tell you why you might use a cup to measure baking materials.

Name ______________________

Practice 12-2

Add Doubles Plus One

Write the sum.

1. $\begin{array}{r} 4 \\ +4 \\ \hline 8 \end{array}$ $\begin{array}{r} 4 \\ +5 \\ \hline \end{array}$ $\begin{array}{r} 5 \\ +4 \\ \hline \end{array}$

2. $\begin{array}{r} 5 \\ +5 \\ \hline \end{array}$ $\begin{array}{r} 5 \\ +6 \\ \hline \end{array}$ $\begin{array}{r} 6 \\ +5 \\ \hline \end{array}$

3. $\begin{array}{r} 9 \\ +9 \\ \hline \end{array}$ $\begin{array}{r} 9 \\ +10 \\ \hline \end{array}$ $\begin{array}{r} 10 \\ +9 \\ \hline \end{array}$

4. $\begin{array}{r} 8 \\ +8 \\ \hline \end{array}$ $\begin{array}{r} 8 \\ +9 \\ \hline \end{array}$ $\begin{array}{r} 9 \\ +8 \\ \hline \end{array}$

5. 6 + 6 = ____ 1 + 2 = ____ 8 + 9 = ____

6. 6 + 5 = ____ 8 + 8 = ____ 7 + 8 = ____

7. 7 + 6 = ____ 4 + 3 = ____ 7 + 7 = ____

Problem Solving

Solve. Write the number sentence.

8. Meg made an ant farm.
   She put in 8 red ants. ____ + ____ = ____
   She put in 9 black ants.
   How many ants did Meg put in? ____ ants

9. A fish had 6 teeth on the top. ____ + ____ = ____
   It had 5 teeth on the bottom.
   How many teeth did the fish have? ____ teeth

Notes for Home Your child added using a doubles fact, such as 6 + 6 = 12, to solve other facts.
Home Activity: Have your child line up shoes to show a doubles plus one fact.

Name ______________________

Practice 12-3

Add 3 Numbers

Use a paper clip and pencil. Spin.
Write the number in the box. Add.

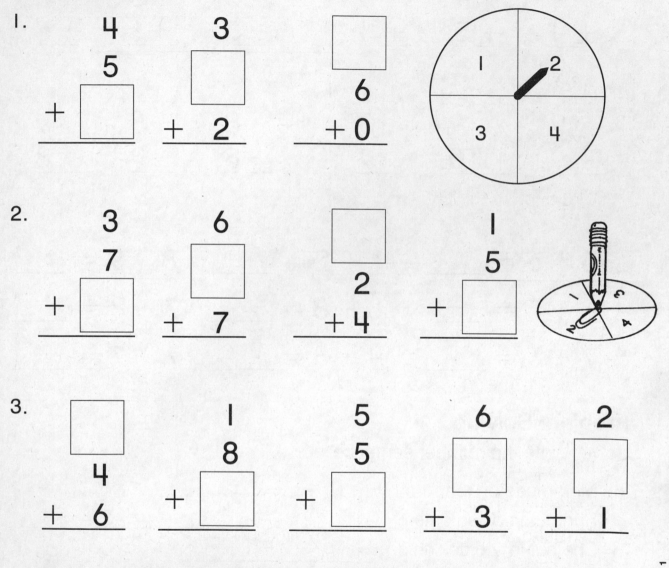

1.

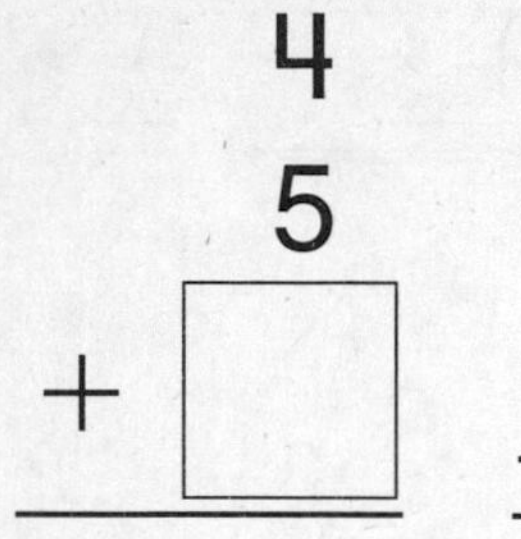

4
5
+ ☐

3
☐
+ 2

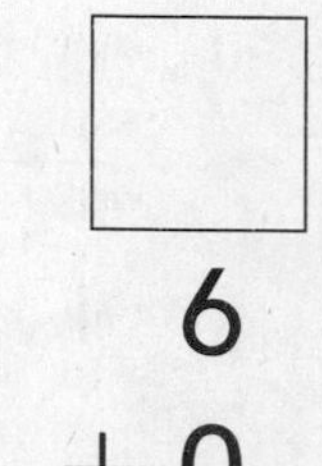

☐
6
+ 0

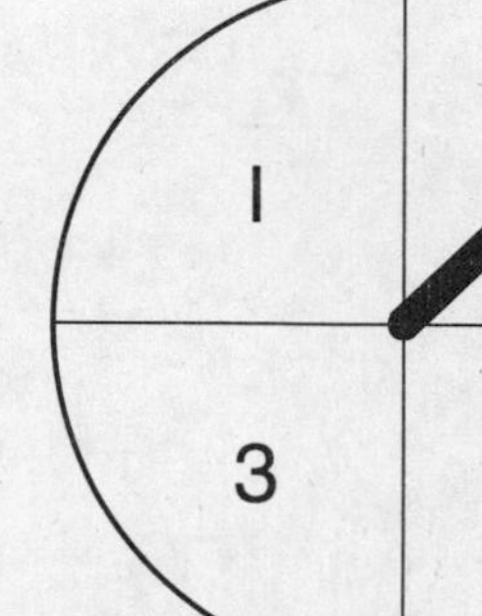

2.

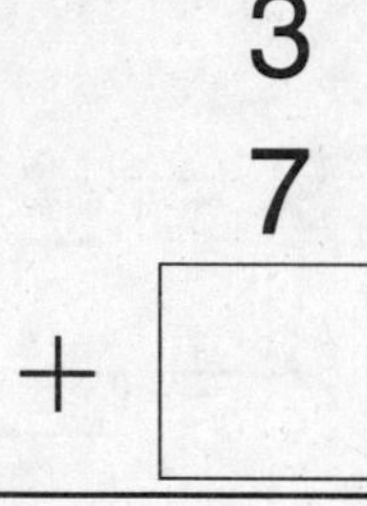

3
7
+ ☐

6
☐
+ 7

☐
2
+ 4

1
5
+ ☐

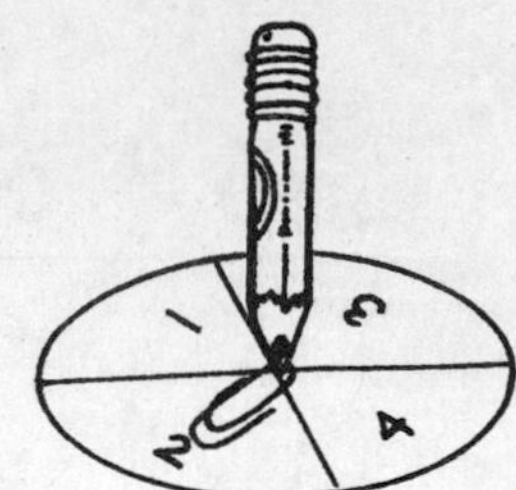

3.

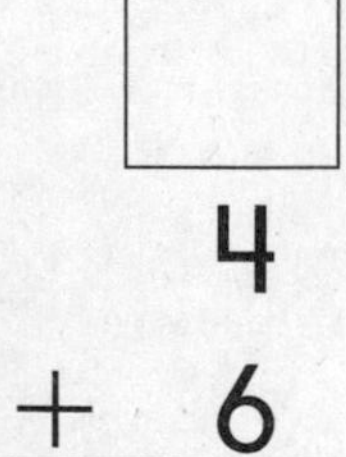

☐
4
+ 6

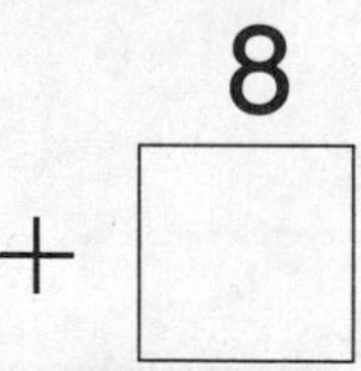

1
8
+ ☐

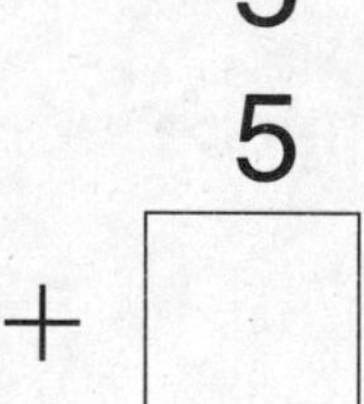

5
5
+ ☐

6
☐
+ 3

2
☐
+ 1

Mental Math

4. Coach had 3 bags of soccer balls.
He had 16 balls in all.
Color the 3 bags Coach had.

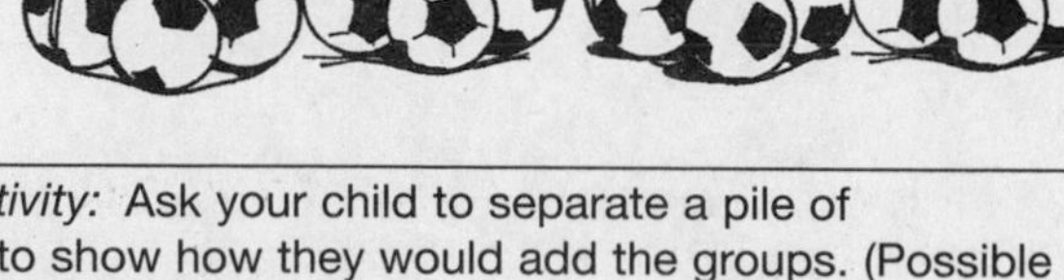

Notes for Home Your child added three numbers. *Home Activity:* Ask your child to separate a pile of 18 rocks into 3 groups. Have them write a number sentence to show how they would add the groups. (Possible answer: 5 + 5 + 8 = 18. I would add the doubles first and then add on 8 more.)

Name ______________________________

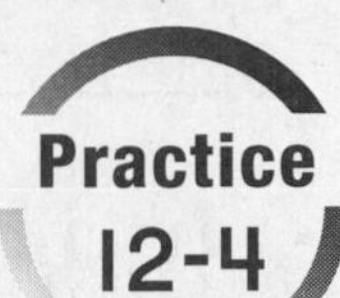

Explore Making 10 to Add 7, 8, or 9

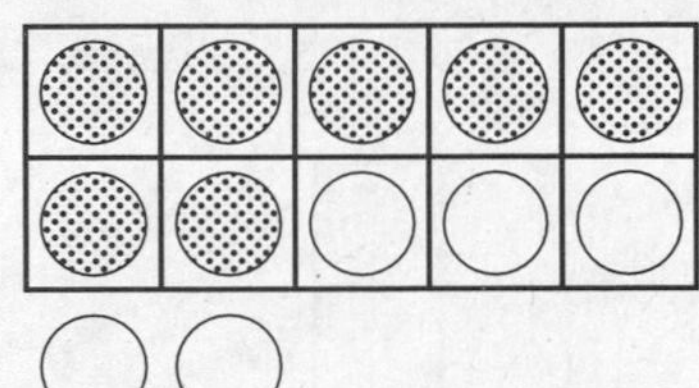

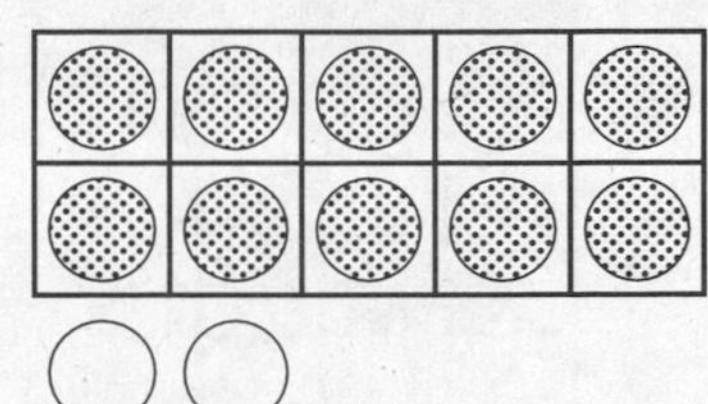

7 + 5 = 12   10 + 2 = 12

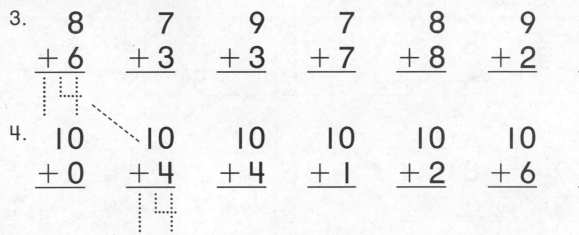

Use and .

Write the sum. Match.

3.
8	7	9	7	8	9	7
+ 6	+ 3	+ 3	+ 7	+ 8	+ 2	+ 8
14						

4.
10	10	10	10	10	10	10
+ 0	+ 4	+ 4	+ 1	+ 2	+ 6	+ 5
	14					

Problem Solving

3. Pedro has 9 rocks.
He found 5 more.
How many rocks does
he have now?

______ rocks

How many rocks will not fit in the box?

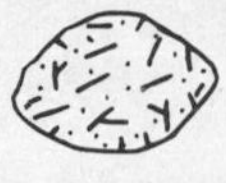

______ rocks

Notes for Home Your child matched facts such as 7 + 5 = 12 and 10 + 2 = 12. *Home Activity:* Ask your child to tell you a story problem for 8 + 8. Help him or her draw a ten frame to solve the problem.

Name ______________________________

Make 10 When Adding 7, 8, or 9

Practice 12-5

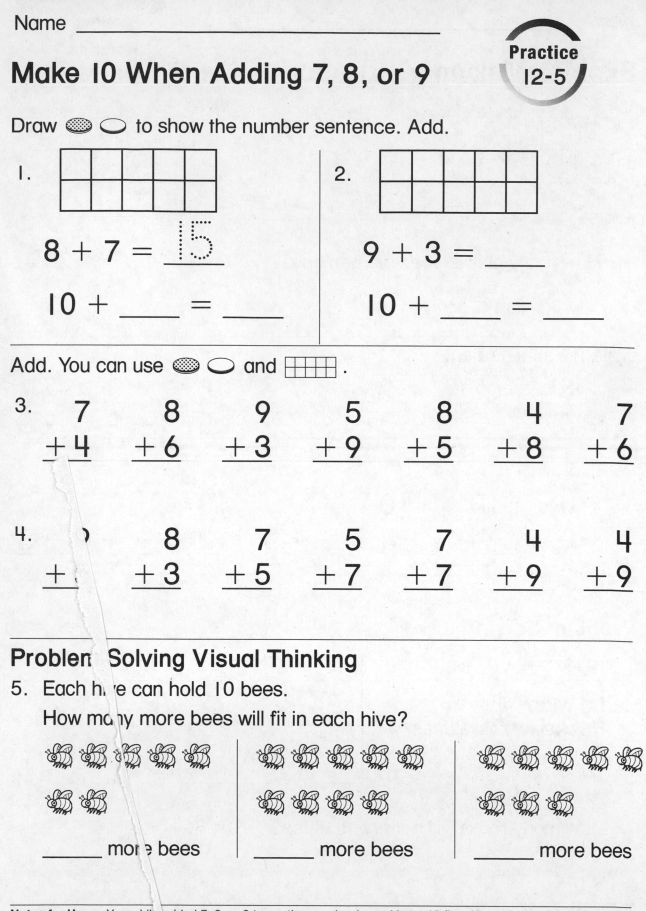

Draw ● ○ to show the number sentence. Add.

1. 

$8 + 7 =$ 15

$10 +$ ____ $=$ ____

2. 

$9 + 3 =$ ____

$10 +$ ____ $=$ ____

Add. You can use ● ○ and ten-frame.

3.

7	8	9	5	8	4	7
+ 4	+ 6	+ 3	+ 9	+ 5	+ 8	+ 6

4.

[illegible]	8	7	5	7	4	4
+ [illegible]	+ 3	+ 5	+ 7	+ 7	+ 9	+ 9

Problem Solving Visual Thinking

5. Each hive can hold 10 bees.

How many more bees will fit in each hive?

____ more bees

____ more bees

____ more bees

Notes for Home Your child added 7, 8, or 9 to another number by making a 10 first. *Home Activity:* Ask your child to write a number sentence for each bee hive problem. (7 + 3 = 10, 9 + 1 = 10, 8 + 2 = 10)

Name ___________________________________

Practice 12-6

Problem Solving:
Choose a Strategy

Solve. Use [counters] and [ten-frames] or draw a picture.

1. A hen has 4 yellow chicks.
   She has 9 tan chicks, too.
   How many chicks does the hen have?

   ______ chicks

---

2. 19 seals go fishing.
   13 seals catch fish.
   How many seals do not catch fish?

   ______ seals

---

3. A zoo has 6 lions.
   It has 4 tigers.
   6 leopards live there, too.
   How many big cats are at the zoo?

   ______ big cats

Tell a Math Story

4. Tell a math story about the picture.

Notes for Home Your child solved problems by drawing a picture or using objects. *Home Activity:* Ask your child to use pennies or other objects to retell the math story.

Name ____________________________________

Practice
Chapter 12
A

Mixed Practice: Lessons 1–6

Write the sum. Circle the doubles.

1.

5	4	6	7	9	8	4
+ 6	+ 4	+ 7	+ 5	+ 9	+ 9	+ 5

2.

7	9	5	4	6	7	3
+ 8	+ 4	+ 5	+ 7	+ 9	+ 7	+ 3

Add.

3.

2	4	3	1	6	5	4
1	3	5	4	2	3	2
+ 6	+ 5	+ 3	+ 7	+ 8	+ 6	+ 9

Problem Solving

Solve. Use and 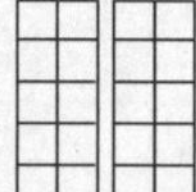 or draw a picture.

4. Marcy found 14 paper clips in her desk.
   She gave 9 to Martha.
   How many paper clips does
   Marcy have now?

   ________ paper clips

Journal

5. Draw a picture to show a doubles fact. Write the fact.

Notes for Home Your child practiced adding two and three numbers and solving problems by drawing a picture or using objects. *Home Activity:* Ask your child how she or he could use 6 + 6 = 12 to help find the answer for 6 + 7. (13)

Name ______________________________

Practice
Chapters 1–12
A

Cumulative Review

Add or subtract.

1. 6 + 3 = ____	4 + 9 = ____	5 + 6 = ____
9 − 6 = ____	13 − 9 = ____	11 − 5 = ____

Problem Solving

Count these coins. Record the coins in the table.

2.       

	Pennies	Nickels	Dimes
How many coins?			

Test Prep

Fill in the ○ for the correct answer.

Count the money.

3. 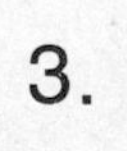       

39¢ ○ 31¢ ○ 41¢ ○ 45¢ ○

4.     

74¢ ○ 40¢ ○ 27¢ ○ 47¢ ○

Notes for Home Your child reviewed addition and subtraction, making a table, and counting money.
Home Activity: Ask your child to make a table to show the number of shapes he or she can find in the kitchen.

Name ______________________

Practice 12-7

Relate Addition and Subtraction

Add. Use the addition fact to help you subtract.

You can use counters.

1. $5 + 6 =$ 11 $\quad 11 - 5 =$ ___

2. $7 + 4 =$ ___ $\quad 11 - 4 =$ ___

3. $9 + 2 =$ ___ $\quad 11 - 9 =$ ___

4. $11 + 0 =$ ___ $\quad 11 - 11 =$ ___

5. $7 + 5 =$ ___ $\quad 12 - 7 =$ ___

6. $9 + 3 =$ ___ $\quad 12 - 9 =$ ___

Add or subtract.

Draw a line to match an addition with a subtraction fact.

7. $8 + 4 =$ ___ .... $12 - 8 =$ ___

8. $3 + 9 =$ ___ $\quad 11 - 7 =$ ___

9. $7 + 4 =$ ___ $\quad 12 - 3 =$ ___

Write About It

10. Complete the number sentences.
Draw or write a story to go with them.

$3 + 8 =$ ___

$11 - 3 =$ ___

Notes for Home Your child used an addition fact such as 8 + 4 = 12 to solve a related subtraction fact such as 12 - 8 = 4. *Home Activity:* Ask your child to name a subtraction fact that uses the same numbers as 6 + 5 = 11. (11 - 5 = 6 or 11 - 6 = 5)

Name ______________________

Practice 12-8

Use Doubles to Subtract

Add or subtract.

1. $6 + 6 =$ 12 $5 + 5 =$ ___ $8 + 8 =$ ___

   $12 - 6 =$ ___ $10 - 5 =$ ___ $16 - 8 =$ ___

2. $4 + 4 =$ ___ $9 + 9 =$ ___ $7 + 7 =$ ___

   $8 - 4 =$ ___ $18 - 9 =$ ___ $14 - 7 =$ ___

Subtract. Write the addition fact that helps.

3. $6 - 3$; 3 + 3 = 6

4. $18 - 9$; ☐ + ☐ = ☐

5. $12 - 6$; ☐ + ☐ = ☐

Problem Solving Patterns

6. Draw the missing dots on the last domino. Tell how you solved the puzzle.

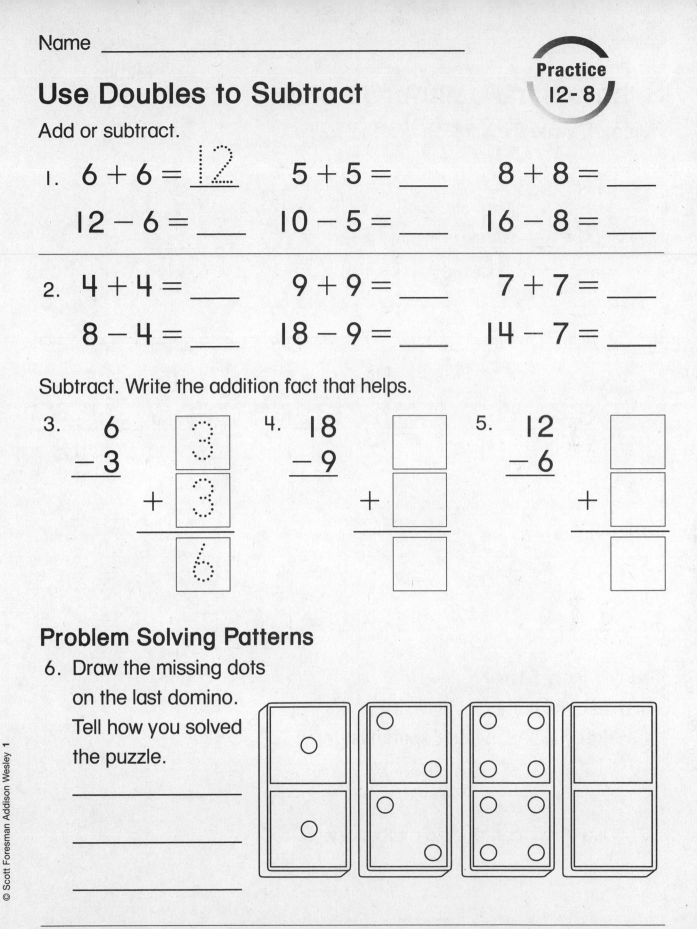

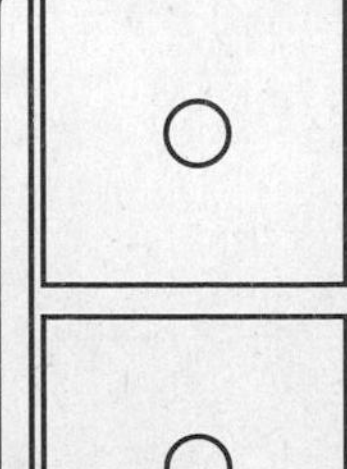
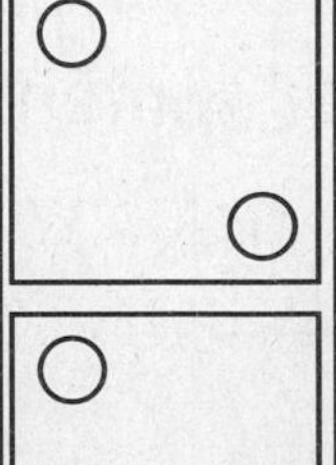
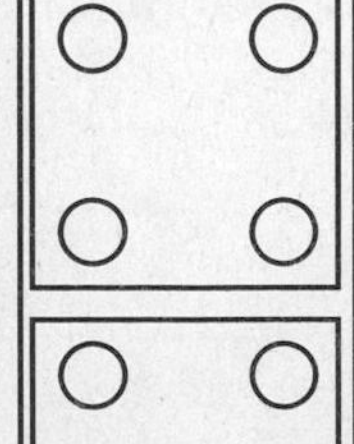

____

____

____

Notes for Home Your child used an addition double such as 5 + 5 to solve a related subtraction fact such as 10 – 5. *Home Activity:* Ask your child to write an addition fact and a subtraction fact for the last domino. (8 + 8 = 16, 16 – 8 = 8)

Name ______________________

Practice 12-9

Subtraction Facts for 13 and 14

Subtract. Write the addition fact that helps.

1. $13 - 8 = [5]$ $\quad 8 + [5] = 13$

2. $14 - 5 = [\ ]$ $\quad 5 + [\ ] = 14$

3. $14 - 8 = [\ ]$ $\quad 8 + [\ ] = 14$

$14 - 2 = [\ ]$ $\quad 2 + [\ ] = 14$

$13 - 6 = [\ ]$ $\quad 6 + [\ ] = 13$

Subtract.

4. 13 − 5 = ___ 13 − 7 = ___ 13 − 9 = ___

5. 14 − 4 = ___ 14 − 9 = ___ 14 − 1 = ___

Tell a Math Story

6. Use these numbers: 8, 6, 14.
   Write an addition and subtraction fact.

   _____ + _____ = _____ _____ − _____ = _____

7. Use each fact to tell a math story.

Notes for Home Your child subtracted facts from 13 and 14. *Home Activity:* Ask your child to tell how the math stories in Exercise 7 are alike and different.

Name ______________________

Practice 12-10

Subtraction Facts for 15 to 18

Complete the addition fact.
Write the subtraction facts.

You can use ⬭ ⬭ .

1. 7 + 9 = 16   16 − ____ = 9

16 − ____ = 7

Mixed Practice

Subtract.

2.

12	13	14	15	17	17	18
− 3	− 5	− 7	− 9	− 9	− 8	− 9

3.

13	16	16	15	14	16	18
− 7	− 7	− 8	− 6	− 5	− 9	− 0

Problem Solving Critical Thinking

5. Mark the coins to buy 2 bags of elephant food.

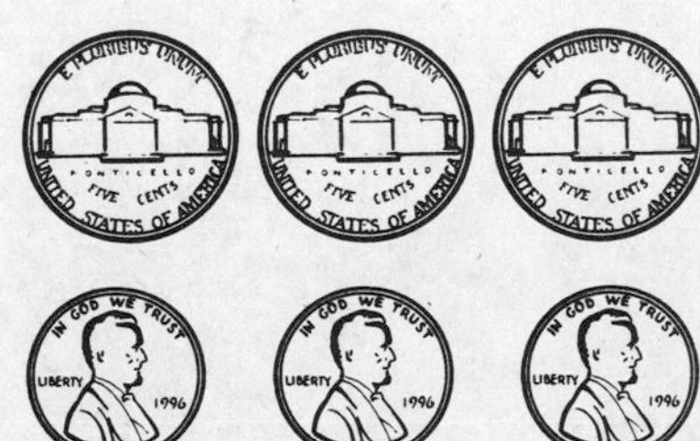

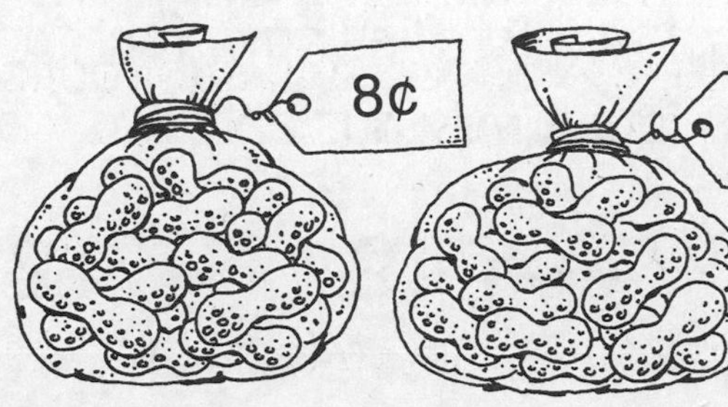

How much money will you have left? _____¢

Notes for Home Your child subtracted facts such as 15 − 7 = 8 and 15 − 8 = 7. *Home Activity:* Ask your child to use real money to show how much they would have left if they bought only one bag of food in Exercise 4. (11¢)

Name ________________________________

Fact Families

Practice 12-11

Complete the fact family. You can use [counters].

1. $9 + 3 =$ ____ $12 - 3 =$ ____

   $3 + 9 =$ ____ $12 - 9 =$ ____

2. $8 + 7 =$ ____ $15 - 8 =$ ____

   $7 + 8 =$ ____ $15 - 7 =$ ____

3. $6 + 8 =$ ____ $14 - 6 =$ ____

   $8 + 6 =$ ____ $14 - 8 =$ ____

4. **Write your own** fact family.

   ____ + ____ = ____ ____ − ____ = ____

   ____ + ____ = ____ ____ − ____ = ____

Problem Solving Critical Thinking

5. Most fact families have four facts.
   This fact family has only two facts. Why?

   $6 + 6 = 12$ $12 - 6 = 6$

   Which other fact families have only two facts?

   ____

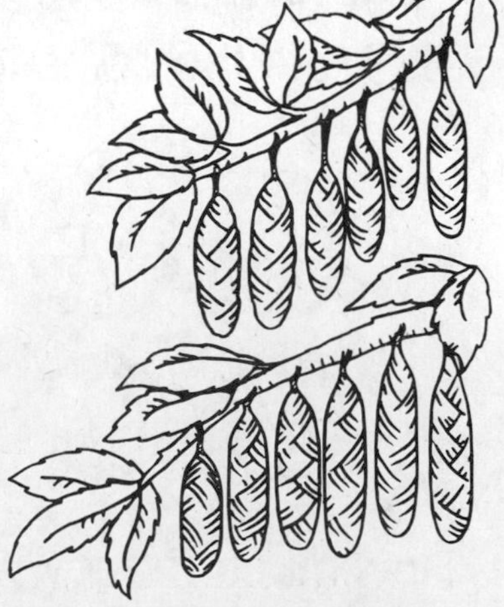

Notes for Home Your child added and subtracted using fact families. *Home Activity:* Ask your child to draw a picture to illustrate the fact family in Exercise 3.

Name ___________________________________

Problem Solving:
Choose an Operation

Circle add or subtract.

Complete the number sentence. Solve.

1. 12 penguins are on a hill. **add** **subtract**
   4 slide down the hill.
   How many are left?

   There are 8 penguins left. 12 ◯ ___ = ___

2. 6 brown cows come into the barn. **add** **subtract**
   7 tan cows came in too.
   How many cows are in the barn?

   There are ____ cows in the barn. ___ ◯ ___ = ___

3. 8 bats are in a cave. **add** **subtract**
   8 more bats fly in.
   How many bats are there all together?

   There are ____ bats. ___ ◯ ___ = ___

Tell a Math Story

4. Use the picture to tell a math story.
   Write a number sentence to go with your story.

____

Notes for Home Your child solved problems by deciding whether to add or subtract. *Home Activity:* Ask your child to name words used in math stories that help them to know to add. (The list should include in all and all together.)

Name ___________________________

Mixed Practice: Lessons 7–12

Add or subtract.

1. $\begin{array}{r} 8 \\ +7 \\ \hline \end{array}$ $\begin{array}{r} 15 \\ -7 \\ \hline \end{array}$

2. $\begin{array}{r} 14 \\ -5 \\ \hline \end{array}$ $\begin{array}{r} 14 \\ -9 \\ \hline \end{array}$

3. $\begin{array}{r} 6 \\ +7 \\ \hline \end{array}$ $\begin{array}{r} 13 \\ -6 \\ \hline \end{array}$

Subtract.

4. $\begin{array}{r} 18 \\ -9 \\ \hline \end{array}$ $\begin{array}{r} 15 \\ -8 \\ \hline \end{array}$ $\begin{array}{r} 16 \\ -8 \\ \hline \end{array}$ $\begin{array}{r} 13 \\ -5 \\ \hline \end{array}$ $\begin{array}{r} 14 \\ -8 \\ \hline \end{array}$ $\begin{array}{r} 17 \\ -8 \\ \hline \end{array}$ $\begin{array}{r} 14 \\ -7 \\ \hline \end{array}$

Problem Solving

Circle add or subtract.

Complete the number sentence. Solve.

5. Mother bear picked 15 berries. **add** **subtract**

   She gave her cub 6 berries.

   How many are left for Mother?

   Mother bear has ____ berries.

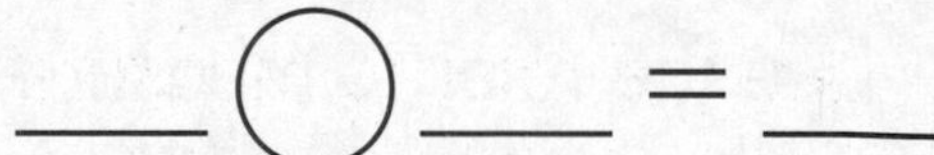

Journal

6. Write or draw a math story about 15 penguins.

   Write a number sentence for your story.

Notes for Home Your child practiced addition and subtraction facts to 18, and choosing addition or subtraction to solve a problem. *Home Activity:* Ask your child how he or she could use 6 + 5 = 11 to help answer 11 – 5 and 11 – 6.

Name ______________________________

Cumulative Review

Practice
Chapters 1–12
B

1.

3	6	2	1	4	5	3
2	1	3	3	0	5	3
+ 3	+ 1	+ 5	+ 7	+ 8	+ 1	+ 3

Problem Solving

2. Count the money. ______

3. Circle what you can buy.

Test Prep

Fill in the ○ for the correct answer.

Use the ruler to measure.

4.

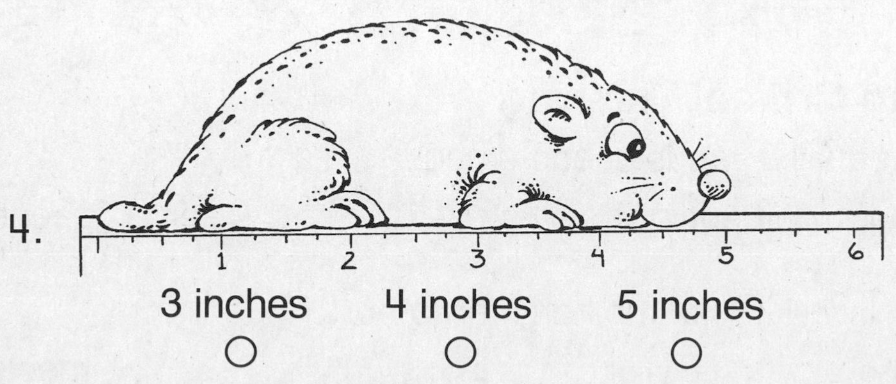

3 inches ○   4 inches ○   5 inches ○

Notes for Home Your child reviewed adding three numbers, counting money, and measurement. *Home Activity:* Ask your child to show you a group of real coins equal to the price of each object in Exercise 3.

Name ______________________________

Practice 13-1

Explore Adding Tens

46 and 3 tens more is 76.

Use a [hundred chart] to add tens to these numbers.

1	2	3	4	5	6	7	8	9	10
11	12	13	14	15	16	17	18	19	20
21	22	23	24	25	26	27	28	29	30
31	32	33	34	35	36	37	38	39	40
41	42	43	44	45	46	47	48	49	50
51	52	53	54	55	56	57	58	59	60
61	62	63	64	65	66	67	68	69	70
71	72	73	74	75	76	77	78	79	80
81	82	83	84	85	86	87	88	89	90
91	92	93	94	95	96	97	98	99	100

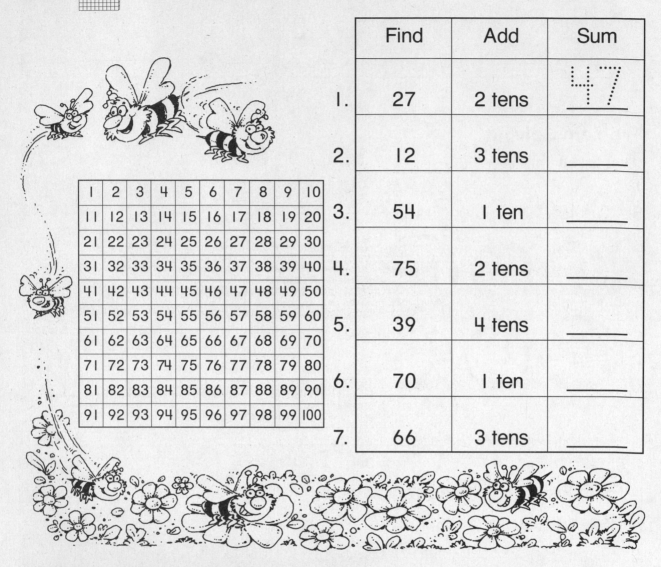

	Find	Add	Sum
1.	27	2 tens	47
2.	12	3 tens	______
3.	54	1 ten	______
4.	75	2 tens	______
5.	39	4 tens	______
6.	70	1 ten	______
7.	66	3 tens	______

Problem Solving Critical Thinking

8. Jed's hamster eats 10 seeds at each meal. How many seeds will it eat in 5 meals? ______ seeds

9. How many meals will it take the hamster to eat 70 seeds? ______ meals

Notes for Home Your child explored adding tens using a 100 chart. *Home Activity:* Ask your child to count by tens starting with his or her age. (Possible answer: 6, 16, 26, 36, 46, 56, 66, 76, 86, 96.)

Name ______________________________

Practice 13-2

Add Tens

Add. Use tens/ones mat and tens and ones blocks.

1.

tens	ones
2	0
+ 3	4
5	4

2.

tens	ones
4	5
+ 4	0

3.

tens	ones
1	0
+ 5	2

4.

tens	ones
5	1
+ 3	0

5. 26 + 10   44 + 40   16 + 50   30 + 22   40 + 57   60 + 17

6. 80 + 14   60 + 26   49 + 10   23 + 20   50 + 31   12 + 20

7. 50 + 23   14 + 20   17 + 40   30 + 62   40 + 28   55 + 10

Problem Solving Patterns

8. Brian uses a calculator to find the total for these packets of seeds.
He presses these keys once:
[2] [5] [+] [1] [0]
He presses [=] 4 times.
He sees 35, 45, 55, 65.
What pattern did Brian use to add? ______

Seeds for Brian's Garden
25 tomato seeds
40 carrot seeds

Notes for Home Your child added two-digit numbers and tens. *Home Activity:* Set out a small sum of coins. Ask your child to add 2, 3, or 4 dimes to the coins and to calculate the total amount.

Name ______________________________

Practice 13-3

Add Tens and Ones

Add. Use tens/ones mat and tens and ones blocks.

1.

tens	ones
2	4
+ 1	5

tens	ones
5	1
+ 2	6

tens	ones
1	6
+ 5	2

tens	ones
6	3
+ 3	2

2. $41 + 21$ $36 + 11$ $50 + 5$ $61 + 28$ $22 + 23$ $18 + 31$

3. $81 + 4$ $28 + 41$ $13 + 33$ $15 + 53$ $34 + 43$ $32 + 22$

4. $94 + 4$ $27 + 51$ $38 + 50$ $40 + 8$ $25 + 52$ $15 + 40$

Problem Solving Critical Thinking

5. Use tens/ones mat and tens and ones blocks to find 4 ways to get the sum of 56.

tens	ones
□	□
+ 4	4
5	6

tens	ones
□	□
+ 3	5
5	6

tens	ones
□	□
+ 5	2
5	6

tens	ones
□	□
+ 2	3
5	6

Notes for Home Your child added numbers like 36 + 12. *Home Activity:* Look at a calendar. Ask your child to add the number of days in his two favorite months.

Name ______________________________

Practice 13-4

Regroup with Addition

Use tens/ones mat and base-ten blocks.

	Show this many.	Add this many.	Do you need to regroup?	Solve.
1.	24	3	yes (no)	24 + 3 = 27
2.	56	7	yes no	56 + 7 = ____
3.	44	5	yes no	44 + 5 = ____
4.	19	4	yes no	19 + 4 = ____
5.	67	8	yes no	67 + 8 = ____
6.	35	6	yes no	35 + 6 = ____

Mental Math Algebra Readiness

What's My Rule? What number does each robot add?

7. 32 + ____ = 36

14 + ____ = 18

55 + ____ = 59

This robot adds ____.

8. 21 + ____ = 27

60 + ____ = 66

43 + ____ = 49

This robot adds ____.

Notes for Home Your child combed materials to find sums for number sentences like 28 + 6.
Home Activity: Ask your child to explain how they know when to regroup ones when adding. (Regroup when there are ten or more ones.)

Name ______________________________

Practice 13-5

Problem Solving: Use Objects

Use | tens | ones | and .

Write the number sentence. Solve.

1. 26 sparklers lit the sky.
   3 firecrackers made a BOOM!
   How many fireworks did Jimmy see? 

   fireworks

2. 40 flags are on top of a float.
   Then 14 more flags are put around it.
   How many flags are there now? ____________________ flags

3. One band has 17 drums.
   Another band has 30 drums.
   How many drums are there in all? ____________________ drums

4. 31 children ate tomato soup at lunch.
   6 children ate chicken soup.
   How many children ate soup? ____________________ children

Visual Thinking

Solve.

5. 25 stars are on this quilt.
   How many are on the back?

   ______ stars

Notes for Home Your child solved problems involving addition. *Home Activity:* Ask your child to use beans, rocks or other small objects to check their answer to Exercise 4. (31 children + 6 children = 37 children)

Name ______________________________

Mixed Practice: Lessons 1–5

Use [tens | ones] and [tens and ones blocks]. Add.

1.

50	40	14	47	85	60
+ 16	+ 41	+ 30	+ 20	+ 10	+ 16
42	35	27	24	51	73
+ 46	+ 24	+ 42	+ 13	+ 22	+ 12

Circle yes or no to tell if you need to regroup. Solve.

2. 37 + 2 = _____ yes no
3. 24 + 7 = _____ yes no
4. 15 + 6 = _____ yes no
5. 74 + 3 = _____ yes no

Problem Solving

Use [tens and ones blocks]. Write the number sentence. Solve.

6. 26 frogs jump in a pond.
13 more frogs jump in.
How many frogs are in the pond now? _____

____________________ frogs

7. 44 girls go to camp.
27 boys go to camp.
How many children go to camp? _____

____________________ children

Journal

8. Write an addition math story using 10 and 17.

Notes for Home Your child practiced the concepts, skills, and problem solving taught in lessons 1-5.
Home Activity: Ask your child to use dimes and pennies to solve Exercise 3. Remind them to regroup 10 pennies as 1 dime when possible. (2 dimes and 4 pennies + 7 pennies = 3 dimes and 1 penny, or 31¢.)

Name ______________________

Practice
Chapters 1–13
A

Cumulative Review

How many tens and ones?

1. 51 _____ tens _____ one
2. 60 _____ tens _____ ones
3. 97 _____ tens _____ ones
4. 34 _____ tens _____ ones
5. 46 _____ tens _____ ones
6. 23 _____ tens _____ ones
7. 15 _____ ten _____ ones
8. 78 _____ tens _____ ones

Problem Solving

Write a number sentence.

9. The boys flew 13 kites.
5 kites got caught in trees.
How many kites are left?

____

10. One kite had 7 tails.
Kim added 7 more.
How many tails are are left?

____

Test Prep

Fill in the O for the correct answer.

Add.

11. 5 + 3 + 2
○ 9
○ 10
○ 11

12. 3 + 4 + 6
○ 13
○ 14
○ 15

13. 2 + 5 + 8
○ 13
○ 14
○ 15

14. 9 + 6 + 1
○ 16
○ 17
○ 18

Notes for Home Your child reviewed place value concepts, problem solving, and addition skills.
Home Activity: Ask your child to name 5 numbers that have no ones. (Possible answers include: 10, 20, 30, 40, 50.)

Name ______________________________

Practice 13-6

Subtract Tens

Subtract.

Use tens/ones mat and tens and ones blocks.

1.

tens	ones
4	7
− 2	0
2	7

tens	ones
2	5
− 1	0

tens	ones
6	3
− 4	0

tens	ones
8	1
− 3	0

2.

$$\begin{array}{r} 25 \\ -\ 10 \\ \hline \end{array} \quad \begin{array}{r} 37 \\ -\ 20 \\ \hline \end{array} \quad \begin{array}{r} 43 \\ -\ 10 \\ \hline \end{array} \quad \begin{array}{r} 56 \\ -\ 20 \\ \hline \end{array} \quad \begin{array}{r} 68 \\ -\ 30 \\ \hline \end{array} \quad \begin{array}{r} 72 \\ -\ 10 \\ \hline \end{array}$$

Problem Solving

3. **Write your own** problem.
Write a problem about the carrots and rabbits in the picture.
Tell if you add or subtract. Write a number sentence. Solve.

____

____

____

Notes for Home Your child subtracted tens from a two-digit number. *Home Activity:* Ask your child to count backwards by tens starting with any number between 50 and 100. How is this like subtracting tens?

Name ______________________________

Subtract Tens and Ones

Use  and . Subtract.

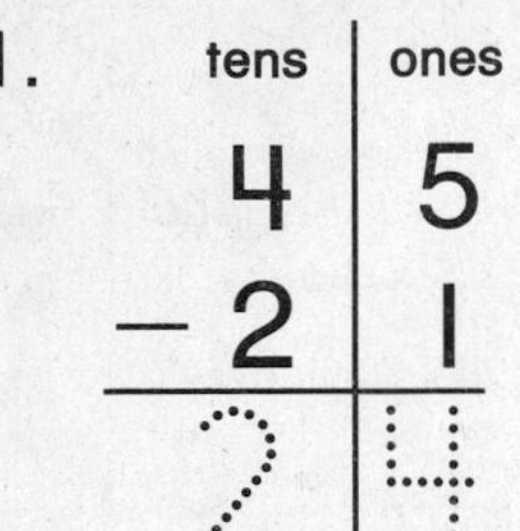

1.

tens	ones
4	5
− 2	1
2	4

tens	ones
8	3
− 1	2

tens	ones
9	2
− 3	2

tens	ones
5	6
−	5

2. $24 - 11$ $36 - 14$ $52 - 31$ $47 - 22$ $85 - 54$ $74 - 42$

Mixed Practice Add or subtract.

3. $23 - 10$ $37 - 6$ $47 - 31$ $58 - 20$ $62 - 51$ $75 - 14$

4. $23 + 16$ $37 + 42$ $47 + 50$ $58 + 21$ $62 + 22$ $75 + 13$

Problem Solving

Solve.

5. Nicki has this many fireflies.
   She lets 23 go.
   How many does she have left?

   ______ fireflies

Notes for Home Your child subtracted number sentences like 34 – 22. *Home Activity:* Ask your child to tell a subtraction math story about something that recently happened to him or her.

Name ____________________

Practice 13-8

Regroup with Subtraction

Use tens | ones and [tens and ones blocks].

	Show this many.	Subtract this many.	Do you need to regroup?	Solve.
1.	24	3	yes (no)	24 − 3 = ____
2.	56	7	yes no	56 − 7 = ____
3.	44	5	yes no	44 − 5 = ____
4.	19	4	yes no	19 − 4 = ____
5.	62	6	yes no	62 − 6 = ____
6.	35	7	yes no	35 − 7 = ____
7.	71	8	yes no	71 − 8 = ____

Problem Solving

Write a number sentence. Solve.

8. Mark's soccer team has 21 players.
5 are sick on game day.
How many players can play?

____________________ players

Notes for Home Your child worked with tens and ones to find differences for number sentences like 23 – 7. *Home Activity:* Ask your child to explain when they need to regroup in subtraction. (You must regroup tens and ones when there are not enough ones to subtract from.)

Name ______________________________

Practice 13-9

Problem Solving: Choose an Operation

Circle add or subtract.
Write a number sentence.

1. Brett picked up 46 shells at the beach.
   He found 12 more.
   How many shells did he find in all?

   add **subtract** ____________________ shells

2. 38 crabs dug in the sand.
   22 turtles were digging, too.
   How many more crabs than
   turtles are in the sand?

   add **subtract** ____________________ crabs

3. We made 68 muffins.
   We sold 40 at the bake sale.
   How many muffins are left?

   add **subtract** ____________________ muffins

Estimation

4. Circle the best estimate.
   Fish jump 31 big waves
   and 58 little waves.
   About how many waves were jumped?

   70 **80** **90**

Notes for Home Your child continued solving problems involving addition and subtraction. *Home Activity:* Ask your child to name words that are used in subtraction math stories. (Answers may include: how many more, left, away, and take away.)

Name ______________________________

Mixed Practice: Lessons 6–9

Subtract. Use tens | ones and [blocks].

1. 38 − 20 = ___ 55 − 30 = ___ 92 − 40 = ___ 17 − 10 = ___ 47 − 30 = ___ 29 − 10 = ___

2. 97 − 61 = ___ 84 − 44 = ___ 26 − 13 = ___ 34 − 22 = ___ 75 − 53 = ___ 28 − 14 = ___

Circle yes or no to tell if you need to regroup. Solve.

3. 37 − 5 = ____ yes no
4. 21 − 7 = ____ yes no
5. 14 − 6 = ____ yes no
6. 50 − 2 = ____ yes no
7. 45 − 4 = ____ yes no
8. 33 − 3 = ____ yes no

Problem Solving

Circle add or subtract. Write a number sentence.

9. K.T. has 32¢.
Pizza costs 75¢.
How much more does K.T.
need to buy pizza? ______________________

add subtract

Journal

10. Write a number story for 25¢ − 10¢.

Notes for Home Your child practiced the concepts, skills, and problem solving taught in lessons 6-9.
Home Activity: Ask your child to share a time when they used subtraction to solve a problem at home.

Name ______________________________

Practice
Chapters 1–13
B

Cumulative Review

Use the ruler to measure. Write the length.

1.

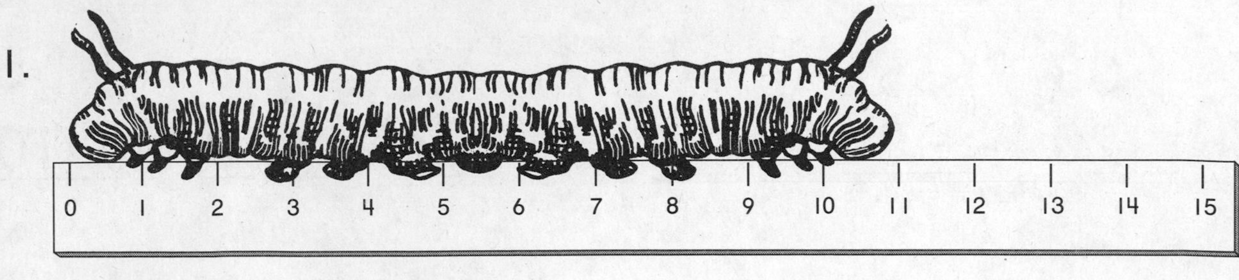

about _____ centimeters

Add.

2. 30 + 10 = ___ 20 + 40 = ___ 30 + 50 = ___

Problem Solving

Solve.

3. Liz sees 13 caterpillars. 5 turn into cocoons. How many caterpillars are left?

_____ caterpillars

4. 17 butterflies are blue. 3 are red. How many more are blue than red?

_____ butterflies

Test Prep

Fill in the ○ for the correct answer.

Subtract.

5. 14 − 7

○ 7
○ 8
○ 9
○ 10

6. 15 − 9

○ 4
○ 5
○ 6
○ 7

7. 12 − 8

○ 4
○ 5
○ 6
○ 7

Notes for Home Your child reviewed measurement, subtraction facts, and problem solving. *Home Activity:* Ask your child to check their answers for Exercises 5-7 by adding. (14 - 7 = 7 and 7 + 7 = 14, 15 – 9 = 6 and 9 + 6 = 15, 12 – 8 = 4 and 8 + 4 = 12)

Name ______________________

Date ______________ Score ______

Write how many.

1.

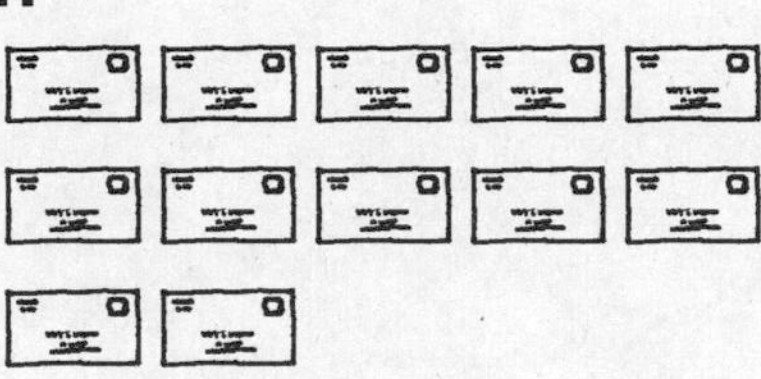

______

2.

______

3.

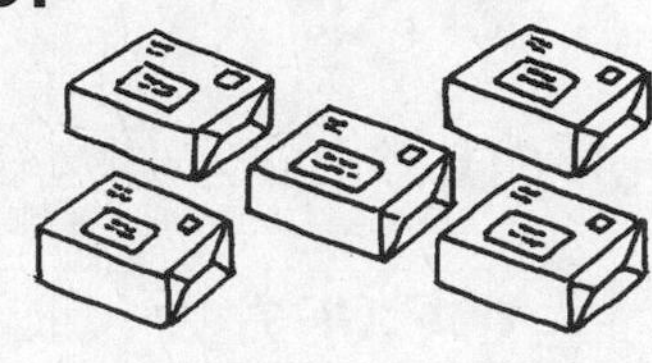

______

4. Complete the graph. Use the pictures above.

In the Mail Bag

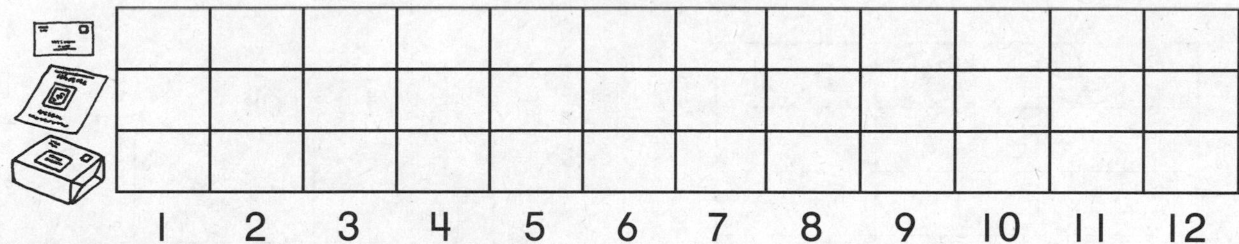

Use the graph. Circle the answer.

5. There are fewer  .

6. How many  ? 0 3 5

7. Write the numbers.

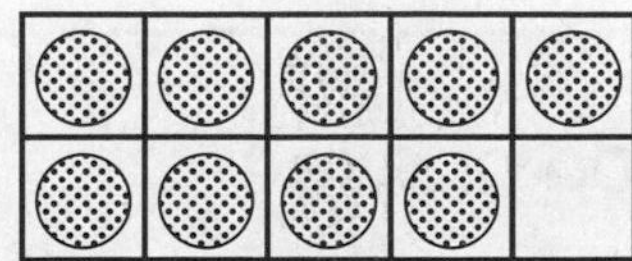

______

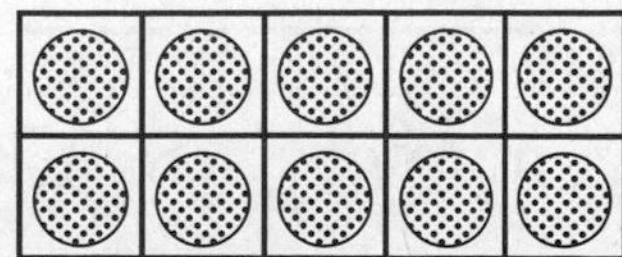

______

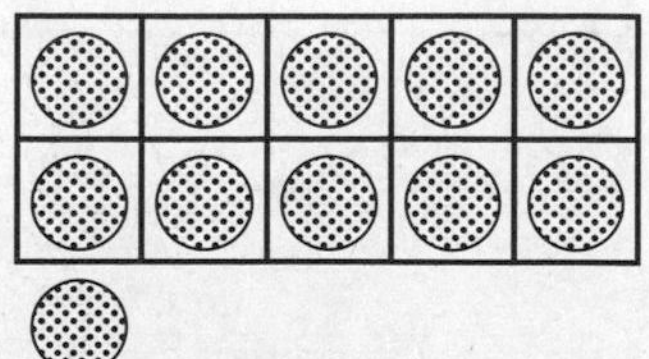

______

8. Complete the pattern. Draw what comes next.

___

Name ______________________________

Date ____________________ Score ______

I. Draw a picture to show the problem.

A cat had 4 .

A dog had 2 .

How many in all?

4 and 2 is ______.

2. How many ways can you put 5 into 2 ?

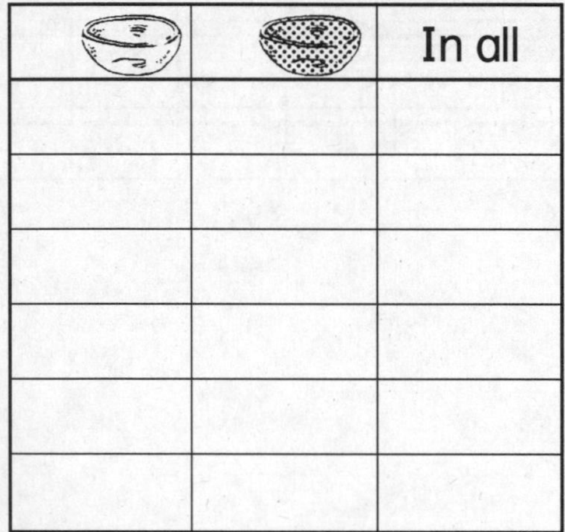

		In all

There are ______ ways.

3. How many are under the ?

10 in all

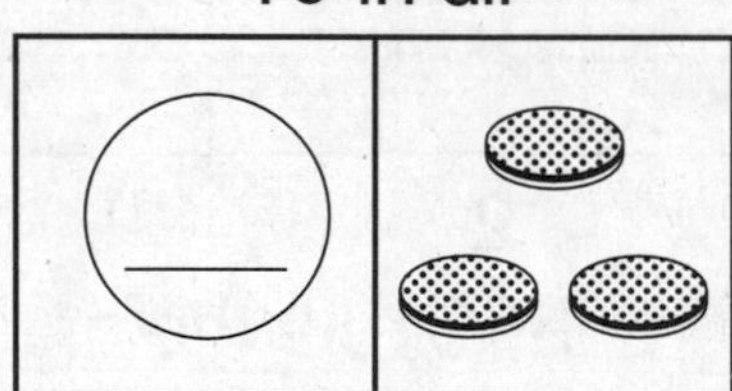

4. Draw 2 more. Write how many.

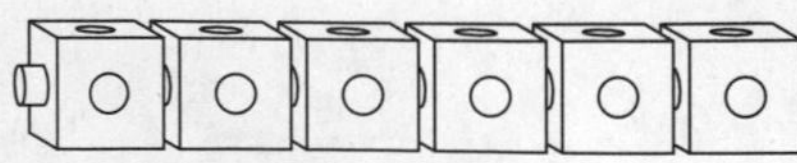

______

5. Circle **odd** or **even**.

odd

even

Name ______________________

Date ______________________ Score ______

Chapter 3 Test
Form
A

1. Complete the number sentences.

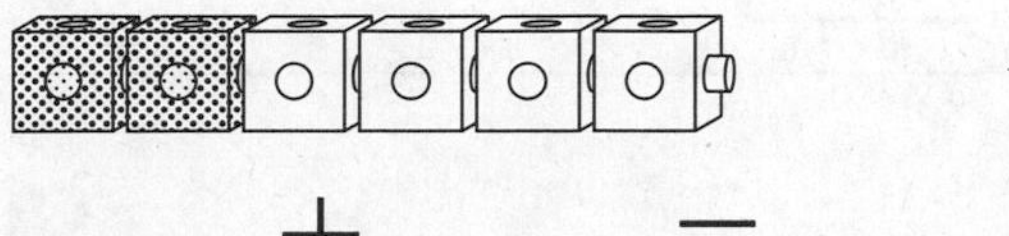

____ + ____ = ____

6 − ____ = ____

2. Subtract.

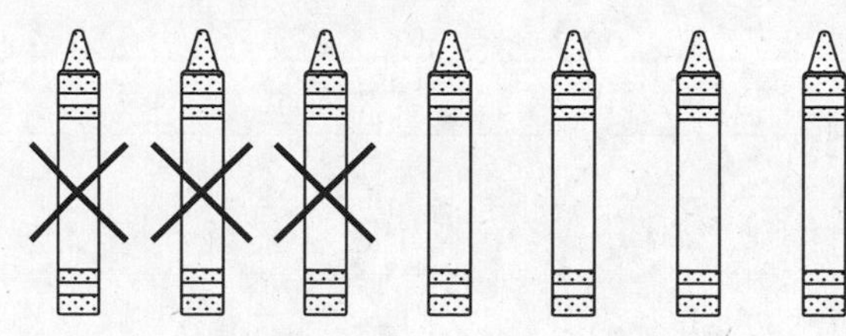

7 − 3 = ____

Add.

3.

$$\begin{array}{r} 4 \\ +3 \\ \hline \end{array} \qquad \begin{array}{r} 2 \\ +6 \\ \hline \end{array} \qquad \begin{array}{r} 8 \\ +3 \\ \hline \end{array}$$

Subtract.

4.

$$\begin{array}{r} 6 \\ -5 \\ \hline \end{array} \qquad \begin{array}{r} 7 \\ -4 \\ \hline \end{array} \qquad \begin{array}{r} 11 \\ -6 \\ \hline \end{array}$$

5. Read the math story. Use counters.
Complete the number sentence.

There are 8 .

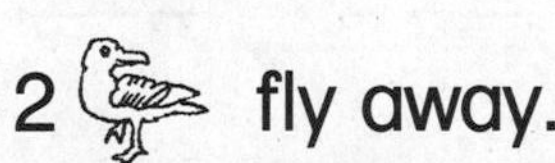
2 fly away.

How many are there now? ____ ○ ____ = ____

6. Draw a picture.
Write the number sentence.

9 eat.

3 more come.

How many are there now? ____ ○ ____ = ____

Name ______________________

Date ______________ Score ______

Add.

1. $7 + 2 =$ ____ $9 + 3 =$ ____ $8 + 2 =$ ____

2.

5	3	1	8	7	3	9
+ 3	+ 5	+ 8	+ 1	+ 3	+ 7	+ 2

3.

6	3	5	7	8	5	0
+ 0	+ 5	+ 1	+ 0	+ 1	+ 6	+ 9

Subtract.

4. $10 - 1 =$ ____ $9 - 2 =$ ____ $11 - 2 =$ ____

5.

9	6	8	8	10	6	9
− 9	− 0	− 2	− 8	− 5	− 2	− 0

6.

8	8	7	11	8	9	11
− 5	− 4	− 3	− 5	− 8	− 1	− 5

Problem Solving

7. Write a number sentence.

Nicky has 10 .

He gives 2 away. How many are left? ______________

Name ______________________

Date ______________________ Score ______

Chapter 5 Test
Form
A

1. Circle the solid that can roll.

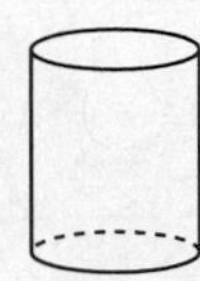 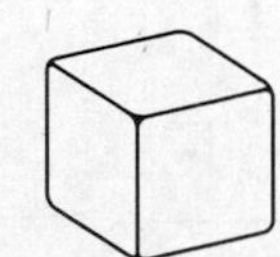

2. Draw the fold line.

3. Make the same size and shape.

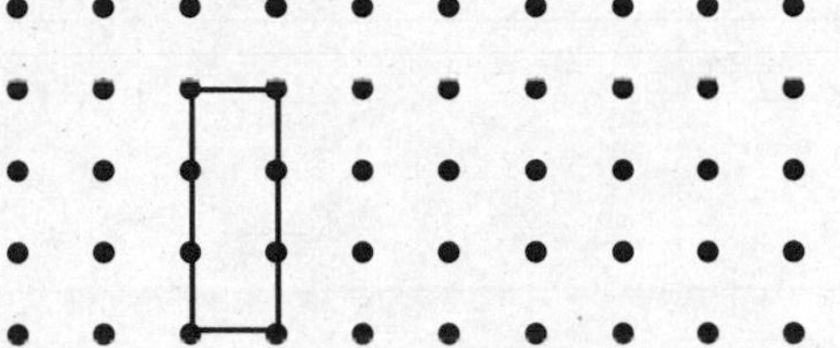

4. Make 3 fair shares.

  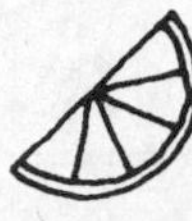

Circle the answer.

5. What part of the spinner is gray?

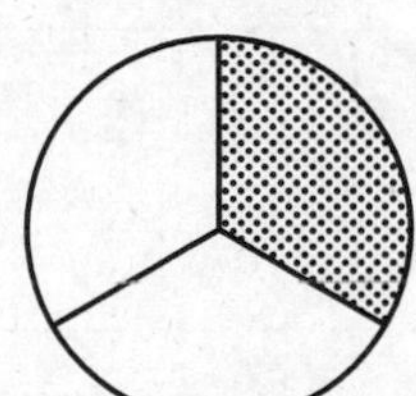

$\frac{1}{2}$ $\frac{1}{3}$ $\frac{1}{4}$

6. How much of the set is shaded?

One third

One fourth

7. Look at the picture. Complete the table to show how many.

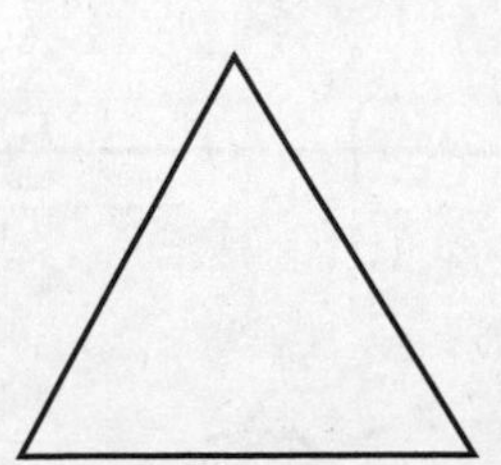  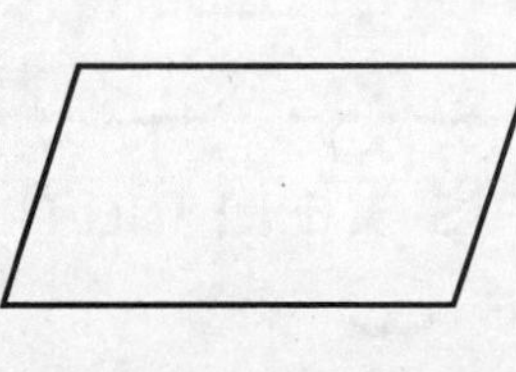 

	3 corners	4 corners	5 corners
Number of shapes			

Name ______________________

Date ______________ Score ______

Add.

1. $\begin{array}{r} 6 \\ +6 \\ \hline \end{array}$ $\begin{array}{r} 4 \\ +5 \\ \hline \end{array}$ $\begin{array}{r} 3 \\ +4 \\ \hline \end{array}$

Subtract.

2. $\begin{array}{r} 10 \\ -5 \\ \hline \end{array}$ $\begin{array}{r} 8 \\ -4 \\ \hline \end{array}$ $\begin{array}{r} 12 \\ -7 \\ \hline \end{array}$

3. Use ▢. Complete the fact family.

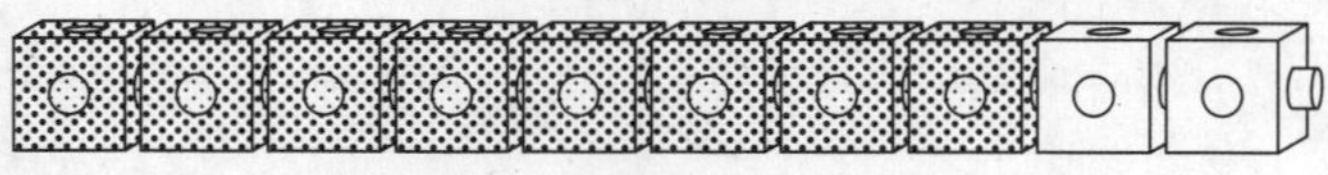

8 + 2 = ____ ____ − ____ = ____

____ + ____ = ____ ____ − ____ = ____

Use the chart to solve. Write the totals.

4. How many worms were in a puddle? ______

5. How many worms were on a leaf and under a rock in all? Write the number sentence.

____ + ____ = ____

Worms We Found		
Place	Tally	Total
Under a rock	///	
In a puddle	~~////~~ ~~////~~ //	
On a leaf	~~////~~ /	

6. Guess how many ants are in the hill. Then check to find the answer. You can use ⬭ ⬭.

Try ______

5 + ______ = ______

Try ______

5 + ______ = ______

12 ants in all

Name ______________________________

Date ____________________ Score ______

1. Estimate how many.

about 20 40 60

Circle groups of 10.
Write the numbers.

_____ tens and _____ extra is _____.

---

2. Count by 2s. 2, 4, 6, _____, _____, _____, _____, 16

3. Count by 5s. 5, 10, 15, _____, _____, _____, _____, 40

Read the graph.

	Cherries We Picked
Jon	
Liz	

4. How many cherries did Jon pick? _____

5. How many more does Jon have than Liz? _____

---

6. Color.

fourth green
first red

Name ______________________

Date ______________ Score ____

You can use [ten rod] and [one cube].

1. Count how many.

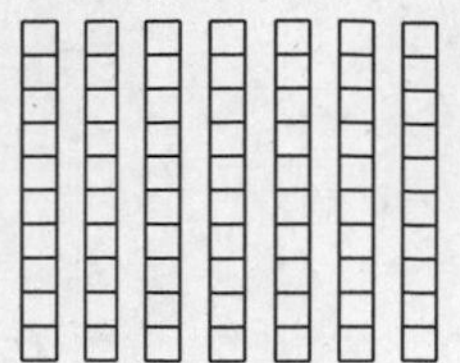

Add 2 more. Do you need to exchange 10 ones for 1 ten?

yes no

Write how many tens and ones.

tens	ones

2. Estimate how many.

Make groups of 10.

About 20 30 40

3. Write the missing numbers.

31	32		34	35
41		43		

Write the numbers that come before, after, and between.

4. ____, 54, ____

5. ____, 38, 39, ____

Answer the questions.

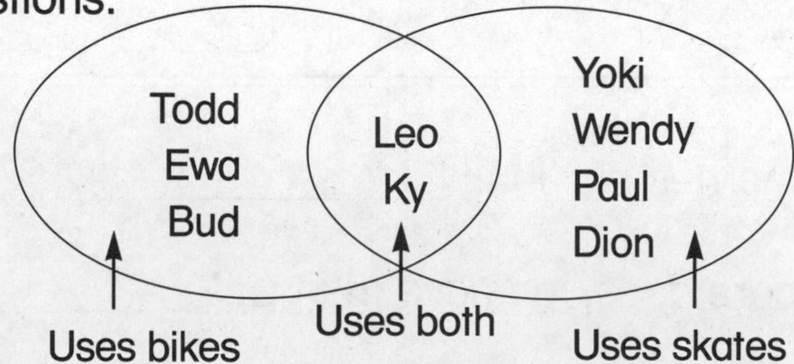

6. How many use bikes? ____

7. Who uses bikes and skates? ______________________

Name ______________________

Date ____________________ Score ______

Chapter 9 Test
Form
A

Count the money. Write the amount.

1.

_____ ¢

2.

_____ ¢

3. Count your money.

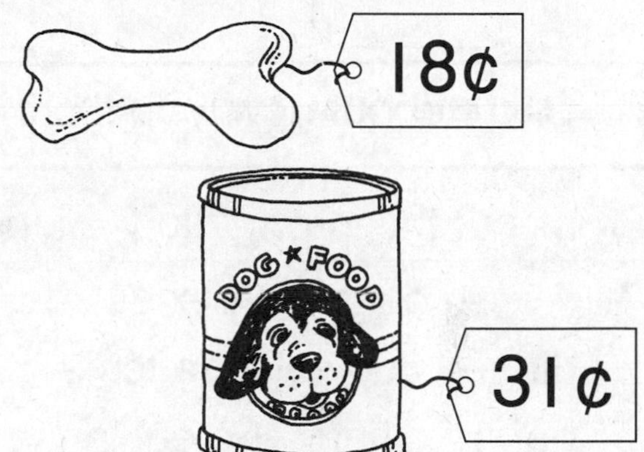

Write the amount. _____ ¢

Circle what you can buy.

4. Find 3 ways to show 17¢.

Make a list.

Name ______________________________

Date ____________________ Score ______

Chapter 10 Test
Form
A

These times tell about a show. Write the times.

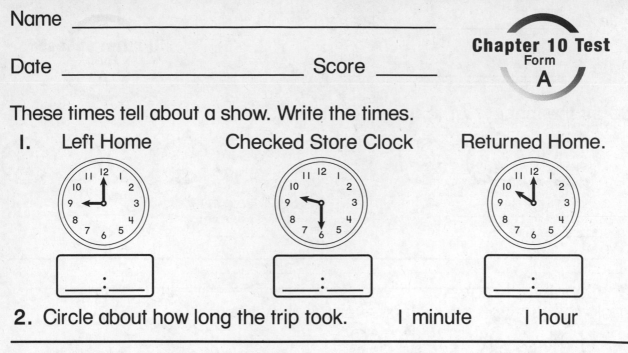

1. Left Home

___:___

Checked Store Clock

___:___

Returned Home.

___:___

2. Circle about how long the trip took. I minute I hour

Cross out the information you do not need. Solve.

3. Alyssa does the dishes after dinner. Jon sets the table before dinner. We eat in the kitchen. Who works first?

____

4. The sun was shining at 3:00. At 4:00, it began to rain. At 5:00, we saw a rainbow. How long after the rain began did we see the rainbow?

____

---

5. Write I st, 2nd, and 3rd to put the pictures in order.

_____

_____

_____

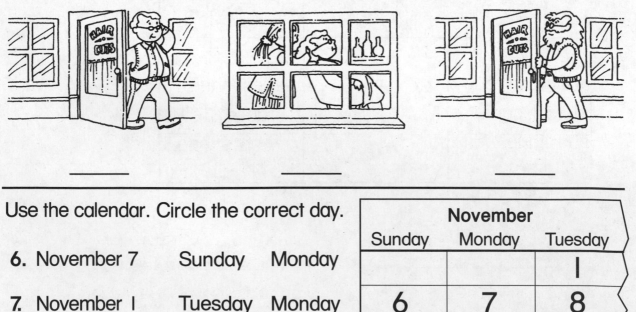

Use the calendar. Circle the correct day.

6. November 7 Sunday Monday

7. November I Tuesday Monday

November		
Sunday	Monday	Tuesday
		I
6	7	8

Name ______________________

Date ______________ Score ______

Measure. Tell about how many.

I. about ______ inches

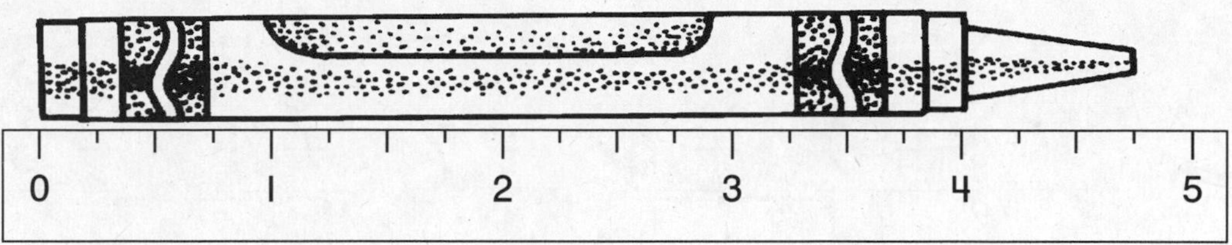

Circle the tool you need to answer the question.

2. How much will  hold?

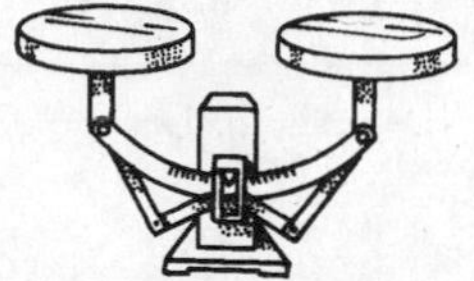

Circle the best answer.

3. A pen is about 5 ______ long. inches feet

Circle the words that tell about each object.

4. 

less than I cup
about I cup
more than I cup

5. 

less than I liter
about I liter
more than I liter

6. 

lighter than I kilogram
about I kilogram
heavier than I kilogram

7. 

lighter than I pound
about I pound
heavier than I pound

Name ______________________

Date ______________ Score ______

Add.

1.

				4	3	5
9	9	6	8	5	4	3
+ 9	+ 7	+ 6	+ 6	+ 7	+ 1	+ 6

Add or subtract.

2.

5	13	16	7	17	17	8
+ 8	− 8	− 9	+ 9	− 8	− 9	+ 9

3. 12 − 6 = ____ 15 − 7 = ____ 14 − 5 = ____

4. Complete the fact family.

7 + 6 = ____ 13 − 6 = ____

6 + 7 = ____ 13 − 7 = ____

5. Solve. Draw a picture or use objects.
Complete the number sentence.

Lia played 16 soccer games this season.
Her team lost 9 games.
How many games did her team win?

Name ______________________________

Date ______________________ Score ______

Add or subtract. You can use , and □.

1. $\begin{array}{r} 60 \\ +39 \\ \hline \end{array}$ $\begin{array}{r} 32 \\ +14 \\ \hline \end{array}$ $\begin{array}{r} 15 \\ +51 \\ \hline \end{array}$

2. $\begin{array}{r} 82 \\ -31 \\ \hline \end{array}$ $\begin{array}{r} 49 \\ -20 \\ \hline \end{array}$ $\begin{array}{r} 76 \\ -53 \\ \hline \end{array}$

Circle yes or no to tell if you need to regroup. Solve.

3. 64 + 7 = ____
yes no

4. 38 − 2 = ____
yes no

5. 44 + 2 = ____
yes no

6. 31 − 5 = ____
yes no

Circle **add** or **subtract**.
Write a number sentence. Solve.

5. There are 47 books in a box.
Dennis takes out 21 books.
How many books are left in the box?

add subtract ______________________ books

6. Rosa spends 46¢ for paper.
She also spends 32¢ for a pencil.
How much money does she spend?

add subtract ______________________

Name ______________________________

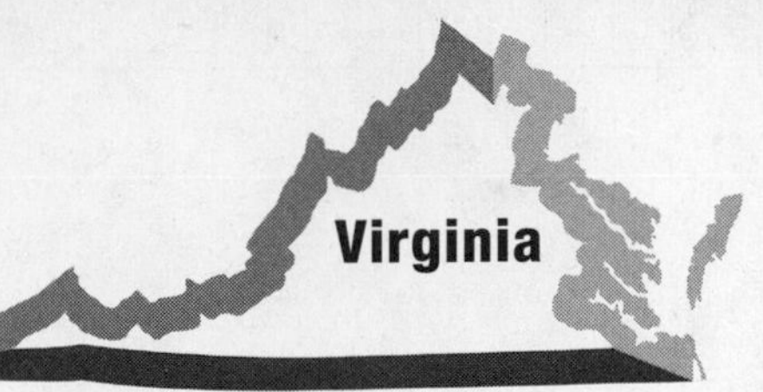

Explore Shapes

This triangle has
3 corners, but only one
is a square corner.

Complete the chart.

Shape	Sides	Corners	Square corners
1.	4		
2.			
3.			
4.			

5. Draw me.
I have 3 sides.
I have 3 corners.
I have no square corners.

6. Draw me.
I have 4 sides.
I have 4 square corners.

Notes for Home Your child found the number of sides, corners, and square corners in shapes.
Home Activity Have your child draw around the bottom of a cup and the bottom of a box and tell you the number of sides, corners, and square corners in each shape.
Virginia Mathematics Standards of Learning: (1.16) The students will draw and describe triangles, squares, rectangles, and circles according to the number of sides, corners, and square corners.

Name ______________________________

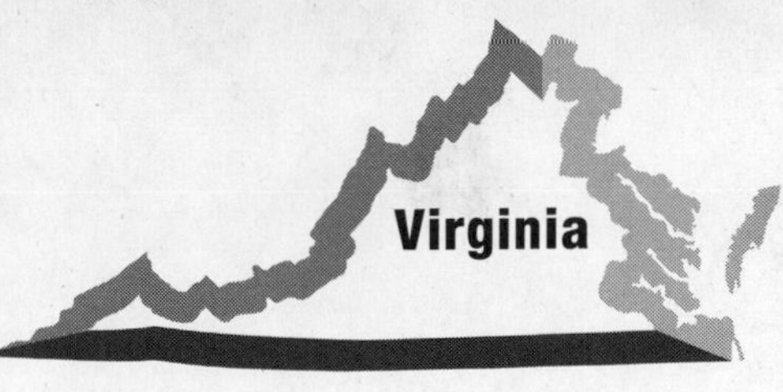

Objects in Space

Sam is in the water. Amy is **close by**.
Amy is holding the shovel **up**. She put the pail **down**.
The bone is **near** Fido. The airplane is **far** away.
The umbrella is **above** Amy. Amy is **below** the umbrella.
The sandals are **next to** the ball.
The pail is **beside** Amy.

1. Put a red X next to Amy.
2. Put a yellow X near Fido.
3. Put a blue X above the bird.
4. Put an orange X beside Sam.
5. Put a green X on Sam's raised arm.
6. Find the pail. Put a purple X close by.

Notes for Home Your child has learned to use the words *close by, up, down, near, far, above, below, next to,* and *beside. Home Activity:* Use these words in such a way that allows your child to identify the location of objects. ***Virginia Mathematics Standards of Learning:*** (1.15) The students will describe the proximity of objects in space (near, far, close by, below, up, down, beside, and next to).